EPOXY RESINS

Epoxy Resins

THEIR APPLICATIONS AND TECHNOLOGY

HENRY LEE • KRIS NEVILLE

Technical Director   *Project Engineer*

The Epoxylite Corporation, El Monte, California

McGRAW-HILL BOOK COMPANY, INC.

New York   Toronto   London   1957

EPOXY RESINS

THE MAPLE PRESS COMPANY, YORK, PA.

PREFACE

The epoxy resins are one of the newest and most versatile of the modern plastics. They have penetrated into more industries and more manufacturing operations in a shorter space of time than any of their predecessors. A year after production reached commercially significant proportions, they were being employed for industrial castings, surface coatings, high-strength adhesives, durable laminates, cold solders, lightweight foams, and potting compounds for all varieties of electrical and electronic apparatus. Not only have they replaced conventional plastics for many applications, but they are moving into fields previously invulnerable to the plastics invasion of the 1940s.

Industrial chemists, engineers, and designers are suddenly confronted with thermosetting materials with which they are completely unfamiliar. How do these new materials work, what are their strong points and their weak points and, most importantly, how can they be used intelligently for a specific application? These questions must be answered, if the advantageous properties of the epoxies are to be applied to the solution of today's complex technological problems.

This book is intended to provide theoretical and practical information on these new plastics and to answer many of the questions which will occur to the user. The book discusses the technical background and general chemistry of the resins and indicates the specific formulations that can be developed and the application techniques that have proved successful.

The chemist will find a review of the synthesis, curing mechanisms, and curing agents involved in this new class of materials. The electronics engineer will find data on the potting of electrical components and their performance in high humidities; the power engineer will learn how epoxy resins have solved many of the application problems of electrical apparatus in corrosive environments; the paint and varnish formulator will find data on the formulation of both solvent and solvent-free coatings of unusually durable properties; the tool and die maker will find a detailed

v

discussion of the casting resins which are creating a revolution in metal-working; the aircraft and missile engineer will find suggestions for light-weight sandwiches, high-compressive-strength laminates, high-temperature adhesives and chemically resistant sealants; the chemical engineer will find details on laminates for lightweight ducts and piping to handle corrosive fluids; and the automotive engineer will meet a versatile metal adhesive and body-patching compound.

Although the chemical literature on epoxy resins and epoxy materials is growing rapidly, we have sought to cite the chief or representative works rather than to produce a comprehensive bibliography. We believe this to be in keeping with the needs of the widespread audience for whom this book was prepared.

The authors wish to acknowledge the helpful assistance of Dr. S. O. Greenlee, formerly of S. C. Johnson and Son, Inc.; Don Masson, Bob Klees, Henry Greenhood, Bruce Godard, Charles Pitt, J. L. Rodgers, and Dr. John Wynstra of the Bakelite Co.; F. S. Swackhammer, Ed Gould, Al Lane, Paul Nielsen, and Sydney Shell of Shell Chemical Co.; Ward Kissell, B. I. Zolin, and W. W. Cooner of E. I. du Pont de Nemours & Co., Inc.; Wayne Churchill, Donald E. Fish, and Alan J. Breslau of Thiokol Chemical Co.; George Firth of Applied Plastics Co.; Robert Jenkins of Convair; Dr. Frank W. Long, T. C. Dauphiné, Dr. S. J. Nelson, and Paul Robitschek of Hooker Electrochemical Co.; Elliot Dorman and D. M. Joseph of Ciba Co., Inc.; J. M. Thomas, G. V. Jenks, and Dr. H. G. Cooke of Jones-Dabney Co., Inc.; George Epstein of Aerojet-General Corp.; William G. Strunk of Westvaco Chloro-Alkali Division, Food Machinery and Chemical Corp.; Lowell E. Peterson and Donald E. Floyd of General Mills, Inc.; Dr. A. M. Partansky and James W. Conners of Dow Chemical Co.; Dr. W. R. R. Park of Case Institute of Technology; Dr. Norman Kharasch of the University of Southern California; Dr. Adolf Damusis of the Sherwin-Williams Co.; Russ Houghton of Houghton Laboratories; John Delmonte of Furane Plastics; Robert Sumers of National Aniline; Leonard Moreland, George Larsen, Stan Rejda, Kenneth Keith, and Charles Doane (who coined the word "Epoxylite") of Larsen-Hogue Electric Co.; Bob Sandman of Sandman Electric Co.; F. J Ackerman; and many others who made this text possible. In particular the technical assistance of Mary MacInnis, R. E. Jones, and E. Sandel Hunt of The Epoxylite Corporation was most vital.

Henry Lee
Kris Neville

CONTENTS

Chapter 3. *Primary Aliphatic Amines and Their Adducts as Curing Agents*   **63**

Chapter 4. *Amines (Continued), Amides, and Latent Curing Agents*   **90**

EPOXY RESINS

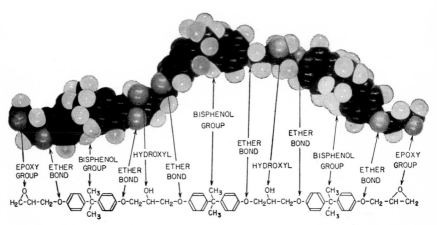

Atom model of epoxy-resin molecule compared with structural symbols (diglycidyl ether of bisphenol A, degree of polymerization of 2).   Magnification, approx ×100,000,000. (*Devoe & Raynolds* Co.)

1
EPOXY RESINS—THEIR SYNTHESIS AND CHARACTERIZATION

The epoxy resins are the newest of the major industrial plastics. They were first synthesized by Pierre Castan in Switzerland and S. O. Greenlee in the United States late in the 1930s. In common with phenolic and polyester resins, the epoxy resins are thermosetting materials. When converted by a curing agent, the thermosetting resins become hard, infusible systems. The system may be visualized as a network cross-linked in all three dimensions. In a plane it might appear:

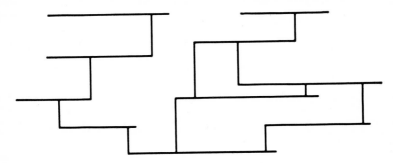

from which it will be seen that movement of a molecule in any direction is opposed by the crosslinking arrangement.

Thermoplastic resins, on the other hand, such as polyethylene and polyvinyl chloride may be thought of as permanently fusible compounds composed of long linear chains lying together in three dimensions, but not interconnected. In a plane, the system might appear:

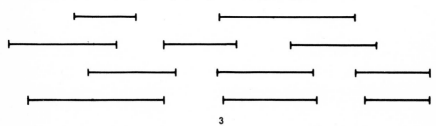

from which it will be seen that movement of a molecule in any direction is not restricted by crosslinking with surrounding molecules.

In practical effect, the thermoplastic materials will soften progressively with heat or flow with pressure, whereas the thermosetting materials will retain their dimensional stability throughout their design range. The classification, however, while justified on the basis of structure, is not to be taken as an absolute criterion of performance. Some thermosetting compounds are designed for an extremely limited range and at higher temperatures will distort more readily than the high-heat-resistant thermoplastic compounds.

In certain other respects, the two classes of materials also differ. Thermoplastic materials, for instance, are formed under heat and pressure into the desired shapes. This need not be the case with all thermosetting compounds. For example, a low-viscosity epoxy resin and a suitable fluid curing agent can be combined at room temperature and poured into a prepared mold; within a few minutes, the mold can be stripped away to reveal a solid, dimensionally stable block of resin. Other differences, both in kind and degree, combine to make the thermosetting resins as a class useful in many industrial applications for which the thermoplastics are chemically unsuited.

The thermosetting epoxy resins possess a number of unusually valuable properties immediately amenable to use in the formulation of adhesives, sealing liquids, cold solders, castings, laminates, and coatings. The more important of these properties are:

1. *Versatility.* Numerous curing agents for the epoxies are available, and the epoxies are compatible with a wide variety of modifiers. Hence, the properties of the cured epoxy-resin system can be engineered to widely diverse specifications.

2. *Good handling characteristics.* Many epoxy systems can be worked at room temperature, and those which cannot require only moderate heat during mixing. Before the curing agent is incorporated, the resins have indefinite shelf life, provided they are properly made and do not contain any caustic. The ratio of curing agent to resin is not as critical as with some thermosetting materials. It should be held fairly close to the empirically determined optimum amount if best results are to be obtained, and weighing should be done with care. If too much or too little curing agent is present, the solvent resistance and heat-distortion temperature will be reduced. In general, however, a few per cent error in either direction may be tolerated in most applications, and some curing agents permit even wider margins. Cure can be accomplished in almost any specified time period by regulation of cure cycles and proper selection of curing agent. In many cases, pot life, viscosity, and cure schedules can

be accommodated to the production situation without seriously influencing the properties of the cured system.

3. *Toughness.* Cured epoxy resins are approximately seven times tougher than cured phenolic resins. The relative toughness has been attributed to the distance between crosslinking points and the presence of integral aliphatic chains:

$$-CH_2-CH-CH_2-O-\left\langle \bigcirc \right\rangle -\overset{\overset{\displaystyle CH_3}{|}}{\underset{\underset{\displaystyle CH_3}{|}}{C}}-\left\langle \bigcirc \right\rangle -O-CH_2-CH-CH_2-$$

Typical cured epoxy-resin structure

Typical cured phenolic-resin structure

4. *High adhesive properties.* Epoxy resins have high adhesive strengths arising from the polarity of aliphatic hydroxyl $\left(\begin{smallmatrix} OH \\ | \\ -C- \end{smallmatrix} \right)$ and ether (C—O—C) groups present in the initial resin chain and in the cured system. The polarity of these groups serves to create electromagnetic bonding forces between the epoxy molecule and the adjacent surface. The epoxy groups, likewise, will react to provide chemical bonds with surfaces, such as metals, where active hydrogens may be found. Since the resin passes relatively undisturbed (i.e., with slight shrinkage) from the liquid to the solid state, the bonds initially established are preserved.

5. *Low shrinkage.* The epoxy resins differ from many thermosetting compounds in that they give off no by-products during cure and, in the liquid state, are highly associated. Cure is by direct addition, and shrinkage is on the order of <2 per cent for an unmodified system, indi-

cating that little internal rearrangement of the molecules is necessary. The condensation and crosslinking of phenolic and polyester resins, on the other hand, yield significantly higher shrinkage values.

6. *Inertness.* Cured epoxy resins are very inert chemically. The ether groups, the benzene rings, and, when present, the aliphatic hydroxyls in the cured epoxy system are virtually invulnerable to caustic attack and extremely resistant to acids.

Compare this inertness with the effect of caustic on a weakly acidic phenolic resin:

| Phenolic resin | Caustic | Soluble sodium phenolate | Water |

and an ester-linked polyester resin:

| Polyester resin | Caustic | Sodium salt | Alcohol |

In the case of the phenolic resin, the sodium phenolate formed is readily soluble and when present will cause the ultimate disintegration of the resin chain. In the case of the polyester, the ester linkage is hydrolyzed back to the original alcohol and salt of the carboxyl group.

The chemical inertness of the cured epoxy system is enhanced by the dense, closely packed structure of the resinous mass, which is extremely resistant to solvent action.

STRUCTURE OF THE BASIC EPOXY-RESIN MOLECULE

The epoxy-resin molecule is characterized by the reactive epoxy or ethoxyline groups

which serve as terminal linear polymerization points. When crosslinking or cure is accomplished through these groups or through hydroxyls or other groups present (Chap. 2), an unusually tough, extremely adhesive, and highly inert solid results. In its simplest and idealized form, the epoxy molecule is represented by the diglycidyl ether of bisphenol **A**

$$CH_2\!\!-\!\!CH\!\!-\!\!CH_2\!\!-\!\!O\!\!-\!\!\langle\ \rangle\!\!-\!\!\underset{\underset{CH_3}{|}}{\overset{\overset{CH_3}{|}}{C}}\!\!-\!\!\langle\ \rangle\!\!-\!\!O\!\!-\!\!CH_2\!\!-\!\!CH\!\!-\!\!CH_2$$

The most widely used liquid epoxy resins, those having viscosities in the 8,000- to 20,000-centipoise range, are predominantly of this structure. Since the commercial resins are not molecularly distilled, they contain some percentages of higher-weight homologs, branched-chain molecules, isomers, and occasionally monoglycidyl ethers in combination with the basic structure. The high-viscosity liquid and the solid commercial resins are predominantly composed of more highly polymerized products considered as homologs of diglycidyl ether of bisphenol A.

Since the diglycidyl ether of bisphenol A and its higher homologs can be considered representative of the class, this type is discussed in detail.

SYNTHESIS OF THE BASIC EPOXY-RESIN MOLECULE

The usual raw materials for the synthesis of the diglycidyl ether of bisphenol A are epichlorohydrin and bisphenol A. These are derived from natural gas or coking by-products.

Epichlorohydrin

Epichlorohydrin is a colorless, mobile liquid having an irritating chloroform-like odor. It is represented by the formula

$$Cl\!\!-\!\!CH_2\!\!-\!\!CH\!\!-\!\!CH_2$$

Epichlorohydrin is extremely reactive and usually combines through the epoxy group with a substance containing an active (i.e., an easily reacted) hydrogen atom. It is available commercially at 98 per cent purity.

Epichlorohydrin is customarily produced by the chlorination of propylene, the resulting allyl chloride being reacted with hypochlorous acid to produce dichlorohydrin, with this being exposed to sodium hydroxide at elevated temperatures to strip off one hydrogen and one chlorine atom. The initial steps are the same as though glycerol were being prepared.

The complete reaction from propylene to epichlorohydrin can be expressed as follows:

(1) $CH_2=CH-CH_3$ + Cl_2 → $CH_2=CH-CH_2-Cl$ + HCl
     Propylene   Chlorine   Allyl chloride   Hydrochloric acid

(2) $CH_2=CH-CH_2-Cl$ + H_2O/Cl_2 → $Cl-CH_2-\overset{\overset{\textstyle OH}{|}}{C}H-CH_2-Cl$
    Allyl chloride   Water/chlorine   Dichlorohydrin

(3) $Cl-CH_2-\overset{\overset{\textstyle OH}{|}}{C}H-CH_2-Cl$ + $NaOH$ $\overset{\Delta}{\rightarrow}$ $CH_2\overset{O}{\overbrace{}}CH-CH_2-Cl$
    Dichlorohydrin   Sodium hydroxide   Epichlorohydrin

As will become apparent from the subsequent discussion, reaction (3), dehydrohalogenation, actually accounts for the formation of the epoxy groups in the diglycidyl ether of bisphenol A molecule.

Bisphenol A

Bisphenol A or bis (4-hydroxyphenyl) dimethylmethane

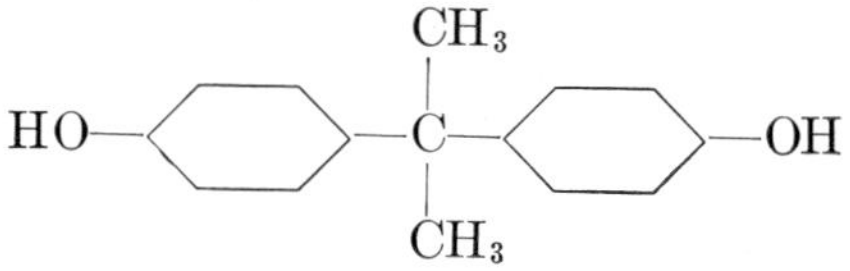

Bisphenol A

requires two basic intermediates for synthesis, acetone and phenol.

As with all aromatics, bisphenol A is based on the very stable benzene ring. It is the most easily prepared of the dihydric phenols and is available commercially as a flaked solid in relatively pure form with a melting point of 153°C.

Several commercial processes are used in the manufacture of bisphenol. A typical process would involve benzene, obtained from coal gas or water gas, as a starting point. Benzene is treated with hydrochloric acid and oxygen to produce chlorobenzene. Sodium hydroxide is added to yield sodium phenolate, and the phenol is released by the addition of carbon dioxide. Acetone can be obtained by treating propylene with sulfuric acid to produce isopropyl alcohol. This is then oxidized under mild conditions to acetone. Acetone is combined with phenol to give bisphenol A. The reactions are as follows:

Phenol

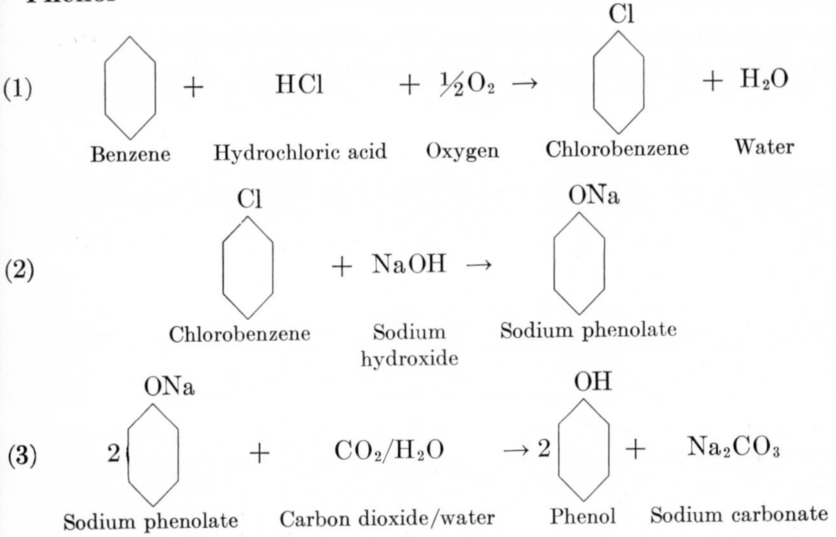

(1)

$$\text{Benzene} + \text{HCl} + \tfrac{1}{2}O_2 \rightarrow \text{Chlorobenzene} + H_2O$$

Benzene   Hydrochloric acid   Oxygen   Chlorobenzene   Water

(2)

$$\text{Chlorobenzene} + \text{NaOH} \rightarrow \text{Sodium phenolate}$$

Chlorobenzene   Sodium hydroxide   Sodium phenolate

(3)

$$2\,\text{Sodium phenolate} + CO_2/H_2O \rightarrow 2\,\text{Phenol} + Na_2CO_3$$

Sodium phenolate   Carbon dioxide/water   Phenol   Sodium carbonate

Acetone

(1)
$$CH_2{=}CH{-}CH_3 + H_2SO_4/H_2O \rightarrow CH_3{-}\underset{|}{\overset{OH}{CH}}{-}CH_3$$

Propylene   Sulfuric acid/water   Isopropyl alcohol

(2)
$$CH_3{-}\underset{|}{\overset{OH}{CH}}{-}CH_3 + O_2 \rightarrow CH_3{-}\overset{O}{\overset{||}{C}}{-}CH_3$$

Isopropyl alcohol   Oxygen   Acetone

Bisphenol A

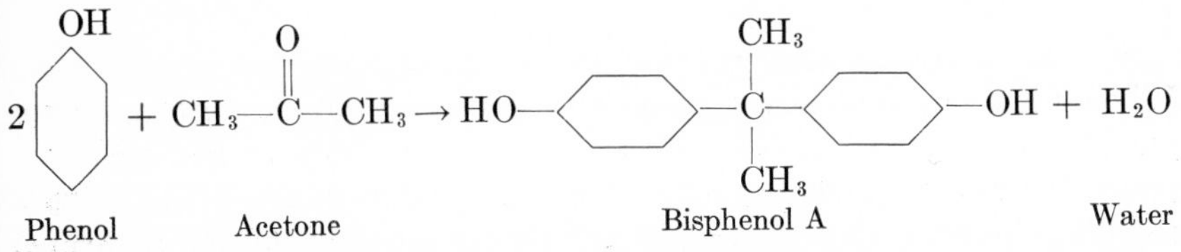

$$2\,\text{Phenol} + CH_3{-}\overset{O}{\overset{||}{C}}{-}CH_3 \rightarrow \text{Bisphenol A} + H_2O$$

Phenol   Acetone   Bisphenol A   Water

Because of the ready availability of phenol and acetone and the ease of manufacture, bisphenol A has been the chief dihydric phenol used in epoxy-resin manufacture.

Diglycidyl Ether of Bisphenol A

Diglycidyl ether of bisphenol A is obtained by reacting epichlorohydrin with bisphenol A in the presence of a caustic:

$$(1) \quad \text{⬡—OH} + \overset{O}{\overset{\displaystyle\diagup\diagdown}{CH_2\text{—}CH}}\text{—}CH_2\text{—}Cl \xrightarrow{\text{NaOH}}$$

$$\text{⬡—O—}CH_2\text{—}\overset{OH}{\overset{|}{CH}}\text{—}CH_2\text{—}Cl$$

$$(2) \quad \text{⬡—O—}CH_2\text{—}\overset{OH}{\overset{|}{CH}}\text{—}CH_2\text{—}Cl \xrightarrow{\text{NaOH}}$$

$$\text{⬡—O—}CH_2\text{—}\overset{O}{\overset{\displaystyle\diagup\diagdown}{CH}}\text{—}CH_2 + HCl$$

It has been suggested that some of the caustic forms phenolate and water as an intermediate step in the reaction. In addition, the caustic serves to neutralize the hydrochloric acid formed as a by-product. Reaction (2) is the same as the reaction involved in converting dichlorohydrin to epichlorohydrin, indicating that the former reactant may be used in the synthesis of the diglycidyl ether (1-1).

In order to obtain the diglycidyl ether of bisphenol A, 2 mols of epichlorohydrin are theoretically required for each mol of bisphenol A:

$$2(\overset{O}{\overset{\displaystyle\diagup\diagdown}{CH_2\text{—}CH}}\text{—}CH_2\text{—}Cl) + \text{HO—⬡—}\overset{CH_3}{\overset{|}{\underset{|}{\underset{CH_3}{C}}}}\text{—⬡—OH} \rightarrow$$

$$\overset{O}{\overset{\displaystyle\diagup\diagdown}{CH_2\text{—}CH}}\text{—}CH_2\text{—O—⬡—}\overset{CH_3}{\overset{|}{\underset{|}{\underset{CH_3}{C}}}}\text{—⬡—O—}CH_2\text{—}\overset{O}{\overset{\displaystyle\diagup\diagdown}{CH}}\text{—}CH_2$$

When, however, the stoichiometric 2:1 ratio is employed, the monomeric yield is less than 10 per cent, with the remaining material being higher-molecular-weight condensation and polymerization products. In order to obtain high yields of the monomeric product, excess epichlorohydrin is employed, the stoichiometric amount being doubled or tripled. Yields of 70 per cent or more are then possible. Amounts ten times in excess have also been suggested, the "purity" of the diglycidyl ether being a function of the excess.

The use of excess epichlorohydrin offers an additional advantage in that the epichlorohydrin serves as a reaction medium, making it unnecessary to employ a foreign solvent in the synthesis. The reaction is conducted in an inert atmosphere, with the alkalinity of the solution being carefully controlled by the stepwise addition of caustic as necessary. An account from the literature (1-2) describes the process:

A solution of 228 grams (1 mol) of bisphenol A in 370 grams (4 mols) of epichlorohydrin was maintained at from 105 to 110°C under an atmosphere of nitrogen. While the solution was continuously stirred, 80 grams (2 mols) of sodium hydroxide in the form of a 30 per cent aqueous solution was added dropwise over a period of 16 hours. The rate of addition was maintained so that the reaction mixture remained just on the neutral side as indicated by its failure to color phenolphthalein.

The organic layer of the reaction products was separated, dried with sodium sulfate, and fractionally distilled under vacuum. The stereoisomers were volatilized in the form of water-white, somewhat viscous liquids, having the following characteristics:

Boiling point at 0.05 mm 210–230°C, refractive index n_D^{20} 1.5707..... 170 grams
Boiling point at 0.05 mm 230–240°C............................ 15 grams
The total yield amounted to 54 per cent.

In Chap. 2, the discussion of curing mechanisms indicates that caustic catalyzes polymerization via the epoxy groups; it therefore follows that, during synthesis, the introduction of the caustic to neutralize the hydrochloric acid and preserve catalytic action must be done in a carefully controlled manner if high monomeric yields are to be obtained.

An alternate procedure has been suggested in the patent literature (1-3) and involves a two-step process. The first step consists of reacting the bisphenol A and epichlorohydrin in the presence of 0.1 to 0.2 per cent of a Friedel-Crafts type catalyst:

The monomeric material is then treated with a dehydrohalogenating compound, such as the aluminates, silicates, and zincates, in a substantially or completely nonaqueous medium

$$\text{(structure)}\quad \text{—O—CH}_2\text{—}\underset{|}{\overset{\overset{\displaystyle OH}{|}}{CH}}\text{—CH}_2\text{—Cl} \xrightarrow{\ Na_2SiO_3\cdot5H_2O\ }$$

$$\text{(structure)}\quad \text{—O—CH}_2\text{—CH}\overset{O}{\overbrace{\ \ }}\text{CH}_2 + HCl$$

It is claimed that dehydrohalogenating compounds in the above classes have little or no tendency to produce polymerization or hydrolysis of the epoxy products so formed.

SYNTHESIS OF HIGHER-MOLECULAR-WEIGHT EPOXY RESINS

As is seen from the preceding discussion, it is possible to synthesize higher-molecular-weight epoxy resins by reacting epichlorohydrin and bisphenol A in the presence of excess caustic. The general formula for such a resin may be written:

$$CH_2\overset{O}{\overbrace{\ \ }}CH\text{—CH}_2\text{—}\left[\text{O—}\underset{CH_3}{\overset{CH_3}{C}}\text{—}\text{—O—CH}_2\text{—}\underset{}{\overset{OH}{CH}}\text{—CH}_2\text{—}\right]_n$$

$$\text{—O—}\underset{CH_3}{\overset{CH_3}{C}}\text{—}\text{—O—CH}_2\text{—CH}\overset{O}{\overbrace{\ \ }}CH_2$$

Generalized epoxy-resin molecule

where n is the number of repeated units in the resin chain. When $n = 0$, the molecular weight is 340; when $n = 10$, about 3,000. It should be noted that each such molecule contains as many alcoholic hydroxyls as there are n groups and, provided that the molecule is linear with no side branches, no more than two epoxy groups. The number of repeated units may be estimated by determining the epoxide or hydroxyl equivalent by techniques discussed subsequently.

Synthesis of higher-weight molecules requires not only the consumption of the initial epoxy groups in the epichlorohydrin but also, in order to link successive bisphenol groups, the consumption of the groups formed by dehydrohalogenation:

(1) $\sim\!\!\!\bigcirc\!\!\!-\!OH + Cl\!-\!CH_2\!-\!CH\overset{O}{\diagup\diagdown}CH_2 \xrightarrow{NaOH}$

$\sim\!\!\!\bigcirc\!\!\!-\!O\!-\!CH_2\!-\!CH\overset{O}{\diagup\diagdown}CH_2 + HCl$

(2) $\sim\!\!\!\bigcirc\!\!\!-\!O\!-\!CH_2\!-\!CH\overset{O}{\diagup\diagdown}CH_2 + HO\!-\!\bigcirc\!\!\!\sim \xrightarrow{NaOH}$

$\sim\!\!\!\bigcirc\!\!\!-\!O\!-\!CH_2\!-\!\underset{OH}{CH}\!-\!CH_2\!-\!O\!-\!\bigcirc\!\!\!\sim$

It should, therefore, be possible to govern the degree of polymerization by regulating the ratio of epichlorohydrin/bisphenol A in the reaction when employing caustic in excess of the amount required to catalyze the reaction and neutralize the formed hydrochloric acid. Table 1-1 presents data for various mol ratios in terms of resultant molecular weight. In actual practice, it is reported that a slight excess of epichlorohydrin (over the apparently stoichiometric ratio for a given molecular weight) is employed (1-4, 1-5).

A description from the literature illustrates the synthesis of higher-molecular-weight resins (1-4) using 1.12 mols epichlorohydrin/1 mol bisphenol A and employing heat and pressure to regulate the reaction:

The apparatus used was a 7½-gallon steam-jacketed pilot-plant kettle, capable of operating under pressure and equipped with a heavy-duty anchor-type agitator, a thermometer, a hot-water inlet, an adjustable level water take-off line, a gas pressure line with gage and pressure regulator, a vapor outlet line and a loading port and a sight glass in the top of the kettle.

TABLE 1-1. Effect of Varying Reactant Ratios on Molecular Weight of Epoxy Resins (1-20)

Mol ratio epichlorohydrin/ bisphenol A	Mol ratio NaOH/epichlorohydrin	Softening point, °C	Molecular weight	Epoxide equivalent	Epoxy groups per molecule
2.0	1.1	43	451	314	1.39
1.4	1.3	84	791	592	1.34
1.33	1.3	90	802	730	1.10
1.25	1.3	100	1,133	862	1.32
1.2	1.3	112	1,420	1,176	1.21

The kettle was loaded with a mixture of 14,950 parts of water, 1,483 parts of commercial caustic soda (98.5 per cent NaOH), 17 parts of sodium orthosilicate, and 6,835 parts of bisphenol. After agitation for several minutes at 50°C, 3,000 parts of epichlorohydrin were added to the reaction mixture and the loading port was closed immediately, agitation being continued. With the exothermic heat of reaction and external heat, the reaction temperature was brought to 115°C over a period of 30 minutes. Compressed air was introduced and the pressure inside the kettle was adjusted to 25 psi, and held there during a 30-minute reaction period at 115°C. The pressure was then increased to 30 to 35 psi to cause the taffylike resinous product to settle to the bottom of the kettle, and as much as possible of the upper water layer was removed with the adjustable-level water take-off line. The taffylike resin was then washed free from the salt and alkali by introducing preheated hot water to the kettle and simultaneously allowing water to flow from the kettle. During the washing period, the resin was continuously agitated. The pressure in the kettle was held at 30 to 35 psi, and the temperature was gradually increased from 120°C to 135°C. After 2½ hours of continuous washing, the water coming from the kettle was neutral. It is important that all of the unreacted alkali, when present, be removed to prevent further polymerization of the resin. After washing was completed, as much water as possible was removed from the kettle through the water take-off line. The air-pressure line was closed and the steam pressure in the jacket increased to raise the temperature of the resin to 137 to 138°C. The steam formed on heating the taffylike resin was slowly released, and, after the pressure had been completely released, the loading port was opened and the last traces of water were removed by heating the resin to 140°C. The resin was continuously agitated during the drying process. The hot resin was then poured from the kettle into a receptacle and allowed to cool.

A second process is available for the synthesis of higher-weight resins which obviates the difficulties involved in washing the contaminants from the heavier compounds. The process requires two steps: (1) the synthesis of a convenient chain molecule, say predominantly $n = 3$; and (2) the reaction of this material with a calculated charge of bisphenol A in the presence of a suitable polymerization agent, which further reacts the terminal epoxy groups with the terminal phenolic hydroxyls of the bisphenol A. This polymerization takes place without the evolution of by-products.

SYNTHESIS OF POLYHYDRIC PHENOL POLYETHER ALCOHOLS

Theoretically it should be possible to create molecules of immense size from epichlorohydrin and bisphenol A; if, for instance, an equimolar ratio were employed, a molecule would be formed equal to the combined weight of all the component adducts, with an aromatic hydroxyl at one end of the chain and an epoxy group at the other. In practice, of course, the reaction starts at many reactive points simultaneously, and as the

molecular weight increases, the resin mobility decreases.   For ester coatings, in which the hydroxyls on the chain are of greater interest than the
epoxy groups, it is desirable to regulate the length of the polymeric chain,
and to accomplish this, monofunctional reactants, such as phenol or
ethylene oxide, can be employed in calculated amounts to end-stop
growth and yield polyhydric phenol polyether alcohols of almost any
given degree of polymerization (1-6).   These higher-weight molecules
will contain a numerous and determinate (1-7) number of alcoholic
hydroxyls capable of direct esterification and are useful in coating
formulations.

Polyhydric phenol polyether alcohols, although containing few if any
epoxy groups, are by custom referred to in the industry as epoxy resins,
since they are synthesized from the basic reactants for diglycidyl ether of
bisphenol A.

SYNTHESIS OF MIXED RESINS

Likewise classifiable as epoxy resins are monoglycidyl ether molecules
containing, for a second reactive point, a mono-olefinic ether.   The
entire mass of such a monomer can be polymerized through one reactive
group to the virtual exclusion of the other; and subsequently, crosslinking
can be accomplished through the remaining terminal group by a different
reactive mechanism.   Representative of this class is allyl glycidyl mixed
diether of bisphenol A (1-8):

$$CH_2\overset{O}{-}CH-CH_2-O-\langle\rangle-\underset{CH_3}{\overset{CH_3}{C}}-\langle\rangle-O-CH_2-CH=CH_2$$

Such materials as epoxidized polyester from tetrahydrophthalic anhydride and diethylene glycol may be formulated to contain a plurality of
epoxy and olefin groups.   These compounds may subsequently be converted in coating formulations by esterification with organic acids and
polymerization through the olefins (1-9).

SYNTHESIS OF OTHER EPOXY RESINS

The number of potentially useful reactants for the synthesis of epoxy
resins is quite large.   All varieties of polyhydric phenols, polyalcohols,
polyfunctional halohydrins, and polyepoxides have been suggested as

intermediates in the patent literature. A few of these are identified in Table 1-2.

Epichlorohydrin and dichlorohydrin are used almost to the exclusion of other epoxy-containing compounds in commercial epoxy-resin synthesis because of their wider availability and lower cost. Butadiene dioxide, however, is a particularly interesting alternative. Since two epoxy groups are initially present, dehydrohalogenation is not required during synthesis, no by-products are formed, and chlorine will not be present, even in small amounts, in the diglycidyl ether (1-10).

Numerous epoxy-type resins and epoxy-containing molecules are also theoretically available from the olefins. The epoxidation of olefins by oxygen and selective metal catalysts, by perbenzoic acid, by acetaldehyde monoperacetate, and by peracetic acid, for example, have been studied for many years and are gaining in industrial importance each year. The introduction of a commercially feasible process for the manufacture of acetic acid through the peracetic acid route, which involves epoxidation of an olefin as a step, promises much in the way of new resins, new diluents, and new epoxy-type products (1-11). The reactions involved here are:

$$CH_3-\overset{\overset{O}{\|}}{C}-H \xrightarrow[0°C]{O_2} CH_3-\overset{OH—\cdots O}{\underset{O——O}{CH}} C-CH_3 \rightarrow$$

Acetaldehyde   Acetaldehyde
                                    monoperacetate

$$CH_3-\overset{\overset{O}{\|}}{C}-O-OH + CH_3-\overset{\overset{O}{\|}}{C}-H$$

Peracetic acid   Acetaldehyde

$$CH_3-\overset{\overset{O}{\|}}{C}-O-OH + R-HC{=}CH-R' \rightarrow$$

Peracetic acid   Olefin

$$R-\overset{O}{\overset{/\backslash}{CH——CH}}-R' + CH_3-\overset{\overset{O}{\|}}{C}-OH$$

Epoxidized molecule   Acetic acid

As an example of the versatility that the peracetic acid process gives to the resin chemist, a crosslinked polybutadiene rubber (which contains terminal and internal olefin groups) was epoxidized to varying degrees with peracetic acid in an effort to combine the thermal and electrical properties of the butadiene with the low-temperature curing properties of the epoxy group. Epoxidation of up to 39 per cent of the internal olefin

TABLE 1-2. Possible Intermediates for the Synthesis of Epoxy Resins

Halohydrins

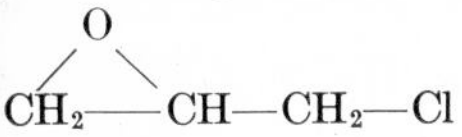

$$CH_2\!\!-\!\!CH\!\!-\!\!CH_2\!\!-\!\!Cl$$ (epoxide O bridging CH₂—CH)
Epichlorohydrin

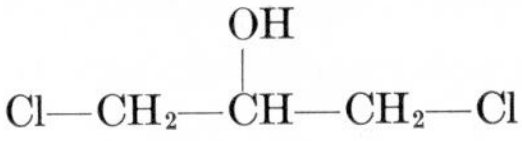

$$Cl\!\!-\!\!CH_2\!\!-\!\!\overset{OH}{CH}\!\!-\!\!CH_2\!\!-\!\!Cl$$
Dichlorohydrin

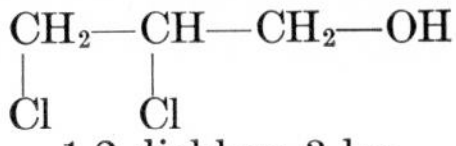

$$CH_2\!\!-\!\!CH\!\!-\!\!CH_2\!\!-\!\!OH$$
$$\quad|\qquad|$$
$$\;Cl\qquad Cl$$
1,2-dichloro-3 hydroxypropane

Diepoxies

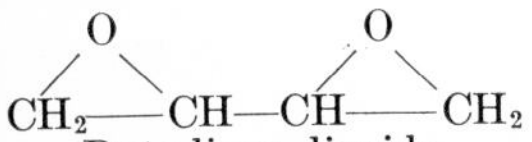

$$CH_2\!\!-\!\!CH\!\!-\!\!CH\!\!-\!\!CH_2$$ (epoxide O bridges at each end)
Butadiene dioxide

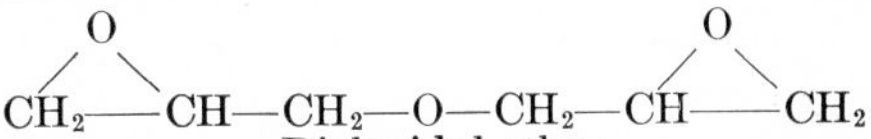

$$CH_2\!\!-\!\!CH\!\!-\!\!CH_2\!\!-\!\!O\!\!-\!\!CH_2\!\!-\!\!CH\!\!-\!\!CH_2$$ (epoxide O bridges at each end)
Diglycidyl ether

Mononuclear di- and trihydroxy phenols

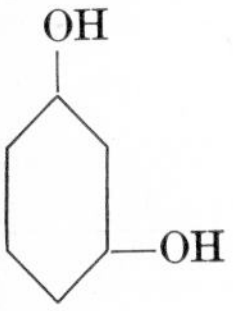

Resorcinol

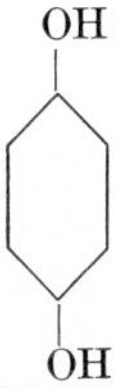

Hydroquinone

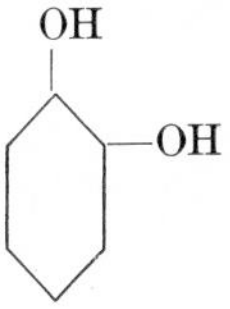

Pyrocatechol

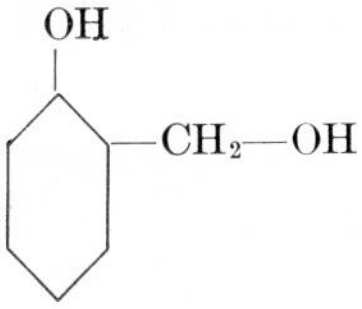

Saligenin

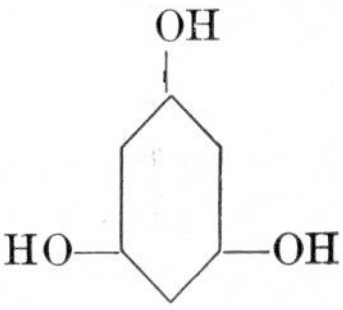

Phloroglucinol

Polynuclear polyhydroxy phenols

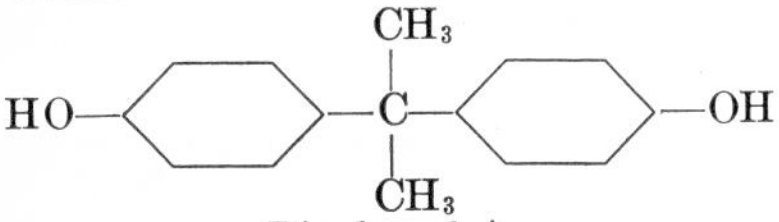

Bisphenol A

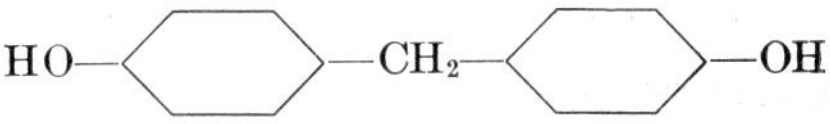

Bisphenol F

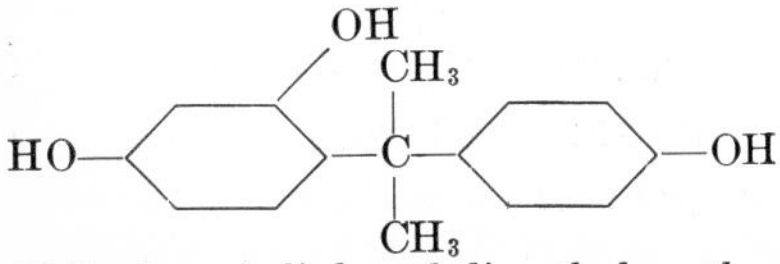

Trihydroxyl diphenyl dimethyl methane

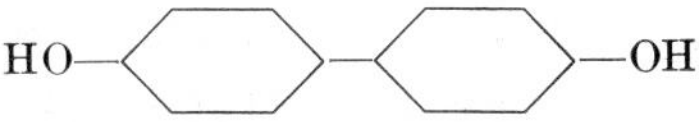

4,4′ dihydroxy biphenyl

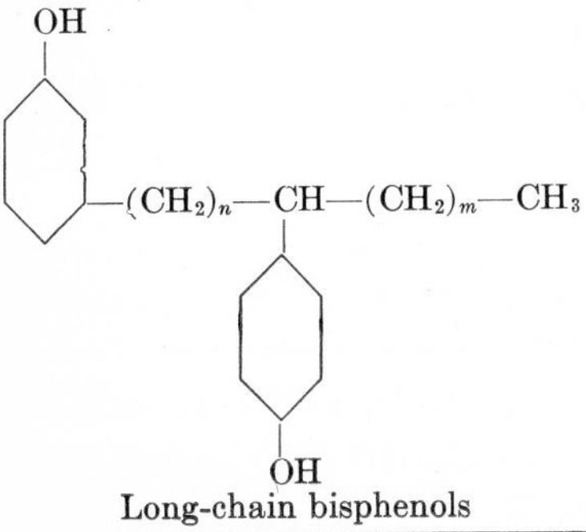

Long-chain bisphenols

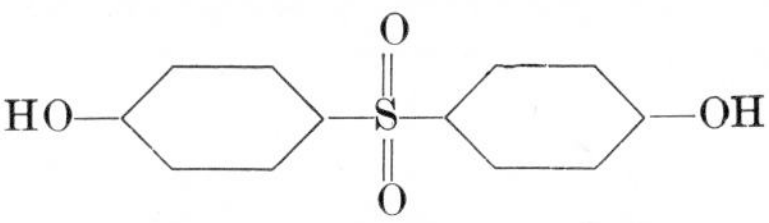

Dihydroxyl diphenyl sulfone

TABLE 1-2. Possible Intermediates for the Synthesis of Epoxy Resins (Continued)

Polynuclear polyhydroxy phenols (Continued)

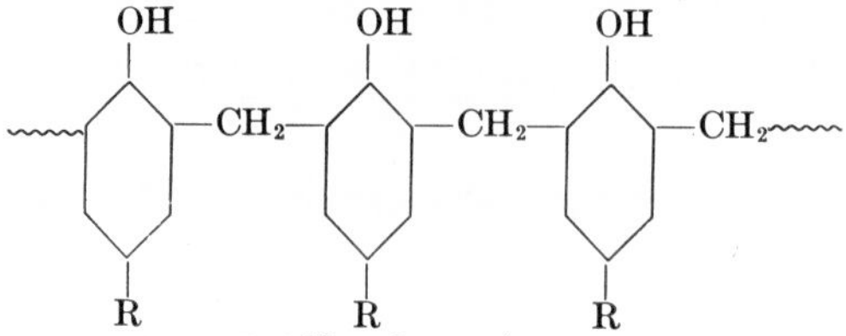

Novolac resins

Polyalcohols

$$CH_2\!-\!CH_2$$
$$\ \ |\qquad\ \ |$$
$$OH\quad OH$$
Ethylene glycol

$$CH_3\!-\!CH\!-\!CH\!-\!CH_3$$
$$\qquad\ \ |\quad\ \ |$$
$$\qquad OH\quad OH$$
2,3 butanediol

$$CH_2\!-\!CH\!-\!CH_2$$
$$\ \ |\qquad\ |\qquad\ |$$
$$OH\quad OH\quad OH$$
Glycerol

$$HO\!-\!CH_2\!-\!CH\!-\!CH\!-\!CH_2\!-\!OH$$
$$\qquad\qquad\ \ |\quad\ \ |$$
$$\qquad\qquad OH\quad OH$$
Erythritol

groups gave a resin which, when cured with polyfunctional amines or acid anhydrides, formed a flexible thermoset resin with good electrical properties (1-12). The number of such hybrids of rubber and epoxies is expected to increase.

Research is in progress on the synthesis of epoxy molecules for high-temperature adhesives; other special-purpose molecules are also in development.

COMMERCIAL EPOXY RESINS

Although there are a number of possible reactants and a wide variety of possible epoxy-resin molecules, it is believed that only three resin types other than diglycidyl ether of bisphenol A (and its homologs) are of commercial significance in the United States: glycidyl ethers of glycerol, glycidyl ethers of bisphenol F, glycidyl ethers of tetrakis (hydroxyphenyl) ethane (1-13), and epoxylated novolacs (1-14).

The epoxylated novolac resins have the general structure:

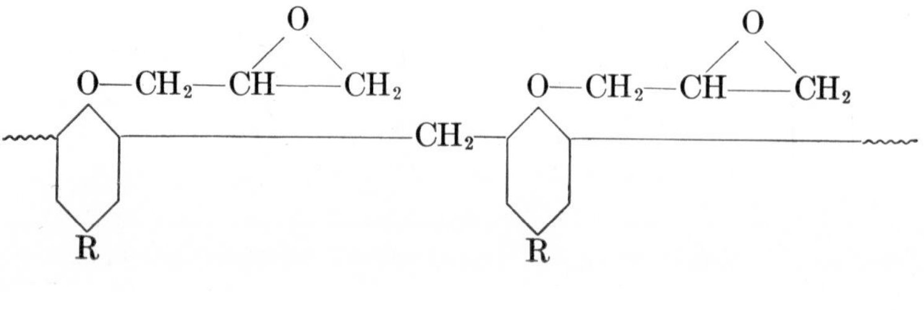

TABLE 1-3. Typical Commercial Epoxy Resins

Resin type*	Melting point, °C (Durrans)	Color, 25°C (Gardner)	Epoxide equivalent	Average molecular weight	Viscosity at 25°C, centipoises or Gardner-Holdt†
Bakelite Co. (Bakelite®):					
ERL-2774............	Liquid	10 (max)	185–200	350–400	10,500–19,500
ERL-3794............	Liquid	5 (max)	170–182	350–400	7,200–19,200
(higher functionality)					
ERL-2795............	Liquid	9 (max)	179–194	340–400	500–900
(contains diluent)					
ERLA-3001..........	25°C	....	....	....	1600–1700‡
(epoxy/phenolic blend)					
EKRA-2002..........	65–75	5 (max)	450–525	900–1,000	C-G
EKRD-2003.........	95–100	6 (max)	875–975	1,400	Q-U
Ciba Co., Inc. (Araldite®):					
502.................	Liquid	4	250	....	3,000
(contains plasticizer)					
6005...............	Liquid	4	190	....	8,000
6010...............	Liquid	4	195	....	16,000
6020...............	Liquid	4	210	....	19,000
6030...............	Liquid	5	225	....	35,000
6040...............	25	5	265	....	90,000
6060...............	60	6	425	....	1000§
6071...............	70	6	485	....	E
6075...............	84	6	690	....	L
6084...............	100	6	935	....	S
6097...............	130	6	1,785	....	Z_1
6099...............	150	8	3,225	....	Z_3
The Dow Chemical Co.:					
DER 331............	Liquid	5 (max)	187–193	350–400	11,000–16,000
DER 332............	Liquid	1 (max)	173–179	340–350	3,600–6,400
DER 334............	Liquid	5 (max)	179–194	....	500–900
DER 661............	74–80	4 (max)	450–525	....	G-H
DER 664............	95–103	4 (max)	875–985	....	R-V
DER 667............	125–131	4 (max)	1,600–2,000	....	Y-Z
Jones-Dabney Co. (Epi-Rez®):					
510.................	Liquid	6	180–200	350–400	9,000–18,000
515.................	20–28	4	235–275	460	A_2-A_1
520.................	65–75	4	450–525	900	C-G_1
522.................	75–85	3	550–650	1,100	F-J
530.................	95–105	3	860–1,015	1,400	Q-U
540.................	127–133	3	1,600–2,000	2,900	X-Z
550.................	145–155	4	2,400–4,000	3,800	Z_2-Z_5

TABLE 1-3. Typical Commercial Epoxy Resins (Continued)

Resin type*	Melting point, °C (Durrans)	Color, 25°C (Gardner)	Epoxide equivalent	Average molecular weight	Viscosity at 25°C, centipoises or Gardner-Holdt†
Shell Chemical Co. (Epon®):					
562................	Liquid	5 (max)	140–165	300	150–210
(aliphatic based)					
815................	Liquid	8 (max)	175–210	340–400	500–900
(contains diluent)					
820................	Liquid	8 (max)	175–210	350–400	4,000–10,000
828................	Liquid	12 (max)	175–210	350–400	5,000–15,000
834................	Liquid	10 (max)	225–290	450	A_2-A_1
864................	40–50	8 (max)	300–375	700	A_1-B
1001...............	64–76	8 (max)	450–525	900–1,000	C-G
1004...............	95–105	6 (max)	870–1,025	1,400	Q-U
1007...............	125–132	8 (max)	1,650–2,050	2,900	Y-Z_1
1009...............	145–155	11 (max)	2,400–4,000	3,800	Z_2-Z_5
1310...............	77	....	208	77	
(tetraglycidyl ether)					

* Based on bisphenol A unless otherwise noted.
† In 40 per cent butyl carbitol.
‡ At 60°C.
§ At 130°C.
All values taken from sales literature of suppliers.

Because they have a functionality greater than two, they provide somewhat higher heat-distortion temperatures and better high-temperature performance than do bisphenol A resins. Epoxylated novolacs having 2.5 to 3 epoxy groups per molecule can, in some systems, offer 30 to 40°C improvement in heat-distortion temperatures (1-15). Their commercial importance is expected to increase.

Throughout the text, unless otherwise indicated, typical values for cured-resin systems are based on diglycidyl ether of bisphenol A type resins, these accounting for by far the majority of resin production.

The first major resin producers in the United States were Bakelite Company, Division of Union Carbide and Carbon Corporation (Bakelite®), Ciba Company (Araldite®), The Dow Chemical Co., Jones-Dabney Company, a subsidiary of Devoe and Raynolds, Inc. (Epi-Rez®), and Shell Chemical Corporation (Epon®). Table 1-3 presents selected properties of the epoxy resins marketed by these resin suppliers. The Borden

Co. (Epiphen®) has introduced a line of resins not based on epichlorohydrin and bisphenol.

RESIN CHARACTERIZATION

The six chief characteristics of epoxy resins which may be used as
guides to their structure and usefulness are:
1. Viscosity.
2. Epoxide equivalent.
3. Hydroxyl equivalent.
4. Average molecular weight and molecular-weight distribution.
5. Softening point.
6. Heat-distortion temperature of cured resin.

Viscosity

Viscosity is a useful index to handling properties as well as to the
general molecular weight of the resin.   Viscosities of the liquid resins are
commonly measured with rotating cylinder or spindle viscometers such
as the Brookfield.   For measuring the viscosity of solid resins, a 40 per
cent solution by weight in butyl carbitol is commonly used.   The solution
is suitable for use in capillary or orifice viscometers.   Table 1-3 indicates
the viscosity range for commercial resins.

Epoxide Equivalent

The epoxide equivalent is the weight of resin in grams which contains
1 gram chemical equivalent of epoxy.   Low-molecular-weight resins have
an epoxide equivalent in the 175 to 200 range; higher-weight resins, correspondingly higher values, since in each such molecule there are long
chains between the epoxy groups.   If the resin chains are assumed to be
linear with no side branching and it is further assumed that an epoxy
group terminates each end, then the epoxide equivalent (weight) is one
half of the average molecular weight of the resin.

The term epoxy value is also employed and represents the fractional
number of epoxy groups contained in 100 grams of resin.   The two terms
are essentially equivalent.   Dividing the epoxy value into 100 gives the
epoxide equivalent.

Epoxide equivalents are determined by reacting a known quantity of
resin with a known quantity of hydrochloric acid and back-titrating the
remaining acid to determine its consumption.

The technique is based on the reaction:

$$\underset{\displaystyle \sim\!\!\sim\!\!\sim\!\!-CH\!\!-\!\!-CH_2}{\overset{\displaystyle O}{\overbrace{\qquad\qquad}}} + HCl \rightarrow \underset{\displaystyle \sim\!\!\sim\!\!\sim\!\!CH\!\!-\!\!CH_2\!\!-\!\!Cl}{\overset{\displaystyle OH}{\underset{\displaystyle |}{}}}$$

The reaction is usually accomplished by adding to 1 gram of resin an excess of pyridine containing pyridine hydrochloride (made by adding

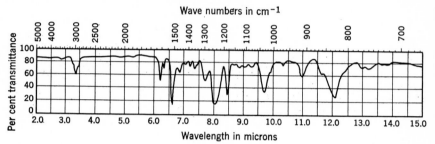

FIG. 1-1. Infrared spectrum for commercial bisphenol-type epoxy resin, mol. wt 400 (1-16).

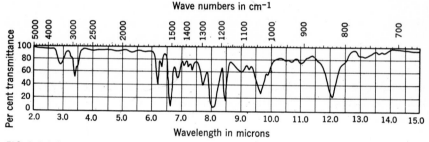

FIG. 1-2. Infrared spectrum for commercial bisphenol-type epoxy resin, mol. wt 1,000 (1-16).

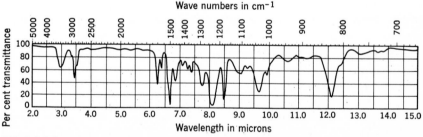

FIG. 1-3. Infrared spectrum for commercial bisphenol-type epoxy resin, mol. wt. 4000 (1-16).

16 ml of concentrated hydrochloric acid per liter of pyridine), boiling for 20 minutes, and back-titrating the excess pyridine hydrochloride with 0.1 normal sodium hydroxide, using phenolphthalein as an indicator.

Infrared spectroscopy may also be used to measure epoxide equivalents. Figures 1-1 to 1-3 show the infrared spectra of three commercial resins in the 2- to 15-micron range (1-16).   Absorption-band characteristics of epoxy resins are in evidence at $\sim$2.95, 7.44, 9.05, $\sim$10.60, 10.95, and 11.60 μ.   The bands at 10.95 and 11.60 μ have been attributed to the epoxy group, the band at 2.9 μ to the hydroxyl group, and the band at 3.5 μ to the methylene group.

TABLE 1-4. Infrared Band Intensity Changes as a Function of Resin Molecular Weight (1-16)

Wave length, μ	Average molecular weight of resin						
	350–400	450	700	900–1,000	1,400	2,900	3,800
2.90	0.126	0.186	0.332	0.402	0.409	0.411	0.461
3.37	0.736	0.749	0.701	0.791	0.665	0.726	0.764
6.21	1.00	1.00	1.00	1.00	1.00	1.00	1.00
7.45	0.300	0.284	0.319	0.324	0.267	0.253	0.296
8.45	1.904	2.25	1.88	2.11	1.910	2.22	1.988
9.05	0.340	0.401	0.540	0.600	0.565	0.611	0.593
10.95	0.712	0.578	0.450	0.337	0.260	0.204	0.193
11.60	0.592	0.480	0.393	0.289	0.228	0.180	0.157
12.06	2.01	2.03	1.63	1.81	1.682	1.71	1.573

In going from lower to higher-molecular-weight resins, the bands change in intensity as the percentages of the various groups change.   Using the absorption band at 6.21 μ as a reference, these changes in intensity may be related (Table 1-4).   When the relative absorbances are plotted as a function of either the epoxide equivalent or the chemically determined molecular weight, reasonably smooth curves are obtained.   If the relative absorbance is corrected to take into account the residual absorption at 10.95 μ in the absence of epoxy groups, a corrected absorbance $R_c = R - 0.173$ is obtained.   A plot of log R_c vs. log epoxide equivalent (Fig. 1-4) shows that a linear relationship results.   Similar values have been obtained with the band at 11.60 μ (1-16).

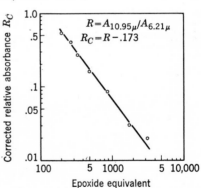

FIG. 1-4. Corrected infrared absorbance vs. epoxide equivalent (1-16).

The effect of organic additives in the resins in even low percentages can be determined by infrared spectroscopy also.   Figure 1-5 presents the analysis of a commercial diglycidyl ether of bisphenol A to which approximately 10 per cent of a reactive diluent (Chap. 6) has been added to improve the fluidity. The marked decrease in transmittance (from 60 to 30 per cent) at 3.5 μ implies a linear hydrocarbon chain, whereas the decrease (from 60 to 35 per cent) at 10.96 μ implies an epoxy group. Such a molecule would be represented by a diluent such as butyl glycidyl ether.

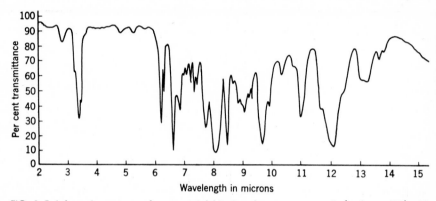

FIG. 1-5. Infrared spectrum of commercial bisphenol-type epoxy resin (mol. wt. 400) with reactive diluent (1-18).

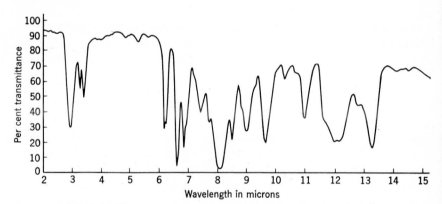

FIG. 1-6. Infrared spectrum for epoxy-phenolic resin blend (1-18).

Figure 1-6 shows the analysis of a blend of epoxy and phenolic resins. Although the epoxy band at 10.96 μ is preserved, the over-all spectrum is changed markedly, with the additional hydroxyl groups present in the phenolic resin evidencing themselves by the low transmission in the 2.9-μ band.

Resins based on polyalcohols such as glycerol instead of bisphenol A give entirely different spectra, but, of course, the hydroxyl and epoxy bands are preserved (Fig. 1-7).

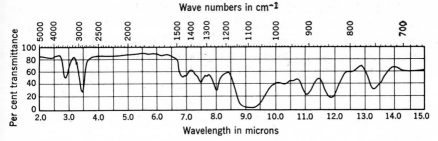

FIG. 1-7. Infrared spectrum for commercial aliphatic-type epoxy resin (1-16).

The theoretical epoxide equivalent of pure diglycidyl ether of bisphenol A is 170.   Typical values for commercial resins are reported in Table 1-3.

Hydroxyl Equivalent

Hydroxyl equivalent is the weight of resin containing one equivalent weight of hydroxyl groups.   Hydroxyl equivalents may be determined by a number of methods: (1) infrared techniques, (2) esterification with acids, (3) reaction with acetyl chloride, and (4) reaction with lithium aluminum hydride.

The first method is similar to that used in determining epoxide equivalents spectroscopically.

The second method involves esterifying the resin with about twice the theoretical amount of linseed-oil acids necessary to react with all the hydroxyl groups at a temperature of 225°C until a constant acid value is obtained and then back-titrating the unreacted linseed acids and calculating the hydroxyl groups plus epoxy content, one epoxy group being taken as equivalent to two hydroxyl groups.

The third method, involving reaction with acetyl chloride, is more common, and the procedure is given in detail:

One to two grams of epoxy resin is dissolved in 10 ml of purified dioxane, in a 250-ml volumetric flask.   The mixture is then warmed to 60°C and swirled to complete solution.   After the mixture has cooled to room temperature, 10 ml of 1.5 M acetyl chloride in toluene is added from a pipette.   It is then swirled gently and chilled to 0°C, at which time 2 ml of c.p. pyridine is added by pipette.   The flask is stoppered, shaken thoroughly, and placed in a water bath at 60 ± 1°C.   The stopper is loosened momentarily to release pressure.   The mixture is held at the temperature for 1 hour and shaken vigorously every 10 minutes.

The flask is then cooled in an ice-water bath.   Then 25 ml of chilled distilled water is added and the mixture shaken well.   It is allowed to stand in the ice bath for 30 minutes, with occasional shaking to decompose the excess reagent.   Next, 25 ml of chilled acetone is added to prevent emulsification.   A few drops of cresol red indicator solution (0.1 per cent in 50 per cent ethanol) are then added, and the mixture is titrated with standard 0.5 N alcoholic sodium hydroxide solution to the first definite violet color, with the flask in the ice water during most of the titration. Any slow fading of the indicator color at the end point is disregarded. Duplicate blank determinations are then made under identical conditions, but omitting the resin sample.   The difference between the average blank and the sample titration is a measure of the hydroxyl content.

Average Molecular Weight and Molecular-weight Distribution

In commercial resins, the structure of the resinous mass varies considerably as to the number of repeated units per molecule.   Thus, a commercial resin might have a small percentage of monomers, where $n = 0$, some polymers of $n = 1$ and $n = 2$, a large percentage of $n = 4$, and a small percentage of $n = 5, 6,$ and 7.   The higher-molecular-weight units would balance out the lower-molecular-weight ones, and the average molecular weight would be representative of a polymer having a composition entirely of $n = 4$.   The properties of the cured resin (i.e., tensile strength, heat-distortion temperature, etc.) would be affected by the actual percentages present.

Average molecular weight may be determined by elevation-of-boiling-point methods.   That is, when a nonvolatile solute is dissolved in a solvent, the vapor pressure of the solute is decreased; as a consequence, the boiling point of the solution is higher than that of the solvent.   The extent of the elevation depends on the concentration.

In addition to average molecular weight, the actual percentages of high- and low-molecular-weight species making up the average may be determined.   In the case of the simple resin synthesized by employing the stoichiometric ratio (i.e., 2:1) of the two basic reactants, a molecular-weight-distribution study was made.   A fractional extraction with normal heptane provided a liquid fraction consisting of a higher-melting-point resin.   The following is an account from the literature (1-17):

By fractional distillation at 1 micron pressure and between 160° and 300°C approximately half of the material distilled and a large part of this distillate was liquid and apparently made up largely of diglycidyl ether of bisphenol with some hydrolyzed epoxides and some polymeric products.   Fractions were thus obtained having an epoxide equivalent of 183 to 185 and fractions having somewhat higher epoxide equivalents up to around 300.   The residual resin had a melting point of about 62.5°C and an epoxide equivalent of about 525.   In referring to average molecular weight based on a standard boiling-point-elevation method, accordingly, and epoxide groups per molecule based on the average molecular weight, these figures do not represent a homogeneous, uniform product but a mixture of monomeric and polymeric liquid and solid resins including diepoxides and polymeric and hydrolyzed products.

Softening Point

Uncured resins may be qualitatively graded by the ring-and-ball softening-point method or Durran's mercury method. These measure the temperature at which the resin reaches an arbitrary softness or viscosity. Typical values are shown in Fig. 1-8.

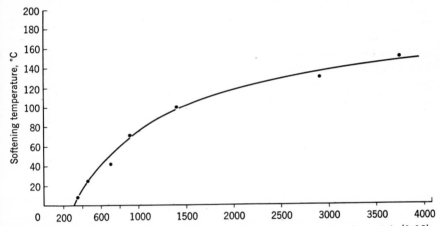

FIG. 1-8. Typical softening-point values for uncured epoxy resins vs. molecular weight (1-19).

In Durran's mercury method, a known weight of the resin is melted in a standard test tube, cooled, and a known quantity of clean mercury is placed on top of the solidified sample. The tube and contents are again heated, and the temperature at which the molten resin rises to the top of the mercury is recorded as the melting point. Since resins in general are not single chemical entities, it is not possible to obtain sharp melting points as is the case with a pure substance. Therefore, any value for the melting point of the resin is empirical and is determined by the conditions under which the test is conducted. Durran's mercury method for determining melting points appears to stabilize these melting-point conditions and to eliminate to a considerable degree the possible personal bias of the observer.

An alternative method is to employ a dilatometer to obtain second-order transition temperatures, i.e., points at which a sharp break in otherwise linear thermal-expansion characteristics occurs, indicating an internal spacial rearrangement caused by expansion of the resin.

Heat-distortion Temperature

The heat-distortion temperature is a valuable criterion for the evaluation of new resins, for the determination of the effects of diluents and impurities present, for the evaluation of new curing agents, and for the determination of the proper amounts of curing agent to employ in a specific resin system. The heat-distortion test is, therefore, of wide utility in the laboratory and in practical research. Unlike the foregoing characterizing techniques, it is employed on a cured-resin system.

Most commonly, heat-distortion temperature is determined by the ASTM procedure (ASTM D648-56). In this test, a standard bar of cured resin, suspended at each end, is loaded in the middle with a weight designed to give a uniform fiber stress of 264 psi. The sample is then immersed in a hot oil bath with a temperature control and a deflection measuring dial indicator. The dial indicator is set at zero and the bath warmed at a rate of 2°C per minute. When deflection of the bar reaches 0.010 inch, the temperature of the bath is reported as the heat-distortion temperature. Heat-distortion temperatures given subsequently in the text have been determined by this or equivalent procedures.

CONCLUSION

This chapter has discussed the relationship of the epoxy resins to more conventional thermosetting plastics in terms of several commercially important properties and has indicated that the epoxy resins commercially available are predominantly based on diglycidyl ether of bisphenol A, synthesized from two widely available commercial reactants, epichlorohydrin and bisphenol A. It was noted that values reported subsequently are, unless otherwise stated, based on the diglycidyl ether of bisphenol A.

The synthesis of lower-molecular-weight species involves the use of excess epichlorohydrin and carefully regulated amounts of caustic; the synthesis of the higher-weight species involves the use of excess caustic and carefully regulated amounts of epichlorohydrin. In both cases, alternate procedures may be used, requiring two-step processes.

High-molecular-weight nonepoxy-containing molecules can be obtained by regulating the degree of polymerization during synthesis by the addition of monofunctional reactants; and mixed diethers can be formed which polymerize by one mechanism and crosslink by a second.

A number of intermediates, other than epichlorohydrin and bisphenol

A, were suggested as feasible reactants for the synthesis of epoxy-resin molecules; and a brief discussion of the chief commercial resins was presented, together with details on techniques used in characterizing the commercial compounds.

References

1-1. Castan, Process for the Manufacture of Thermosetting Synthetic Resins by the Polymerization of Alkylene Oxide Derivatives, U.S. 2,444,333 (1948).
1-2. Werner and Farenhorst, Preparation of Glycidyl Polyethers of Polyhydric Aromatic Alcohols, U.S. 2,467,171 (1949).
1-3. Zech, Epoxide Preparations, U.S. 2,538,072 (1951).
1-4. Greenlee, Manufacture of Epoxide Resins, U.S. 2,694,694 (1954).
1-5. Wynstra, The Chemistry of Epoxy Resins, paper presented at North New Jersey Section, American Chemical Society, March, 1956.
1-6. Greenlee, Polymeric Polyether Polyhydric Alcohols, U.S. 2,558,949 (1951).
1-7. Earhart and Montague, Compositions of Epoxy Resin Esters, *Industrial and Engineering Chemistry*, July, 1957.
1-8. Shokal and Whitehill, Allyl Glycidyl Mixed Diether of Bis (4-hydroxyphenyl)-2,2-propane and Polymers Thereof, U.S. 2,464,753 (1949).
1-9. Greenlee, Pearce, and Kawa, Film Curing by Simultaneous Esterification and Olefin Polymerization, *Industrial and Engineering Chemistry*, July, 1957.
1-10. Greenlee, Polyepoxide Compositions, U.S. 2,592,560 (1952).
1-11. Phillips, Oxidation of Olefins, paper presented at American Chemical Society Meeting, Dallas, Tex., April, 1956.
1-12. Fitzgerald, Carr, Maienthal, and Franklin, Epoxy-Polybutadiene Resins, *Electronics Equipment*, July, 1956.
1-13. Shell Development Co., Technical Data Sheet DS-56:3 (revised April, 1957).
1-14. Hanson and Ringwald, Resins from Phenol-Formaldehyde Condensates and Epichlorohydrin, Brit. 746,824 (1956).
1-15. Partansky and Schrader, Some Thermal Properties of Epoxylated Novolac and Bisphenol A Types Casting Resins, paper presented at Division of Paint, Plastics, and Printing Ink Chemistry, ACS Symposium, Atlantic City, September, 1956.
1-16. Kagarise and Weinberger, Infra Red Spectrophotography of Plastics and Resins, Government Report PB 111438, May, 1954.
1-17. Greenlee, Epoxide Resins, U.S. 2,582,985 (1952).
1-18. Wynstra, Bakelite Company, private communication.
1-19. Shell Chemical Co., sales literature.
1-20. Newey and Shokal, Glycidyl Ether Compositions and Method of Using Same, U.S. 2,575,558 (1951).

2

CURING OF EPOXY RESINS

One of the valuable properties of epoxy resins is their ability to transform readily from the liquid (or thermoplastic) state to tough, hard thermoset solids. This hardening is accomplished by the addition of a chemically active reagent known as a curing agent (or hardener or activator or catalyst). Some curing agents promote curing by catalytic action; others participate directly in the reaction and are absorbed into the resin chain. Depending upon the particular agent, curing may be accomplished at room temperature, with heat produced by exothermic reaction, or may require application of external heat.

This chapter outlines the nature and mechanisms of the curing reaction. It provides a basic, if simplified, three-dimensional concept of the cured-resin system, which will contribute to an understanding of the ultimate structure and, hence, the properties of the thermoset epoxy resin.

Epoxy resins in the pure or uncontaminated state possess indefinite shelf life. They are chemically stable at temperatures up to 200°C. The resins cure into thermoset compounds by three reactions: (1) direct linkage between epoxy groups, (2) linkage of epoxy groups with aromatic or aliphatic hydroxyls, and (3) crosslinkage with the curing agent through various radicals.

Since, however, the epoxy resins cure to hard, infusible materials, the reaction products are not readily amenable to chemical analysis. This fact, coupled with the complexity of the reactions that may occur, poses a number of problems for the investigator. These can, to an extent, be overcome by employing monofunctional reactants, selected for their chemical resemblance to the constituent parts of the actual resin, as models, and, by controlling the conditions of reaction, isolating the competing mechanisms. Thus, phenyl glycidyl ether

$$\underset{CH_2}{\overset{O}{\diagup\diagdown}}\!\!-\!\!CH\!-\!CH_2\!-\!O\!-\!\langle \rangle$$

and tolyl glycidyl ether

$$CH_2-CH-CH_2-O-\hspace{-0.3em}\langle\hspace{1em}\rangle\hspace{-0.3em}-CH_3$$

are representative of the diglycidyl ether of bisphenol A cut in half at the mid-point of the resin chain. Each "half" is free to react as though it were in the resin, but the uncrosslinked reaction products are soluble and amenable to analysis. Similarly, ditolyl glyceryl ether

$$H_3C-\hspace{-0.3em}\langle\hspace{1em}\rangle\hspace{-0.3em}-O-CH_2-CH-CH_2-O-\hspace{-0.3em}\langle\hspace{1em}\rangle\hspace{-0.3em}-CH_3$$

serves as a model of the middle section of higher-molecular-weight hydroxyl-containing resins. Care must be taken, however, in selecting the specific model for the analysis. Model compounds not containing ether linkages, for example, behave in a markedly different fashion from those which more nearly simulate the epoxy-resin structure. By combining properly selected model compounds at the proper ratio, a close approximation of the actual resin may be obtained.

The following discussion represents conclusions obtained from a number of experiments primarily with model compounds. The discussion is based chiefly on the work of Shechter, Wynstra, and Kurkjy (2-1, 2-2, 2-3), Narracott (2-4), and Fisch, Hofmann, and Koskikallio (2-5, 2-6).

POLYMERIZATION THROUGH EPOXY GROUPS

The reactivity of commercial epoxy resins is enhanced by the ether linkage (2-3), which even though separated by a methylene group ($-CH_2-$) from the epoxy ring exerts an extremely strong activating effect. Because of this reactivity, the epoxy group may be readily opened not only by available ions and active hydrogens but even by tertiary (R_3N) amines. The tertiary amines used commercially are discussed in Chap. 4.

With tertiary amine cures, epoxy-epoxy polymerization may occur. The opening of the epoxy group is believed to take place in the following manner (2-4):

$$R_3N + CH_2-CH\sim\sim \rightarrow R\overset{\oplus}{N}_3-CH_2-CH\sim\sim$$
$$\underset{O^{\ominus}}{}$$

Assuming that this ion is capable of opening a new epoxy group,

$$\sim\!\!\sim CH_2\!-\!CH\!\!\sim\!\!\sim \ +\ CH_2\!\!\overset{O}{\overset{\diagup\,\diagdown}{}}\!\!CH\!\!\sim\!\!\sim\ \rightarrow\ \sim\!\!\sim CH_2\!-\!CH\!\!\sim\!\!\sim$$

at the left: $\underset{O^{\ominus}}{\overset{|}{}}$; at the right: $\overset{|}{O}$, then $CH_2\!-\!CH\!\!\sim\!\!\sim$, then $\underset{O^{\ominus}}{\overset{|}{}}$

the reaction may then proceed

$$\sim\!\!\sim CH_2\!-\!CH\!\!\sim\!\!\sim$$
$$\overset{|}{O}$$
$$CH_2\!-\!CH\!\!\sim\!\!\sim$$
$$\overset{|}{O}$$
$$CH_2\!-\!CH\!\!\sim\!\!\sim$$
$$\overset{|}{O}$$
$$CH_2\!-\!CH\!\!\sim\!\!\sim$$
$$\overset{|}{O}$$
$$CH_2\!-\!CH\!\!\sim\!\!\sim$$
$$\overset{|}{O^{\ominus}}$$

to result in a very long chain system. Thus, visualize several epoxy-resin molecules (e.g., diglycidyl ether of bisphenol A) lying beside each other in the liquid state (Fig. 2-1). Supposing that this simplified curing reaction took place between the several molecules, then the cured-resin system would appear as the united, infusible network presented in Fig. 2-2.

However, it is most improbable that the molecules would ever be lined up so uniformly in the liquid uncured state as shown in Fig. 2-2. The head or tail of other molecules would protrude into the system, and the cured resin would have somewhat the appearance shown in Fig. 2-3. Going one step further, it must be remembered that the various molecules can lie in a third dimension, i.e., project up from the plane of the page or down into it, also that the resin can bend and twist to some extent in most of its bonds to assume many contorted shapes.

The polymerization, thus, takes place among molecules in three dimen-

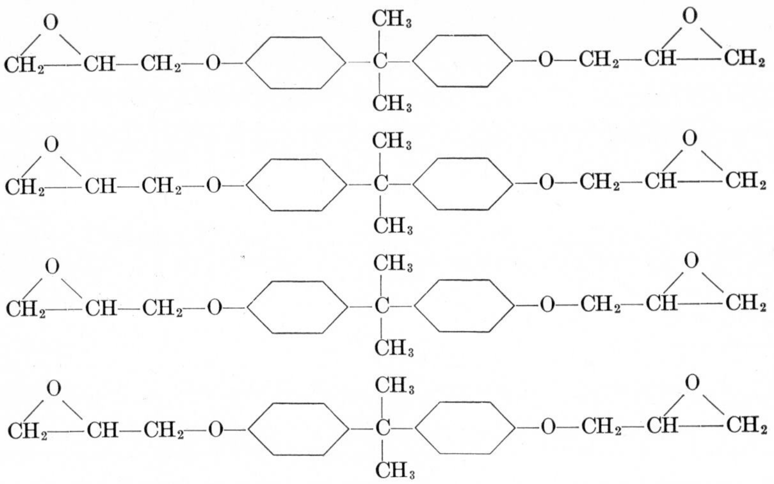

$$CH_2\!-\!CH\!-\!CH_2\!-\!O\!-\!\bigcirc\!-\!\underset{\underset{CH_3}{|}}{\overset{\overset{CH_3}{|}}{C}}\!-\!\bigcirc\!-\!O\!-\!CH_2\!-\!CH\!-\!CH_2$$

$$CH_2\!-\!CH\!-\!CH_2\!-\!O\!-\!\bigcirc\!-\!\underset{\underset{CH_3}{|}}{\overset{\overset{CH_3}{|}}{C}}\!-\!\bigcirc\!-\!O\!-\!CH_2\!-\!CH\!-\!CH_2$$

$$CH_2\!-\!CH\!-\!CH_2\!-\!O\!-\!\bigcirc\!-\!\underset{\underset{CH_3}{|}}{\overset{\overset{CH_3}{|}}{C}}\!-\!\bigcirc\!-\!O\!-\!CH_2\!-\!CH\!-\!CH_2$$

$$CH_2\!-\!CH\!-\!CH_2\!-\!O\!-\!\bigcirc\!-\!\underset{\underset{CH_3}{|}}{\overset{\overset{CH_3}{|}}{C}}\!-\!\bigcirc\!-\!O\!-\!CH_2\!-\!CH\!-\!CH_2$$

FIG. 2-1. Simplified picture of epoxy resins crosslinking under idealized conditions.   Four epoxy molecules side by side, about to react.

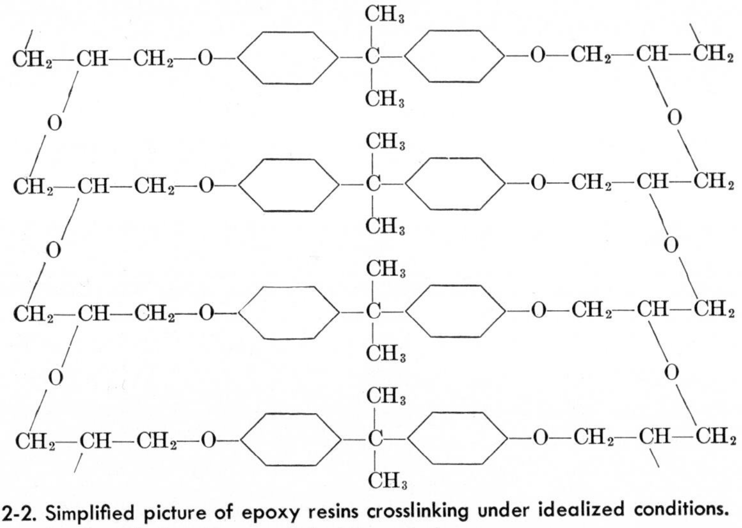

$$CH_2\!-\!CH\!-\!CH_2\!-\!O\!-\!\bigcirc\!-\!\underset{\underset{CH_3}{|}}{\overset{\overset{CH_3}{|}}{C}}\!-\!\bigcirc\!-\!O\!-\!CH_2\!-\!CH\!-\!CH_2$$

FIG. 2-2. Simplified picture of epoxy resins crosslinking under idealized conditions.   Four epoxy molecules side by side, crosslinked through the epoxy groups.

sions to build exceedingly complex structures.   Chain building will be terminated randomly by blocking off of the final activated epoxy, and always some epoxy groups on the ends of polymers will be trapped in corners between other chains and without adjacent groups to react with.

Although the above discussion presents a reasonably accurate description of the cured polymer, the actual mechanisms by which it is achieved

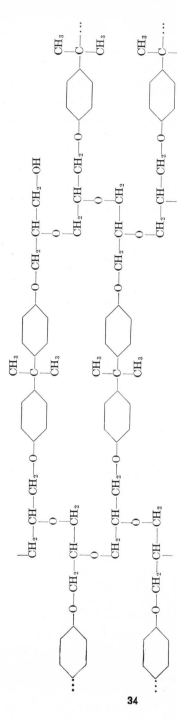

FIG. 2-3. Simplified picture of epoxy resins crosslinking under idealized conditions. Six adjacent molecules are shown as crosslinked. Molecules can extend in all three dimensions to form very complex networks. The polymer shown here is referred to as a "homopolymer" because it is made up entirely of epoxy-resin molecules. When crosslinking agents such as polyfunctional amines and acid anhydrides are used to achieve cure, these are built into the crosslinked chain and considerably change the intermolecular spacing, heat distortion temperature, thermal stability, and chemical resistance. The ease by which epoxy resins form such "heteropolymers" is the basis for the wide range of properties that may be achieved in cured epoxy-resin systems.

34

are somewhat more complex. Even when a tertiary amine is employed as curing agent, it is unlikely that the direct epoxy-epoxy polymerization occurs. Hydroxyl groups along the chain of higher-weight resin species and present from water would necessarily enter in the reaction as an intermediate step. This process is discussed subsequently.

POLYMERIZATION THROUGH HYDROXYL GROUPS

Epoxy groups will react (1) with hydroxyl groups introduced into the resin by the curing agent or modifiers, (2) with hydroxyl groups present in the resin chain of higher-weight homologs, (3) with hydroxyl groups formed as an epoxy group is opened by an active hydrogen during cure, and (4) with various phenolic hydroxyls present as unreacted phenol, bisphenol, resorcinol, etc.

The epoxy groups, if uncatalyzed, do not react readily with the hydroxyl groups present along the higher-weight resin chain as evidenced by the stability of uncontaminated resins at temperatures up to 200°C. However under suitable conditions, once the epoxy-hydroxyl polymerization is started, it proceeds very rapidly.

The first step of the epoxy-hydroxyl reaction may be represented (2-2):

$$R\!-\!OH + CH_2\!-\!CH\!\!\sim\!\!\sim \xrightarrow{\text{catalyst}} \begin{array}{l} RO\!-\!CH_2\!-\!CH\!\!\sim\!\!\sim \quad \alpha \text{ isomer} \\ \qquad\qquad\quad | \\ \qquad\qquad\ OH \\[4pt] HO\!-\!CH_2\!-\!CH\!\!\sim\!\!\sim \quad \beta \text{ isomer} \\ \qquad\qquad\quad | \\ \qquad\qquad\ OR \end{array}$$

Although two isomers are possible, either provides a new hydroxyl group which is susceptible to continued polymerization. Showing further reaction of the α isomer, for example, to proceed through hydroxyls,

$$RO\!-\!CH_2\!-\!CH\!\!\sim\!\!\sim + CH_2\!-\!CH\!\!\sim\!\!\sim \rightarrow$$
$$\qquad\qquad\quad | $$
$$\qquad\qquad\ OH$$

$$RO\!-\!CH_2\!-\!CH\!\!\sim\!\!\sim$$
$$\qquad\qquad\quad |$$
$$\qquad\qquad\ O\!-\!CH_2\!-\!CH\!\!\sim\!\!\sim$$
$$\qquad\qquad\qquad\qquad\quad |$$
$$\qquad\qquad\qquad\qquad\ OH$$

a structure very similar to that postulated for the epoxy-epoxy reaction cured compound will result. The reaction, as before, can continue until a high degree of crosslinking is achieved.

As was noted in the equation, some form of catalyst is required to promote this reaction. The catalyst may be an acid or a base. Acid catalysts are discussed under crosslinking agents, as are the basic primary and secondary amines. The principal agents useful for promoting epoxy-hydroxyl reactions are the inorganic bases, such as sodium hydroxide (employed in resin synthesis) and tertiary amines (employed in resin cure); both impart considerable selectivity to the reaction.

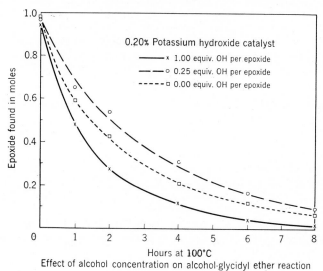

Effect of alcohol concentration on alcohol-glycidyl ether reaction

FIG. 2-4. Alcohol-epoxy reaction in presence of fixed base is virtually independent of alcohol concentration (2-2).

In the case of an inorganic base, the reaction appears to be ionic, that is, prefers to travel through the more readily ionizable hydroxyls of the base than through the alcoholic hydroxyls present in the resin. The concentration of the alcoholic hydroxyls appears to have little influence on the reaction rate (Fig. 2-4).

The reaction is believed (2-2) to proceed through the alkoxide ion as follows:

$$RO^{\ominus} + CH_2 \overset{O}{\diagup\diagdown} CH\text{\textasciitilde\textasciitilde} \rightarrow RO-CH_2-\underset{\underset{O^{\ominus}}{|}}{CH}\text{\textasciitilde\textasciitilde} + HO-R' \rightarrow$$

$$RO-CH_2-\underset{\underset{OH}{|}}{CH}\text{\textasciitilde\textasciitilde} + R'O^{\ominus}$$

The regenerated alkoxide ion is then available to open a second epoxy group.

If a small amount of a nonhydroxyl containing tertiary amine instead of the inorganic base is used as catalyst, the concentration of alcohol determines the reaction rate (Fig. 2-5), indicating here again that the reaction prefers to travel through the hydroxyls rather than by the epoxy-epoxy

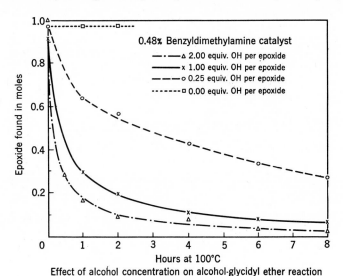

Effect of alcohol concentration on alcohol-glycidyl ether reaction

FIG. 2-5. Alcohol-epoxy reaction in presence of amine catalyst is dependent on alcohol concentration (2-2).

route. This reaction is believed, as in the case of the inorganic base, to be essentially ionic:

(1) $\quad R_3N + \overset{O}{\overset{\triangle}{CH-CH}}\!\sim \rightarrow R_3\overset{\oplus}{N}-CH_2-\underset{\underset{O^{\ominus}}{|}}{CH}\!\sim$

(2) $\quad R_3\overset{\oplus}{N}-CH_2-\underset{\underset{O^{\ominus}}{|}}{CH}\!\sim + R'OH \rightarrow R_3N-CH_2-\underset{\underset{OH}{|}}{CH}\!\sim + R'O^{\ominus}$

The accelerating effect of alcoholic hydroxyls on tertiary amine cures is significant in commercial practice, since a number of hydroxyls may be present in the catalyzed mixture. However, it should be noted that not all tertiary amines are effective catalysts for the epoxies. The greater the steric hindrances at the nitrogen group, the less effective is the catalytic action. This is illustrated in Fig. 2-6.

The reaction mechanism of epoxy groups with phenolic hydroxyls is similar to the epoxy–alcoholic hydroxyl reaction. Below 200°C, the

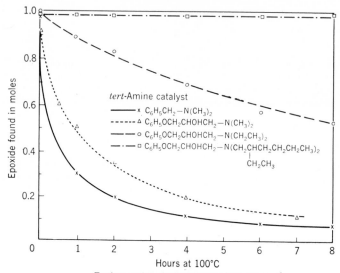

Tertiary amine catalysts tested in reaction of
phenyl-glycidyl ether (1.00 mole) with dipropylene glycol (0.50 mole)

FIG. 2-6. Effect of structure of tertiary amine catalyst on alcohol-epoxy reaction (2-2).

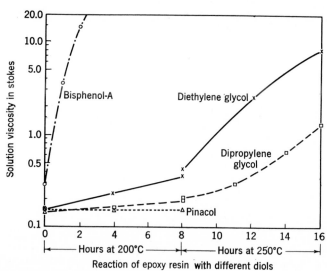

Reaction of epoxy resin with different diols

FIG. 2-7. Phenol-epoxy reaction proceeds faster than alcohol-epoxy reaction when un-catalyzed (2-2).

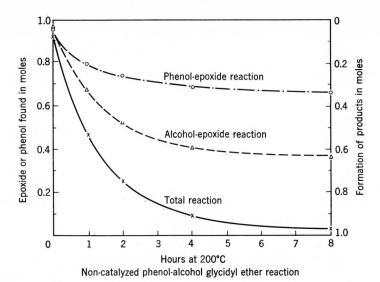

FIG. 2-8. Alcohol-epoxy reaction dominates phenol-epoxy reaction when phenol, alcohol, and epoxy are reacted together (2-2).

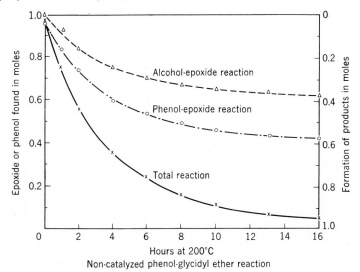

FIG. 2-9. In uncatalyzed phenol-epoxy reaction alcohol-epoxy reaction progresses (2-2).

reaction is extremely sluggish in the uncatalyzed resin, although it does proceed somewhat faster than the uncatalyzed epoxy-alcohol reaction, because of the effect of the acidity of the phenol. The uncatalyzed reaction rates of bisphenol and various alcohols with an epoxy resin are compared in Fig. 2-7.

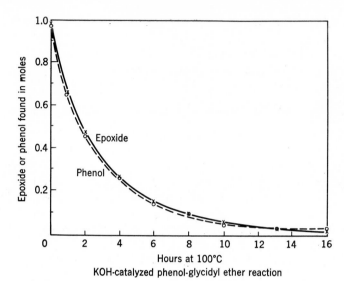

FIG. 2-10. Phenol-epoxy reaction proceeds to exclusion of epoxy-alcohol reaction in presence of caustic (2-2).

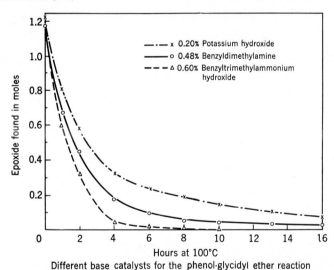

FIG. 2-11. Amine-catalysts provide reactions similar to caustics (2-3).

Uncatalyzed, when phenol, alcohol, and epoxy are present, the phenol-epoxy reaction loses ground to the epoxy-alcohol reactions (Fig. 2-8). In an uncatalyzed mixture, even if alcohol is not initially present, the alcoholic hydroxyls formed during the reaction will compete with the phenol-epoxy reaction (Fig. 2-9).

With a base catalyst, however, the phenol-epoxy reaction excludes the epoxy-alcohol reaction (Fig. 2-10). The catalyst employed affects the rate (Fig. 2-11), but the selectivity or direction imparted to the reaction is unaffected. (The selectivity imparted to this reaction of a phenol with epoxy is important in reducing the epoxy-alcohol reactions during resin synthesis and thereby the possibility of side-chain and branch-polymer formation.)

CURING BY CROSSLINKING AGENTS

Epoxy resins may be cured by using a reactive intermediate to join the resin chains. The principal reactive crosslinking agents are polyfunctional primary and secondary amines and dibasic acids or acid anhydrides. However, polyfunctional phenols such as bisphenol A and resorcinol have also been suggested as crosslinking agents and are sometimes used in conjunction with other curing agents.

Primary and Secondary Amines

Polyfunctional primary (RNH_2) and secondary (R_2NH) amines are widely used as curing agents for epoxy resins. Each primary amine group is theoretically capable of reacting with two epoxy groups. Hence, a polyamine such as ethylene diamine

$$H_2N—CH_2—CH_2—NH_2$$

is capable of reacting with four epoxy groups because of the four active hydrogens attached to the nitrogen atoms.

The reactions possible with primary amines are:

1. Reaction with an epoxy group to form a secondary amine

$$RNH_2 + \overset{O}{\overset{/ \backslash}{CH_2——CH}}\sim\sim \rightarrow R\overset{H}{\overset{|}{N}}—CH_2—\underset{\underset{OH}{|}}{CH}\sim\sim$$

2. Reaction with another epoxy group to form a tertiary amine

$$R\overset{H}{\overset{|}{N}}—CH_2—\underset{\underset{OH}{|}}{CH}\sim\sim + \overset{O}{\overset{/ \backslash}{CH_2——CH}}\sim\sim \rightarrow RN\begin{matrix} \overset{\overset{OH}{|}}{CH_2—CH}\sim\sim \\ CH_2—\underset{\underset{OH}{|}}{CH}\sim\sim \end{matrix}$$

3. Reaction of hydroxyls so formed with epoxy

$$\sim\sim\text{CH}\sim\sim + \overset{\overset{\displaystyle O}{\diagup\diagdown}}{\text{CH}_2\text{—CH}}\sim\sim \rightarrow \sim\sim\text{CH}\sim\sim$$
$$\underset{\displaystyle \text{OH}}{\mid} \qquad\qquad\qquad\qquad \underset{\displaystyle O}{\mid}$$
$$\underset{\displaystyle \text{OH}}{\overset{\displaystyle \mid}{\text{CH}_2\text{—CH}\sim\sim}}$$

Under normal conditions, the two amine-epoxy reactions predominate and proceed at approximately equal rates (Fig. 2-12). The alcohol-epoxy

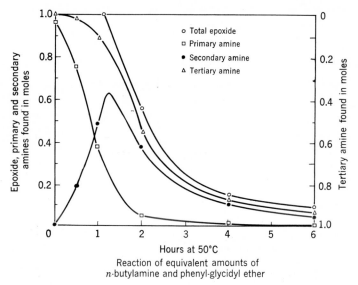

Reaction of equivalent amounts of
n-butylamine and phenyl-glycidyl ether

FIG. 2-12. Progress of amine-epoxy reaction in terms of primary, secondary, and tertiary amines (2-3).

reaction proceeds hardly at all in the presence of the primary and secondary amines (Fig. 2-13). Even with a 25 per cent molar excess of epoxy, the alcohol-epoxy reaction does not progress (Fig. 2-14). It should be noted that although some tertiary amines promote the alcohol-epoxy reaction, as indicated earlier, the tertiary amines formed with the resin from primary and secondary amines are generally too immobile or sterically hindered to catalyze a reaction.

Although, with primary and secondary amine curing agents, the

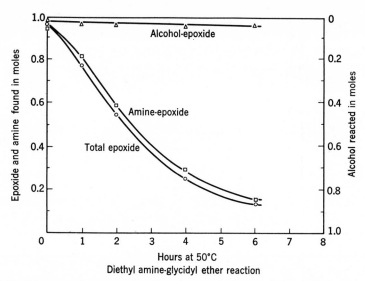

FIG. 2-13. Primary and secondary amine-epoxy reactions exclude alcohol-epoxy reactions (2-3).

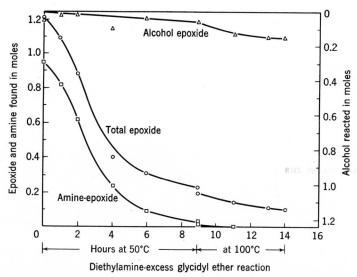

FIG. 2-14. Primary and secondary amine-epoxy reactions exclude alcohol-epoxy reactions even in presence of excess epoxy (2-3).

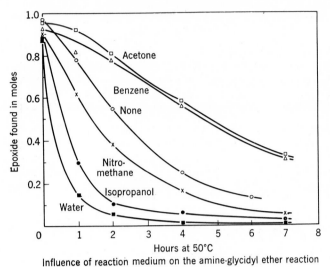

Influence of reaction medium on the amine-glycidyl ether reaction

FIG. 2-15. Influence of reaction medium on amine-epoxy reaction (2-3).

alcohol-epoxy reaction does not appear to progress, a trace of alcoholic hydroxyl or phenolic hydroxyl does, however, speed the epoxy-amine reaction (Fig. 2-15). This acceleration is presumed to be caused by hydrogen bonding effects assisting in the opening of the epoxy ring:

$$R_2NH + CH_2\!\!-\!\!CH\!\!\sim\!\!\sim + HOX \rightarrow$$

Phenol, because of the greater activity of its hydrogen, accelerates the reaction most markedly, indicating that it can be used to speed gel time of primary and secondary amine cures. Likewise, amines containing alcoholic hydroxyls (see ethylene oxide adducts in Chap. 3) react faster than the unmodified amines. Nonhydroxyl containing solvents such as acetone and benzene retard the reaction by diluting the reactants.

Organic Acids

Organic acids are used chiefly to esterify higher-molecular-weight resins for use in surface-coating formulations. The anhydrides of organic acids are used more commonly as crosslinking or curing agents for the liquid epoxy resins.

Four over-all reactions may be considered characteristic of the reaction of epoxy resins in the presence of organic acids.

I. Esterification via epoxy-acid reaction:

$$\underset{\overset{\displaystyle\|}{O}}{\sim\sim\sim C} - OH + CH_2 \overset{O}{\diagup\diagdown} CH \sim\sim\sim \rightarrow \underset{\overset{\displaystyle\|}{O}}{\sim\sim\sim C} - O - CH_2 - \underset{OH}{CH} \sim\sim\sim$$

II. Esterification via hydroxyls present in the resin chain or via the nascent hydroxyls of reaction I:

$$\underset{\overset{\displaystyle\|}{O}}{\sim\sim\sim C} - OH + \underset{OH}{\sim\sim\sim CH} \sim\sim\sim \rightarrow \underset{O - C \sim\sim\sim}{\sim\sim\sim CH} \sim\sim\sim + H_2O$$

III. Etherification (reaction of epoxy with aliphatic hydroxyl):

$$\underset{OH}{\sim\sim\sim CH} \sim\sim\sim + CH_2 \overset{O}{\diagup\diagdown} CH \sim\sim\sim \rightarrow \sim\sim\sim CH \sim\sim\sim$$

IV. Hydration of epoxy groups:

$$H_2O + CH_2 \overset{O}{\diagup\diagdown} CH \sim\sim\sim \rightarrow HO - CH_2 - \underset{OH}{OH} \sim\sim\sim$$

Model studies using monofunctional reactants under conditions which eliminated reaction IV have shown that all the other reactions (I, II, III) are significant. Normally, reaction I proceeded approximately twice as fast as either reaction II or III (Fig. 2-16); however, when reacted in the presence of an alcohol, reaction I was dominated by the

EPOXY RESINS

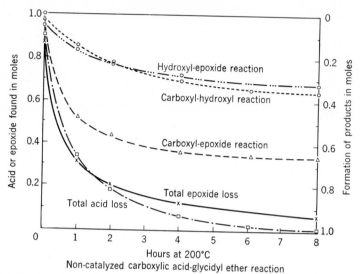

Hours at 200°C

Non-catalyzed carboxylic acid-glycidyl ether reaction

FIG. 2-16. Predominance of acid-epoxy reaction over acid-hydroxyl and epoxy-hydroxyl reaction in uncatalyzed medium (2-2).

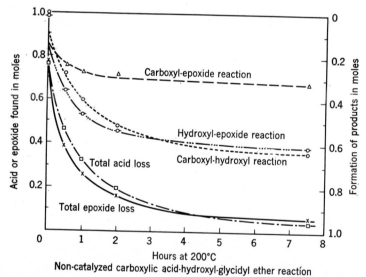

Hours at 200°C

Non-catalyzed carboxylic acid-hydroxyl-glycidyl ether reaction

FIG. 2-17. Domination of acid-hydroxyl and epoxy-hydroxyl reactions over acid-epoxy reaction in presence of alcohol (2-2).

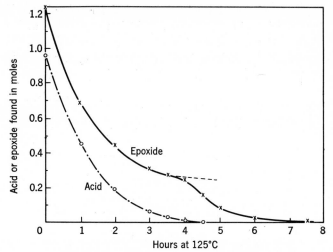

FIG. 2-18. Predominance of acid-epoxy reaction in caustic catalyzed system and excess epoxy. When acid is exhausted, epoxy-alcohol reactions pick up to continue reaction (2-2).

acid-hydroxyl (II) and epoxy-hydroxyl (III) reactions (Fig. 2-17). In this regard, the behavior of the organic acid is seen to resemble the behavior of the phenol system. When base catalyzed, the reaction is highly selective. The base immediately reacts with the acid

$$\underset{\text{C}}{\overset{\text{O}}{\parallel}}\text{—OH} \;+\; \xrightarrow[\text{base}]{\text{KOH}} \; \underset{\text{C}}{\overset{\text{O}}{\parallel}}\text{—O}^{\ominus}$$

and the reaction proceeds ionically through the epoxy group

$$\overset{\text{O}}{\overset{\parallel}{\text{C}}}\text{—O}^{\ominus} + \text{CH}_2\text{—CH}\!\!\!\sim \rightarrow \overset{\text{O}}{\overset{\parallel}{\text{C}}}\text{—O—CH}_2\text{—CH}\!\!\!\sim \;\; \underset{\text{O}^{\ominus}}{}$$

with the acid ion being regenerated

$$\overset{\text{O}}{\overset{\parallel}{\text{C}}}\text{—O—CH}_2\text{—CH}\!\!\!\sim \;+\; \overset{\text{O}}{\overset{\parallel}{\text{C}}}\text{—OH} \rightarrow$$

$$\overset{\text{O}}{\overset{\parallel}{\text{C}}}\text{-O—CH}_2\text{—CH}\!\!\!\sim \;+\; \overset{\text{O}}{\overset{\parallel}{\text{C}}}\text{—O}^{\ominus}$$
$$\underset{\text{OH}}{}$$

Figure 2-18 illustrates the selectivity of the mechanism. Following consumption of the acid (I), the catalyst is regenerated and then proceeds to catalyze the faster epoxy-hydroxyl (III) reaction. The epoxy-organic acid reaction, however, is slower than the epoxy-phenol reaction, as might be expected from the difference in acidity of the phenoxide and carboxylate ions.

Using tertiary amines or quaternary ammonium hydroxide instead of potassium hydroxide, the reaction is equally selective. The acid (I)

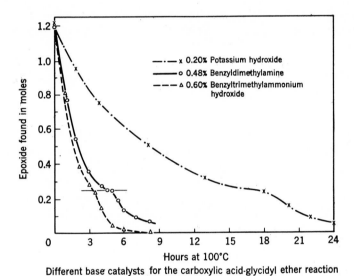

Different base catalysts for the carboxylic acid-glycidyl ether reaction

FIG. 2-19. Predominance of acid-epoxy reaction in presence of tertiary amine and quartenary ammonium compound. When acid is exhausted, epoxy-alcohol reactions pick up to continue reaction (2-2).

reacts and is exhausted first. Remaining epoxy groups then react (III) through the etherification reaction. The organic bases are more active than potassium hydroxide (Fig. 2-19), and in actual practice, they find commercial use as accelerators for acid anhydride cures.

Acid Anhydrides

Acid anhydrides react in a manner similar to organic acids, but the reaction is more complex because of the absence of water in the molecule and the necessity for activating the anhydride structure. The first reaction which occurs is the opening of the anhydride ring by an alcoholic hydroxyl (or salt or a trace of water).

I. Opening of anhydride ring:

| Phthalic anhydride | Alcoholic hydroxyl | Phthalic monoester |

Subsequent to this reaction, five other reactions can occur.

II. Reaction of the nascent carboxylic group with an epoxy group:

Phthalic monoester   Epoxy resin

Phthalic diester

III. Etherification of the epoxy groups with nascent or existing hydroxyl groups (catalyzed by presence of acid):

IV. Reaction of monoester with a hydroxyl to give the diester and water:

| Monoester | Alcoholic hydroxyl | Diester | Water |

V. Hydrolysis of the anhydride by water to give the acid:

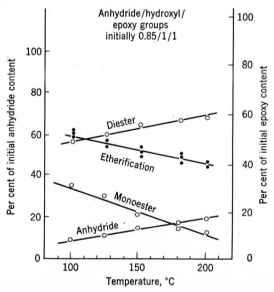

VI. Hydrolysis of the monoester (from reaction I) with water to give the acid and alcohol:

In practice, it is found that reactions I, II, and III are of principal concern and that ester and ether linkages occur at about equal frequency in the cured structure.

Inasmuch as the etherification reaction (III) proceeds rather independently in acid medium, there is considerably more leeway in the amount of

FIG. 2-20. Effect of temperature on chemical bond composition of anhydride-cured epoxy system (2-5).

anhydrides employed as curing agent than in the amount of crosslinking amines. There will, however, usually be an optimum percentage for a given cure cycle with regard to a specific property (heat-distortion temperature, high-temperature weight loss, etc.). Figure 2-20 shows the effect of cure temperature on the predominance of the various reactions.

EFFECT OF CHLORINE CONTENT

In commercial resins, a number of impurities may exist to influence the curing mechanisms. Chief among these is the chloride ion, present from the chlorohydrin step of the synthesis. The free chloride content of commercial resins is very low and appears to have little effect on curing rate. But in higher concentrations, the ion tends to inhibit catalytic cure by neutralizing any base added to give speed and direction to the curing reaction of an organic acid or by blocking the nitrogen of a tertiary amine. Under these circumstances, if the chlorine content varies from batch to batch, this will be reflected in the properties of the cured systems in which all other parameters have been held constant (2-3).

CALCULATION OF AMOUNT OF CURING AGENT TO USE

From the foregoing discussion, it will be seen that the curing reactions determine the percentage of the curing agent required. When the curing agent is of the crosslinking type, it will be recognized that there is a calculated optimum or stoichiometric ratio which theoretically provides exactly the amount of curing agent necessary for complete consumption of the reactive groups in the resin.

The actual value used in practice must then be modified by evaluation of performance and properties, as there are minor phenomena which the theory cannot allow for. When the curing agent is of the catalytic type, the percentages must be arrived at empirically for each system.

With crosslinking amines, the customary method is to allow one epoxy group for each active hydrogen of the reagent. The calculated amount will then result in nearly optimum properties in the cured system, and variations from it should not be greater than 10 to 20 per cent. Excessive amine curing agent, for example, will tend to stop chain building at low molecular weights, thereby embrittling the resin. Too little curing agent will fail to provide for adequate cure. In a typical calculation for diglycidyl ether of bisphenol A and metaphenylene diamine, consider that the resin has a gram-molecular weight of 340 and that one-half this value would contain 1 gram mol of epoxy. Metaphenylene diamine has a gram-molecular weight of 108 and four reactive hydrogens; that is, one quarter of this value would contain 1 gram mol of active hydrogen. Therefore, 27 grams will provide one reactive point for each 170 grams of resin, or approximately 16 parts per 100 of resin will be required. With commercial resins having epoxy equivalents of 175 to 200, 14.5 parts per hundred of resin is customarily employed.

In calculating the amount of anhydride to employ, a similar method is followed. In general, 0.85 gram mol of anhydride carboxyl is used per 1 gram mol of epoxy. The arbitrary reduction of 0.15 from unity is sufficient in most cases to accommodate competing reactions.

The amount of a particular catalytic curing agent to employ with a given epoxy resin is not as critical as the amount of a crosslinking curing agent required. With catalytic curing agents, the general approach is to determine the amount of curing agent that provides a convenient rate of reaction and to consider that, in most cases, this amount can be varied by as much as 50 per cent without seriously affecting the properties of the cured system. With catalytic tertiary amines, for example, the usual range is from 5 to 15 phr (parts per hundred parts resin, by weight). This amount will be sufficient to absorb inhibiting impurities in addition to establishing a convenient rate of polymerization.

Within the permissible range, the lower the amount of catalytic curing agent employed, of course, the lower the reaction rate, and, consequently, the higher temperature and longer cure cycle required to achieve a thoroughly crosslinked system.

In the chapters on curing agents, specific amounts or ranges are recommended.

DEGREE OF CURE

Not only is it necessary to employ the proper amount of curing agent to achieve thorough crosslinking of the system, but it is necessary to discover the cure time and/or cure temperature which will bring about this thorough crosslinking in a practical or convenient period of time.

During the early stages of cure, before the molecules are all crosslinked, semithermoplastic or B-stage resins are in existence. These are hard and frangible and soluble in solvents such as acetone. At this stage, the reaction has been initiated at a number of widely separated points in the resinous mass. With additional cure, crosslinking becomes general and the compound assumes its thermoset nature.

In the epoxy resins, the degree of cure has, by custom, come to refer to the extent to which the epoxy groups have been consumed, and, when present, the extent of consumption of the reactive elements in the curing agent. For practical purposes, a thoroughly cured system is considered one in which the degree of crosslinking is sufficient to provide optimum physical properties for a particular application. Complete cure, requiring consumption of all unsaturated elements, is seldom if ever obtained even under laboratory conditions.

During cure, two reactions are involved: *conversion* (the actual disappearance of reactive elements) and, more importantly, *crosslinking* (the coupling of the molecules into three-dimensional networks through reactive residues to form the desired thermoset resins).

A theoretical method for calculating the optimum cure cycle for a given compound has not been advanced. The thermodynamics and reaction chemistry are exceedingly complex. Some systems will, in practice, require external heat, while others will, once activated, provide their own heat by an exothermic reaction. In general, however, irrespective of the curing agent, postcuring at temperatures higher than ambient (25°C) will produce a system more thoroughly crosslinked and containing fewer unreacted groups. In many cases, low (i.e., ambient or only slightly elevated) temperature gelling appears to promote linear polymerization; the long-chain molecules so formed, later, under the influence of thermal agitation induced by high postcuring temperatures, continue to react and provide a higher degree of cure. Long postcures may be necessary to complete the reaction if the initial gelling cycle is not correct. Similarly, in other cases, low-temperature gelling appears to create molecules with steric hindrances or a degree of unsymmetry such that even high postcure temperatures do not markedly improve the degree of cure (2-7). The anhydride curing agents in particular appear to be very temperature sensitive, and the initial cure temperatures will determine, to some extent, the type of bonds present in the cured system and hence its cured properties. In these cases, long postcures will not as readily offset the effects of the initial cure cycle.

Proper cure cycles are best determined empirically for each application. In the laboratory, heat-distortion tests are widely used as a quick screening method. For ascertaining the effect of curing temperature, it is often desirable to plot cure time divided by heat-distortion temperature against cure time for various curing temperatures. If the heat-distortion temperature is independent of curing temperature within the range of temperatures under consideration, then all the lines so plotted will coincide. If the heat-distortion temperature is dependent on cure temperature, the lines will differ in slope (1-15).

Two other approaches may be used to determine conversion and degree of cure: infrared spectroscopy and chemical analysis by the swollen-particle method. The following discussion is based on material in a series of papers by H. Dannenberg and W. R. Harp (2-8).

Determination of Conversion

Insofar as infrared spectroscopy does not destroy the sample under test, it is one of the best analytical methods. The absorption band at 10.95 μ, which has been assigned to a fundamental vibration of the epoxy ring, progressively disappears as an epoxy resin is cured.

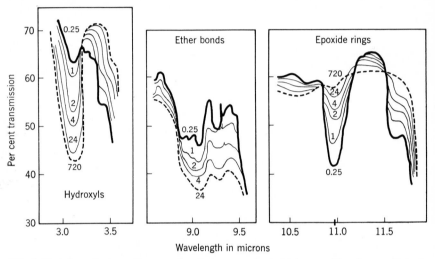

FIG. 2-21. Infrared absorption graphs of epoxy resin during cure with primary aliphatic polyamine (2-10). Numbers indicate cure time in hours at 23°C.

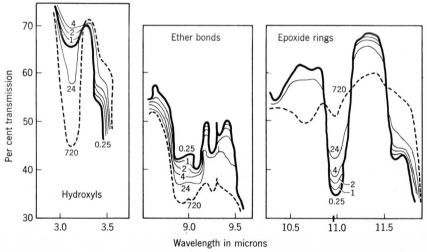

FIG. 2-22. Infrared absorption graphs of epoxy resin during cure with tertiary aliphatic amine (2-10). Numbers indicate cure time in hours at 23°C.

Samples for recording spectra are prepared as films about 0.025 mm thick between rock-salt plates. The curing then takes place in the rock-salt cell, and the spectrum is recorded at various time intervals. Curves showing absorption at various times during cure are presented in Figs. 2-21 and 2-22.

In chemical analysis by the swollen-particle method, the resin sample is reduced to a very small particle size and suspended in a liquid which acts as a swelling agent. The analytical reagent is then allowed to diffuse

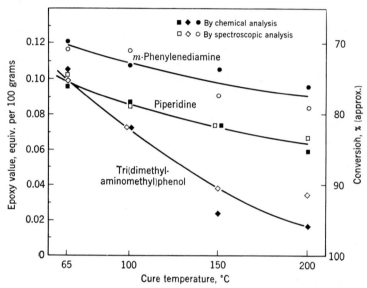

FIG. 2-23. Conversion of epoxy resin as a function of curing agents and curing temperatures (2-8).

into the swollen particle and perform the analytical reaction, and the reaction products diffuse out of the particle. The values obtained by the chemical method are compared with the values obtained by infrared techniques in Fig. 2-23.

The curves connecting the experimental points in Fig. 2-23 show clearly the influence of the cure temperatures on the conversion, as well as the difference in the activity of three curing agents.

Estimation of Crosslinking

The determination of the degree of cure from the amount of chemical conversion is not satisfactory as the sole means for evaluating thermo-setting resins, as is obvious from the discussion of Fig. 2-3. The extent and character of the three-dimensional network formed during cure must be determined.

Since the extent and character of this network are reflected in the heat-distortion temperatures and solvent resistance, these two parameters can provide an indirect but theoretically accurate measurement of the cross-linking within the cured system. These two parameters may be measured directly by (1) deformation under load at elevated temperature and (2) swell volume in solvent solution.

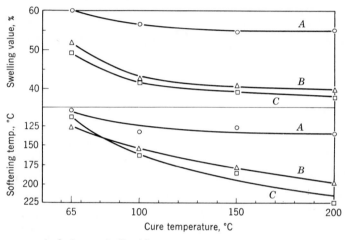

A. Curing agent: Piperidine
B. Curing agent: Tri(dimethylaminomethyl)phenol
C. Curing agent: m-Phenylenediamine

FIG. 2-24. Comparison of swelling values and softening temperatures of cured epoxy resins (2-8).

Conventional methods for the determination of deformation under load at elevated temperatures include ASTM heat-distortion tests (Chap. 1) and hardness tests with conventional hardness testers on preheated specimens. In the case of the cured epoxy systems, the situation is complicated by the fact that the temperatures needed to obtain an easily measurable deformation are frequently higher than the customary cure temperatures and may result in a continuation of cure while the specimen is being prepared for the test. To avoid this source of error, it is desirable to have a test method in which the major part of the specimen is kept at room temperature, with heat applied over a small area and during a limited time only. This is accomplished with a preheated point on a hardness tester. The arbitrary indentation of the hot point may then be used to define a softening temperature.

Figure 2-24 presents the results of such softening-point tests conducted with the same resin systems employed for the conversion experiments. The choice of the curing agent and the cure temperature is seen to have a strong influence on the softening temperatures.

The second of the two properties related to crosslinking is the swelling of the crosslinked materials in solvents. To utilize this property, it is necessary to investigate the amount of swelling at equilibrium conditions. In order to obtain accurate and reproducible results, the swelling must be carried out on finely divided powders of the substance in contact with the vapors of a solvent.

Values obtained by this procedure, expressed as per cent gain of weight, can vary from 60 per cent for an inadequately cured resin to 35 per cent for a very well cured resin.

CHARACTERIZATION OF THE CURED RESIN

The cured-resin system is best characterized by its physical, chemical, and electrical properties. This section discusses the more common of these properties and explains the standard test procedures employed to determine the values for each property. All values as given subse-quently in the text have been determined by these procedures or their equivalents.

By way of introduction, it should be noted that the characterizing properties will vary somewhat from batch to batch of commercial resins, so that systems cured with identical curing agents under identical condi-tions may not necessarily produce identical properties. This is seldom of major consequence on a day-to-day basis, but the changes in the produc-tion techniques for the resins involved may, over a period of a few years, have a considerable cumulative effect on the cured system, and periodic revaluations may be required.

It should be noted, too, that one specific property may be at optimum with one specific curing agent or percentage of curing agent; a second property, with another, etc. Likewise, the values of some characterizing properties may be reduced by extended cure; others, increased. That is, a specific "optimized" system will not be at optimum in all its properties but will represent a compromise designed to accommodate a specific service environment.

Because of variations in batch properties, cure cycles, and design objec-tives, all values subsequently given in the text must be considered typical or representative rather than optimum.

Some of the interrelationships between the various properties can be expressed in a general way. High heat-distortion temperatures, for instance, occur in systems tightly crosslinked through highly stable benzene rings and values may reach the 300°C (600°F) range. Proper cure cycles and thorough postcuring lead to the highest heat-distortion temperature, hardness, chemical resistance, and electrical properties; but as the structures become more tightly crosslinked, tensile, impact, and flexural strengths will be correspondingly reduced. Other relationships, likewise, can be established.

An extremely wide range of values for physical, chemical, and electrical properties may be achieved by modifying epoxy resins and by using differing curing agents. Typical values for unmodified and unreinforced diglycidyl ether of bisphenol A type casting resins are included in the following discussions. Typical values for modified compounds are presented elsewhere in the text.

Physical Properties

In addition to the heat-distortion temperature, discussed in Chap. 1, the major characterizing properties of the physical system of the cured resin are the tensile, compressive, and flexural strengths, the impact resistance, the hardness, and the flammability.

Tensile Strength. Tensile strength is a measure of the pull required to break a sample of material. It is determined by dividing the force at failure by the area of the initial cross section and is expressed in pounds per square inch. Measurement procedures are recorded in ASTM 638-52TD (2-9). Tensile strengths of unmodified resins vary from 8,000 to 12,000 psi.

Compressive Strength. The compressive strength of a material is the measure of its resistance to a crushing force, expressed in pounds per square inch at failure. The value is meaningful when it records the force at which a fracture occurs. If deformation continues without fracture, the parameter compressive yield, in pounds per square inch, provides a better criterion. Compressive yield is the point at which the deformation increases without additional load. Both parameters are measured in accordance with ASTM D695-54. A typical value is 15,000 psi yield, 30,000 psi ultimate.

Flexural Strength. Flexural strength is the resistance of a material to bending stresses. A sample beam of test material is subjected to center loads, and the value at which permanent distortion or failure occurs is recorded in pounds per square inch. The test method is described in ASTM D790-49T. A typical value for flexural strength is 18,000 psi.

Modulus of Elasticity. Young's modulus or stiffness, which is the ratio of stress to unit strain, may also be determined for tension, compression, and flexure by the respective ASTM test procedures. Typical values of all three are 400,000 to 600,000 psi.

Impact Resistance. Impact resistance is a measure of the ability of the material to withstand sudden loading and is usually expressed in foot-pounds or foot-pounds per inch of notch width of specimen at failure. The usual test is the Izod type, in which the specimen is held as a cantilever beam and is broken by a blow delivered at a fixed distance from the edge of the specimen clamp. The specimen is notched to produce a standard degree of stress concentration. This test is described in ASTM D256-54T. A second method, the falling-ball test, records the failure of a test specimen subjected to a sudden impact delivered by standard balls falling a standard distance, the weight of the ball increasing throughout the test. This method is described in Mil-C-16923 Ships. A typical value by the Izod test is 0.2 ft-lb per inch of width; by the falling ball test, 2 ft-lb.

Hardness. Hardness is a measure of the ability of the material to withstand localized indentation and may be expressed in a number of different test scales, depending on the degree of rigidity. Rockwell hardness is determined by procedures described in ASTM Methods E 18, with the M scale being most common for epoxies. The plastics test procedure is explained in ASTM D785-51. Durometers (usually Shore type) are used to measure indentation in softer materials (ASTM D676-55T). A cured epoxy resin gives Rockwell M readings in the neighborhood of 100. Barcol hardness testers are frequently used for materials in the Rockwell range. A typical value is 40 Barcol.

Flammability. Flammability is a measure of the burning rate of the material. Since the epoxy resins are classed as self-extinguishing, the test procedure employed is ASTM D757-49, which provides a measure of the burning rate of a standard sample in inches per minute.

Chemical Properties

The chemical properties of the cured resin may be determined by exposing standard samples of the material to various chemical atmospheres and recording the effects of such exposure on physical properties, such properties being determined before and after exposure by standard test methods. A method reporting the changes in weight, dimensions, and appearance after immersion in various chemical reagents is discussed in ASTM D543-52T. Tests may be conducted to determine the resistance of the compound to accelerated weathering by exposing a sample to artificial sunlight and fog. Other tests, such as salt spray, oxidation, etc., are based on the same principle: that of exposing the sample to the environment and recording performance.

The chemical resistance of cured epoxy resins varies markedly with the type of curing agent and the degree of cure. However, a well-cured epoxy resin is extremely resistant to all but the strongest oxidizing acids, to most caustics, and to most solvents.

Electrical Properties

The chief electrical properties usually reported for the cured resin system are dielectric constant, power factor or dissipation factor, and loss factor (ASTM D150-54T), resistivity (ASTM D/257-54T), dielectric strength (ASTM D149-55T), and arc resistance (ASTM D495-48T). Since electrical properties are sharply affected by temperature, frequency, and relative humidity, values are often reported for several conditions.

Dielectric Constant. Dielectric constant is the ratio of the capacitance of a given dielectric material to the capacitance of a vacuum in the same configuration, or a measure of the effect of the dielectric material on the mutual interaction of electrical bodies. For comparison, the dielectric constant of air is taken as approximately 1. A typical value for an epoxy resin is 3.8.

Power Factor. Power factor is a measure of the electric power loss in a dielectric. It is, in insulations, close in value to the dissipation factor. (The relationship $\cos \theta \sim \sin \delta \sim \tan \delta \sim \delta$ is approximately true, where θ is the alternating-current voltage phase angle and δ is its complement.) Typical values of power factor or dissipation factor are 0.003 to 0.030.

Loss Factor. Loss factor is a product of the power factor and the dielectric constant and represents a quantitative measure of power loss. Typical values are 0.01 to 0.08.

Resistivity. Resistivity is the ability of the material to resist passage of an electrical current: Resistivity may be recorded in terms of volume resistivity (ohm-centimeters) or in terms of surface resistivity (ohms). When reported as electrical resistance, it is a function of both values. A typical value is 10^{13} ohm-cm.

Dielectric Strength. Dielectric strength is a measure of the ability of insulation to withstand voltage. It is calculated from the voltage required to break down an insulation section of given thickness and is expressed in volts per mil. The value will be highly dependent on the thickness of the sample, the thinner the specimen, the higher the calculated dielectric strength per unit thickness. A typical value is 425 volts per mil (0.125 in. thickness).

Arc Resistance. Arc resistance is the ability of an insulating material to withstand bridging by high voltage and low current close to the surface. The breakdown value is reported in seconds and indicates that a path has been formed across the insulation surface. A typical value of an unmodified cured resin is 60 seconds.

CONCLUSION

This chapter has been designed to familiarize the reader with the curing mechanisms and general structure of the cured epoxy resin and to indicate some of the properties by which the structure is characterized.

The structure has been said to consist of a number of molecular chains crosslinked into a tight network through the action of one or more specific curing mechanisms, which may involve the epoxy groups exclusively, the epoxy groups and available hydroxyls, or the epoxy groups and various radicals present in the crosslinking curing agent.

The various specific mechanisms believed to occur during cure with commercial types of curing agents were presented, and on the basis of this, methods for calculating the optimum amounts of a particular curing agent were suggested.

It was further indicated that not only is the curing agent of consequence in determining the ultimate structure, but also the degree to which cure has been completed. This is a function of the time and temperature of the cure cycle and can be expressed in terms of conversion and crosslinking and can be analyzed experimentally.

References

2-1. Shechter, Wynstra, and Kurkjy, Chemistry of Styrene Oxide—A Comparison with Phenyl Glycidyl Ether in Model Compound Reactions, *Industrial and Engineering Chemistry*, July, 1957.

2-2. Shechter and Wynstra, Glycidyl Ether Reactions with Alcohols, Phenols, Carboxylic Acids, and Acid Anhydrides, *Industrial and Engineering Chemistry*, **48**:86–93 (1956).

2-3. Shechter, Wynstra, and Kurkjy, Glycidyl Ether Reactions with Amines, *Industrial and Engineering Chemistry*, **48**:94–97 (1956).

2-4. Narracott, The Curing of Epoxide Resins, *British Plastics*, **26**:120–123 (1953).

2-5. Fisch, Hofmann, and Koskikallio, The Curing Mechanism of Epoxy Resins, paper presented at Symposium of British Society of Chemical Industry, April, 1956.

2-6. Fisch and Hofmann, Über den Härtungsmechanismus der Äthoxylinharze, *Journal of Polymer Science*, **12**:497–502 (1954).

2-7. Peerman, Tolberg, and Floyd, Reaction of Polyamide Resins and Epoxy Resins, *Industrial and Engineering Chemistry*, July, 1957.

2-8. Shell Chemical Co., *Polymer Progress No. 2*, October, 1955.

2-9. American Society of Testing Materials *Standards*, 1955.

2-10. Damusis, Amines as Curing Agents of Ether Resins, paper presented at Division of Paint, Plastics, and Printing Ink Chemistry, ACS Symposium, Atlantic City, September, 1956.

3

PRIMARY ALIPHATIC AMINES AND THEIR ADDUCTS AS CURING AGENTS

The amines were among the first materials to gain general acceptance in the United States as curing agents for the epoxy resins. This chapter presents data on the primary aliphatic (or alkyl) amines as characterized by diethylene triamine and diethylamino propylamine, on various chemical modifications or adducts of these amines, and on amine blends containing these two classes of compounds.

A number of primary aliphatic amines were in quantity production at the time of the discovery of the epoxy resins, and these commercially available materials were the first to be investigated as curing agents. However, with commercially available amines, certain parameters were unnecessarily critical, and a continuing investigation was undertaken to discover amines providing for selective improvement in one or more properties. A number of somewhat specialized aliphatic primary amines are now used in specific applications, and new ones are being proposed at regular intervals.

Concurrently, a second effort is under way, designed to modify the amines specifically for use with the epoxy resins and thereby improve the properties of the better-known materials. Among the improvements sought are longer pot life, lower exotherm, a wider range of combining ratios, and improved handling characteristics. The short pot life of many amines complicates the production situation and requires either the use of continuous mixing equipment or batch replenishment. The high exotherms—the specific value being a function of the mass involved— prohibit the convenient casting of larger shapes. The stoichiometric ratio (usually less than 12 phr*) necessitates more careful weighing operations than are desirable in production-line operations when cured-system parameters are critical. And, of course, since many of the amines are skin-

---

* Throughout the text, the abbreviation phr refers to parts per hundred parts of resin, by weight.

sensitizing agents, their use requires careful attention to ventilation and personal hygiene.

PRIMARY ALIPHATIC AMINES

Polyfunctional primary aliphatic amines give fast cures and provide over-all properties satisfactory for a wide variety of commerical applications. Table 3-1 presents representative amines of this type, together with their structural formulas. Diethylene triamine (DETA) and diethylamino propylamine (DEAPA) are widely used curing agents in this class and are considered in detail.

Diethylene Triamine

DETA is a highly reactive primary and secondary polyamine having a molecular weight of 103. It is a pungent liquid with a viscosity of 7 centi-poises at room temperature. Other physical properties are presented in

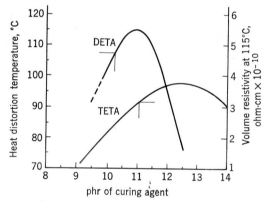

FIG. 3-1. Effect of varying ratios of DETA on heat-distortion temperature and of TETA on volume resistivity (3-1, 3-14).

Table 3-2. DETA possesses five active hydrogens available for cross-linking, and the stoichiometric quantity required is approximately 10 to 11 phr. At this ratio, the initial viscosity of the resin mix will be reduced to about 3,000 centipoises.

The stoichiometric ratio, calculated from the number of active hydrogens, is fairly critical with the unmodified primary-amine curing agents, and the effect of varying ratios of DETA on the heat-distortion temperature and of triethylene tetramine on volume resistivity of thoroughly cured systems is presented in Fig. 3-1 by way of example.

DETA-catalyzed resin will gel and set hard at room temperature within a very short time. The exotherm is vigorous, and temperatures may

TABLE 3-1. Structural Formulas for Typical Primary Aliphatic Amines

Ethylene diamine....... $H_2N-CH_2-CH_2-NH_2$

Diethylene triamine..... $H_2N-CH_2-CH_2-\underset{\underset{H}{|}}{N}-CH_2-CH_2-NH_2$

Triethylene tetramine... $H_2N-CH_2-CH_2-\underset{\underset{H}{|}}{N}-CH_2-CH_2-\underset{\underset{H}{|}}{N}-CH_2-CH_2-NH_2$

Dimethylamino propylamine............... $\underset{CH_3}{\overset{CH_3}{\diagdown}} N-CH_2-CH_2-CH_2-NH_2$

Diethylamino propylamine............. $\underset{CH_3-CH_2}{\overset{CH_3-CH_2}{\diagdown}} N-CH_2-CH_2-CH_2-NH_2$

TABLE 3-2. Physical Properties of Two Representative Primary Aliphatic Amines

Property	Diethylene triamine	Diethylamino propylamine
Molecular weight	103.7	130.2
Boiling point, °C, 760 mm Hg	206.7	169.4
Vapor pressure, mm Hg, 20°C	0.2–0.3	1.2
Freezing point, °C	−39	Below −100
Specific gravity, 20/20°C	0.9542	0.8289
Absolute viscosity, centipoises, 20°C	7.1	1.9
Flash point, °C (Cleveland open cup)	101	59
Weight per gallon, lb at 20°C	7.95	6.90

reach as high as 250°C in ½-lb batches. When larger volumes of resin are employed, the exotherm, if uncontrolled, will be sufficient to volatilize a portion of the DETA, and cured compounds of inferior quality will result. Pot lives at room temperature vary from about 20 minutes in 1-lb batches to 40 minutes in 50-gram batches. Pot lives can be somewhat increased by using only 8 phr DETA, as frequently recommended in the literature.

Although curing at room temperature for a few hours will provide fairly good properties, postcure will result in higher heat-distortion temperature, increased chemical resistance, and improved electrical properties (3-2).

DETA provides tensile strengths in the neighborhood of 12,000 psi and heat-distortion temperatures of up to 120°C in a thoroughly cured system. Typical physical properties of a DETA-cured system (at 8 phr), cured 24 hours at 40°C, are presented in Table 3-3. The chemical resistance of

TABLE 3-3. Typical Physical Properties of Resin Cured with Diethylene Triamine
(Test conditions: room temperature)

Tensile strength, psi...	8,000–9,000
Compressive strength, psi.......................................	16,000
Flexural strength, psi...	17,700
Impact strength, Izod...	0.3–0.4
Hardness, Rockwell M...	99–108
Heat-distortion temperature, °C.................................	66–76*
Modulus of elasticity in flexure, psi.............................	0.54×10^6
Thermal conductivity, cal/(sec)(sq cm²)(°C)(cm).................	4.8×10^{-4}
Flammability, in./min...	0.34–0.36
Shrinkage during cure, in./in...................................	0.004–0.005
Water absorption 24-hr immersion, %...........................	0.11–0.12
Moisture-vapor transmission, at 38°C, relative humidity 95%, g/sq ft/ 24 hr/in. thickness...	<0.01

* See Fig. 3-1 for effect of amount of DETA on heat-distortion temperature.

TABLE 3-4. Typical Electrical Properties of Resin Cured with Diethylene Triamine (3-10)

Property	Frequency, cycles/sec					
	10^2	10^3	10^4	10^5	10^6	10^7
Power factor:						
−40°C..............	0.0220	0.0200	0.0195	0.0175	0.0165	0.0170
−20°C..............	0.0300	0.0500	0.0500	0.0700	0.0900	0.1000
20°C...............	0.0090	0.0400	0.0480	0.0800	0.1000	0.1300
60°C...............	0.0045	0.0100	0.0600	0.0750	0.1100	0.1500
100°C..............	0.0175	0.0165	0.0300	0.0600	0.1200	0.2000
Dielectric constant:						
−40°C..............	3.4	3.35	3.3	3.3	3.2	3.1
−20°C..............	3.8	3.8	3.75	3.7	3.6	3.4
20°C...............	4.1	4.2	4.2	4.1	4.2	4.1
60°C...............	4.3	4.4	4.6	4.6	4.5	4.4
100°C..............	4.5	4.6	4.7	4.8	4.9	5.0

Volume resistivity:	
25°C.................	2×10^{16} ohm-cm
50°C.................	6×10^{14} ohm-cm
75°C.................	5×10^{13} ohm-cm
100°C................	5×10^{12} ohm-cm
125°C................	5×10^{11} ohm-cm

DETA-cured resins is generally good, although this is dependent on the extent of cure. A thoroughly cured system will withstand 20 per cent nitric, 85 per cent sulfuric, and 10 per cent hydrochloric acid, etc., and 1 to 20 per cent concentrations of caustics. Solvent resistance, likewise, is generally good, although the system will disintegrate in methylene dichloride type solvents and concentrated acetic acid–trichloroethylene mixtures. Resistance to weathering is good. Even though the heat-distortion temperature is relatively low, short time exposure to higher temperatures can be tolerated. A 100-gram sample, for instance, was subjected to temperatures of 350°C for 15 minutes without loss of properties. Weight loss after 200 hours at 200°C will be on the order of 3 to 4 per cent. Electrical properties of a DETA-cured system are presented in Table 3-4.

DETA finds widespread use as a general-purpose curing agent for small castings, rigid laminates, medium-strength adhesives, and baking-type solution coatings. It is a skin-sensitizing agent, and proper handling precautions must be observed with its use.

Diethylamino Propylamine

DEAPA is a reactive primary and tertiary amine having a molecular weight of 130.   It is a pungent liquid with a viscosity of 1.9 centipoises at room temperature.   Other physical properties are presented in Table 3-2. It possesses two active hydrogens and contains a tertiary amine group capable of effecting catalytic cure (3-3).   Because of the activity of the unblocked tertiary amine, the quantity required for commercial resins is approximately 7 phr.   At this ratio, the viscosity of the resin mix will be about 2,000 centipoises at room temperature.

DEAPA will gel and set a resin hard at room temperature, but it is somewhat slower acting than DETA.   Pot life of a 1-lb batch at room temperature is about 140 minutes.   Peak exotherms of 170°C are possible.

The effects of cure temperatures and cure times on the various physical properties of a DEAPA-cured system are presented in Figs. 3-2 to 3-7.* Electrical properties of a DEAPA-cured system are presented in Table 3-5.

DEAPA gives cured systems very similar to those provided by DETA, the principal advantage being the longer pot life offered through its use. DEAPA, like DETA, is a good general-purpose curing agent, and like DETA it is also a skin-sensitizing agent.

* These and other three-dimensional cure-cycle graphs used subsequently in this chapter are based on the work of C. F. Pitt (3-4).

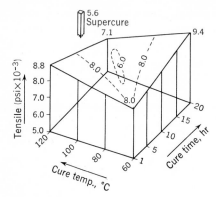

FIG. 3-2. Tensile strength of DEAPA-cured system (3-5).

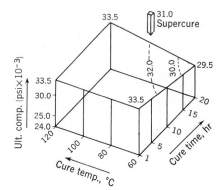

FIG. 3-3. Compressive strength of DEAPA-cured system (3-5).

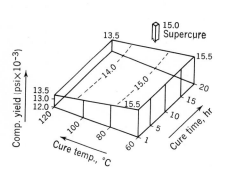

FIG. 3-4. Compressive yield strength of DEAPA-cured system (3-5).

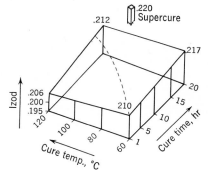

FIG. 3-5. Izod impact strength of DEAPA-cured system (3-5).

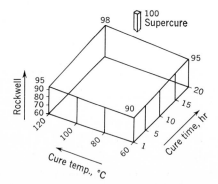

FIG. 3-6. Rockwell hardness (M) of DEAPA-cured system (3-5).

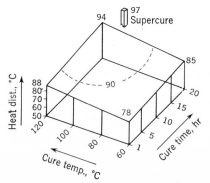

FIG. 3-7. Heat-distortion temperature of DEAPA-cured system (3-5).

TABLE 3-5. Typical Electrical Properties of Resin Cured with
Diethylamino Propylamine (3-9)
(Test conditions: room temperature)

Property	Frequency, cycles/sec			
	10^2	10^5	10^6	10^8
Power factor......................	0.0017	0.0078	0.0121	0.0294
Dielectric constant...............	3.75	3.70	3.64	3.44

MODIFIED AMINES

Various methods may be used to modify the conventional polyfunctional primary amines to make them more suitable for use as curing

TABLE 3-6. Typical Commercial Amine-type Curing Agents

Designation	*Suggested chemical description*
Applied Plastics Co.* (APCO®):	
180.........................	Aliphatic polyamide
320.........................	Modified aromatic amine (liquid)
Bakelite Co. (Bakelite®):	
ERL-2793....................	Aliphatic amine–glycidyl adduct
ZZL-0814....................	Aliphatic amine–ethylene oxide adduct
ZZL-0803....................	Aliphatic amine–cyanoethylation product
ZZL-0812....................	Aliphatic amine–cyanoethylation product
ZZL-0807....................	Aliphatic amine–glycidyl adduct
ZZL-0800....................	Aromatic amine mixture
ZZL-0801....................	Aromatic amine mixture
Ciba Co., Inc. (Araldite®):	
HN 951......................	Aliphatic amine
The Epoxylite Corp.* (Epoxylite®):	
1...........................	Aliphatic amine
1A..........................	Modified aliphatic amine
M...........................	Aromatic amine
7 and 7B....................	Aromatic amine mixtures
Shell Chemical Co. (Epon®):	
A...........................	Diethylamino propylamine
D...........................	Tri (2-ethyl hexoate) salt of tri (dimethyl amino methyl) phenol
CL..........................	Metaphenylene diamine
U...........................	Modified aliphatic amine
T...........................	Modified aliphatic amine
Z...........................	Aromatic amine mixture
BF_3-400.....................	Boron trifluoride amine complex

* Most other resin formulators—for example, Houghton Laboratories and
Furane Plastics—likewise supply proprietary curing agents; the number of such curing
agents prohibits a comprehensive listing.

agents for the epoxy resins. The modifications are offered under proprietary designations by a variety of suppliers (Table 3-6). These modifications may, for convenience, be classed as resin adducts, ethylene oxide adducts, and cyanoethylation products. Other adducts or modifiers which have found use are represented by aliphatic substitutions such as

$$
\begin{array}{ccc}
\text{H} & & \text{H} \\
| & & | \\
\text{R—N—CH}_2\text{—CH}_2\text{—N—CH}_2\text{—CH}_2\text{—NH}_2
\end{array}
$$

where R is a 12-carbon atom aliphatic chain (3-13).

Amine-resin and Amine-glycidyl Adducts

The commercial amine adducts are those synthesized by reacting an amine, such as ethylene diamine or diethylene triamine, with a calculated percentage of commercial diglycidyl ether of bisphenol A or monofunctional glycidyl materials such as butyl glycidyl ether or phenyl glycidyl ether.

$$
\underset{\substack{\text{Mono- or polyfunctional} \\ \text{glycidyl material}}}{\text{R—CH}_2\text{—CH}\overset{\displaystyle O}{\overbrace{\qquad}}\text{CH}_2} + \underset{\text{Polyamine}}{\text{H}_2\text{N—R}'\text{—NH}_2} \rightarrow
$$

$$
\underset{\text{Amine adduct curing agent}}{
\begin{array}{cc}
\text{OH} & \text{H} \\
| & | \\
\text{R—CH}_2\text{—CH—CH}_2\text{—N—R}'\text{—NH}_2
\end{array}}
$$

The principal advantages of the amine adducts are that they provide more convenient mixture ratios and more rapid cures (3-1). The higher percentage of curing agent required offsets minor measuring errors that could be reasonably critical with the unmodified amines. The shorter cure occurs because a portion of the resin is already in a partially "cured" stage and the hydroxyl groups present in the adduct speed the cure by mechanisms indicated in Chap. 2.

A typical adduct of a polyamine with a low-molecular-weight resin will have a viscosity of 5,000 to 13,000 centipoises at room temperature. The stoichiometric amount of the adduct required for commercial liquid resins is 25 phr, at which ratio no appreciable reduction of viscosity in the resin mix is realized (3-5).

Amine adducts will provide extremely fast cures at room temperature. The exotherm is high, falling in the 200 to 250°C range. The pot life is approximately 10 minutes for a 1-lb batch, 20 minutes for a 50-gram batch.

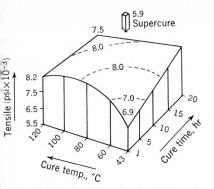

FIG. 3-8. Tensile strength of amine-resin adduct cured system, diglycidyl ether of bisphenol A type resin (3-5).

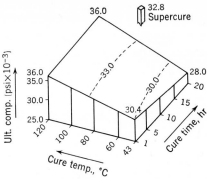

FIG. 3-9. Compressive strength of amine-resin adduct cured system, diglycidyl ether of bisphenol A type resin (3-5).

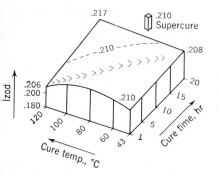

FIG. 3-10. Izod impact strength of amine-resin adduct cured system, diglycidyl ether of bisphenol A type resin (3-5).

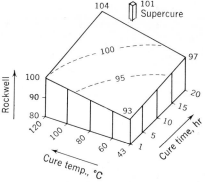

FIG. 3-11. Rockwell hardness (M) of amine-resin adduct cured system, diglycidyl ether of bisphenol A type resin (3-5).

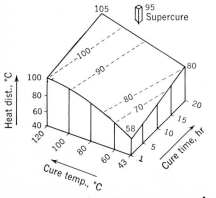

FIG. 3-12. Heat-distortion temperature of amine-resin adduct cured system, diglycidyl ether of bisphenol A type resin (3-5).

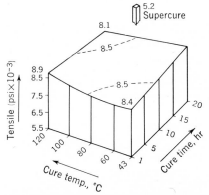

FIG. 3-13. Tensile strength of amine-resin adduct cured system, fluidized epoxy resin (3-5).

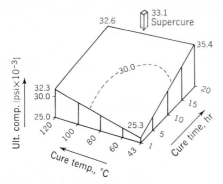

FIG. 3-14. Compressive strength of amine-resin adduct cured system, fluidized epoxy resin (3-5).

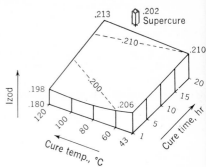

FIG. 3-15. Izod impact strength of amine-resin adduct cured system, fluidized epoxy resin (3-5).

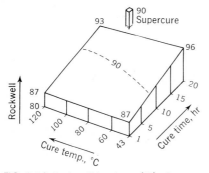

FIG. 3-16. Rockwell hardness (M) of amine-resin adduct cured system, fluidized epoxy resin (3-5).

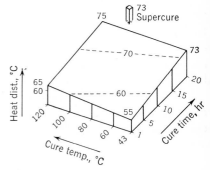

FIG. 3-17. Heat-distortion temperature of amine-resin adduct cured system, fluidized epoxy resin (3-5).

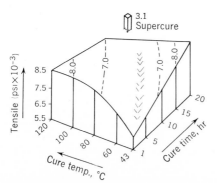

FIG. 3-18. Tensile strength of amine-resin adduct cured system, higher-functionality epoxy resin (3-5).

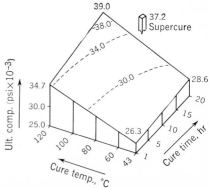

FIG. 3-19. Compressive strength of amine-resin adduct cured system, higher-functionality epoxy resin (3-5).

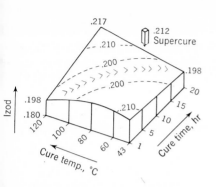

FIG. 3-20. Izod impact strength of amine-resin adduct cured system, higher-functionality epoxy resin (3-5).

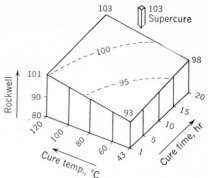

FIG. 3-21. Rockwell hardness (M) of amine-resin adduct cured system, higher-functionality epoxy resin (3-5).

Figures 3-8 to 3-22 present physical properties for three resins cured with an amine adduct, indicating the variations to be expected between a diglycidyl ether of bisphenol A type resin, a fluidized (Chap. 6) diglycidyl ether of bisphenol A type resin, and a liquid epoxy resin of higher functionality.

Table 3-7 presents electrical and chemical properties for a typical commercial resin cured with an amine adduct.

The amine adducts are principally useful in adhesive and laminating formulations, where thin sections must be cured rapidly. Although castings employing such curing agents show less tendency to bubble and froth during cure than is the case with unmodified amines, the high viscosity and the short pot life militate against their use in casting

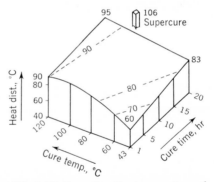

FIG. 3-22. Heat-distortion temperature of amine-resin adduct cured system, higher-functionality epoxy resin (3-5).

formulations. These amine adducts have a skin-irritation potential similar to other polyamines, and caution should be exercised in their use.

Amine–Ethylene Oxide Adducts

The sensitization potential can be reduced by the introduction of selected functional groups on the nitrogen atom. The most effective group is the hydroxyethyl group and its alkyl or aryl derivatives, and for this reason, adducts of ethylene and propylene oxide with polyamines represent a useful class of curing agents (3-1). Depending on the ratio of reactants and the reaction conditions prevailing, the end product will consist predominantly of the mono- or *bis*-hydroxylethyl derivates. The reaction of a polyamine and ethylene oxide, for example, would proceed

$$H_2N\text{---}R\text{---}NH_2 + CH_2\diagup\!\!\!\!\diagdown CH_2 \rightarrow H_2N\text{---}R\text{---}\underset{\underset{O}{|}}{N}\text{---}CH_2\text{---}\overset{\overset{OH}{|}}{C}H_2$$

$$+ CH_2\diagup\!\!\!\!\diagdown CH_2 \rightarrow CH_2\text{---}\overset{\overset{OH}{|}}{C}H_2\text{---}\overset{\overset{H}{|}}{N}\text{---}R\text{---}\overset{\overset{H}{|}}{N}\text{---}CH_2\text{---}\overset{\overset{OH}{|}}{C}H_2$$

The reaction, it will be seen, is closely analogous to that which takes place during the cure of epoxy resins with primary or secondary amines. The amine is reacted with the desired alkylene oxide in the presence of excess water.

TABLE 3-7. Typical Electrical Properties and Chemical Resistance of Resin Cured with Amine-resin Adduct (3-5)

(Test conditions: room temperature)

Electrical properties	Frequency, cycles/sec		
	60	10^3	10^6
Power factor..................	0.009	0.019	0.032
Dielectric constant.............	4.4	4.2	3.7
Loss factor....................	0.03	0.08	0.11

Chemical Resistance

System tested in	*Percentage weight gain, 7 days immersion*
10% caustic....................	Negligible
Ethyl alcohol....................	Negligible
Kerosene......................	Negligible
Toluol........................	Negligible
Ethyl acetate..................	Negligible
30% sulfuric acid...............	0.88
Ethyl ether....................	0.55
Chloroform....................	1.81
Acetic acid....................	2.88
Acetone......................	0.83
Trichloroethylene...............	0.13

Typical oxide adducts may be made from a wide range of aliphatic amines. Typical ethylene oxide and propylene oxide adducts are:

I. Mono-hydroxy diethylene triamine (3-1)

$$H_2N-CH_2-CH_2-\overset{\overset{\displaystyle H}{|}}{N}-CH_2-CH_2-\overset{\overset{\displaystyle H}{|}}{N}-CH_2-CH_2-OH$$

II. Bis-hydroxyl ethyl diethylene triamine (3-1)

$$HO-CH_2-CH_2-\overset{\overset{\displaystyle H}{|}}{N}-CH_2-CH_2-\overset{\overset{\displaystyle H}{|}}{N}-CH_2-CH_2-\overset{\overset{\displaystyle H}{|}}{N}-CH_2-CH_2-OH$$

III. N-(2-hydroxypropyl) ethylene diamine (3-6)

$$H_2N-CH_2-CH_2-\overset{\overset{\displaystyle H}{|}}{N}-CH_2-\overset{\overset{\displaystyle OH}{|}}{CH}-CH_3$$

Although of reduced sensitization potential, the hydroxyalkylated derivatives of ethylene diamine are, to some extent, skin sensitizing; the corresponding derivatives of diethylene triamine, however, appear free of irritation potential (3-15).

Low viscosity and reduced skin-irritation potential are the principal advantages of the oxide adducts. Some of the compounds are very hygroscopic and must be stored in tightly closed containers. High humidities interfere with room-temperature cures, particularly in thin sections. The water absorption (3-6) of N-(2-hydroxypropyl) ethylene diamine at 21°C and 66 per cent relative humidity in a film of 4 mm thickness, for example, is given in the accompanying table.

Time, hours	Increase in weight, %
5	14.5
10	25
20	36.8
30	46.5
40	56
50	59.5
100	79.5
150	90

Slow film cures, a disadvantage in laminating work, can be overcome with the hydroxyalkylated derivatives of diethylene triamine, for example, by the addition of bisphenol A, the amount of bisphenol being considered as an acid accelerator and being ignored in the calculation of stoichiometric requirements (3-15).

With increasing numbers of hydroxyls, it becomes more difficult to mix the curing agent into the resin; thus, N,N'-bis(hydroxyethyl) diethylene triamine cannot be completely dissolved into the resin until exothermic heat promotes solution, whereas N-hydroxyethyl diethylene triamine dissolves in the resin readily at room temperature. Terminal methyl groups, however, improve solubility, even in compounds containing numerous hydroxyls (3-15). However, when incorporating the amine

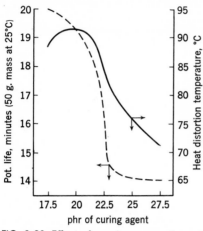

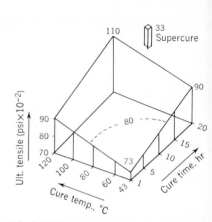

FIG. 3-23. Effect of varying proportions of amine-oxide adduct type curing agent on pot life and heat-distortion temperature (3-5).

FIG. 3-24. Tensile strength of amine-oxide adduct cured system (3-5).

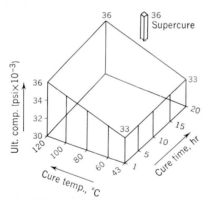

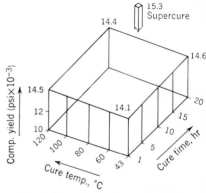

FIG. 3-25. Compressive strength of amine-oxide adduct cured system (3-5).

FIG. 3-26. Compressive yield strength of amine-oxide adduct cured system (3-5).

oxide adducts into the resin, attention must be directed to thorough stirring, since mixing is less easily accomplished than with unmodified polyamines. Incomplete mixing will be reflected in the properties of the cured system.

A typical commercial amine oxide (consisting of a blend of adducts I and II) has a viscosity of 200 to 500 centipoises at room temperature. It provides fast room-temperature cures, and the stoichiometric quantity required for commercial liquid resins is 20 phr.   The pot life is 16 to 18 minutes, with peak exotherms for a 1-lb batch reaching 237°C.   Figure 3-23 shows the effect of varying the mixture ratio on the pot life as well as

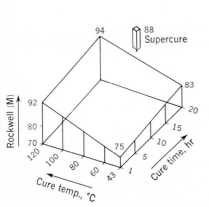

FIG. 3-27. Rockwell hardness (M) of amine-oxide adduct cured system (3-5).

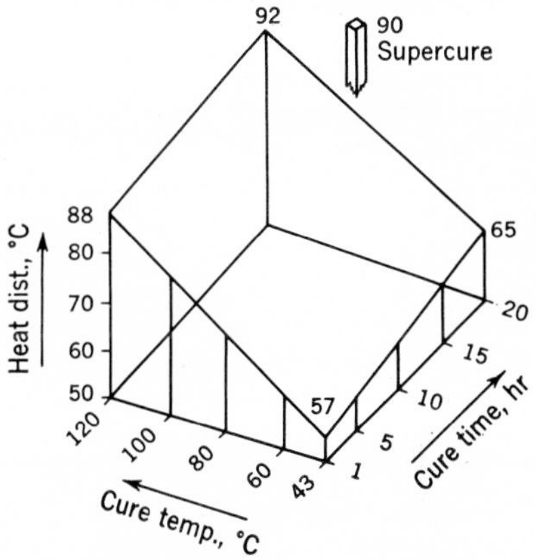

FIG. 3-28. Heat-distortion temperature of amine-oxide adduct cured system (3-5).

on the heat-distortion temperature.   Typical physical properties for this curing-agent system are presented in Figs. 3-24 to 3-28.   Table 3-8 presents electrical and chemical data.

TABLE 3-8. Typical Electrical Properties and Chemical Resistance of Resin Cured with Amine–Ethylene Oxide Adduct (3-5)

(Test conditions: room temperature)

Electrical properties	Frequency, cycles/sec		
	60	10^3	10^6
Power factor..............	0.0150	0.0274	0.0468
Dielectric constant..........	4.66	4.50	3.58
Loss factor................	0.070	0.124	0.167

Chemical Resistance

System tested in	Percentage weight gain, 7 days immersion
10% caustic...................	0.40
30% sulfuric acid..............	5.10
Ethyl ether....................	1.05
Chloroform....................	Disintegrated
Acetic acid....................	Disintegrated
Acetone.......................	Plasticized
Trichloroethylene..............	Plasticized

TABLE 3-9. Pot Life of Various Amine Oxide Adducts (3-15)
(Test conditions: 25°C.   Size of sample: 50 grams.)

Compound	Pot life, min
N-(2-phenyl, 2-hydroxyethyl) DETA	18
N-(hydroxyethyl) DETA	19
N,N'-bis(hydroxyethyl) DETA*	24
N,N'-bis(hydroxyethyl) 3,3'-imino bis(propylamine)	25
N-(hydroxypropyl) DETA	27
N,N-bis(hydroxyethyl) TETA	28
N,N-bis(hydroxypropyl) DETA	29
N,N-bis and tris(hydroxypropyl) DETA	34
N,N'-bis and tris(hydroxyethyl) DETA	54
N-(2-hydroxy,2,4,4, trimethylpentyl) DETA	57
N-(hydroxypropyl) 1,2-diaminopropane	67
N-(hydroxypropyl) m-phenylene diamine	250

* Probably mixture of isomers.

TABLE 3-10. Physical Properties of Resin Cured with Various Amine Oxide Adducts (3-15)

Curing agents	Heat-distortion temperature, °C	Ultimate compressive strength, psi	Compressive yield strength, psi	Ultimate flexural strength, psi	Flexural modulus × 10⁻⁶ psi
N,N'-bis(hydroxyethyl) DETA	58	45,000	12,000	14,500	0.500
N,N'-bis(hydroxypropyl) DETA	68	41,500	13,500	16,500	0.525
N,N'-bis(hydroxyethyl) TETA	76	41,500	13,000	15,500	0.400
N-(hydroxyethyl) DETA	96	41,000	15,000	14,000	0.410
N-(hydroxyethyl) DETA (85 parts) plus N,N'-bis(hydroxethyl) DETA (15 parts)	92	43,000	15,000	15,500	0.420
N-(hydroxyethyl) DETA (85 parts) plus N,N'-bis(hydroxethyl) DETA (15 parts) plus bisphenol A (30 parts)	84	35,000	14,600	16,900	0.475
N-(hydroxypropyl) DETA	94	36,500	15,000	15,500	0.420
N-(hydroxypropyl) m-phenylene diamine	116	45,000	19,000	22,100	0.570
N-(2-hydroxy,2,4,4-trimethylpentyl) DETA	90	35,000	14,000	17,500	0.460
N-(2-phenyl,2-hydroxyethyl) DETA	93	39,000	15,000	12,500	0.525

The pot lives of various other amine oxide adducts are presented in Table 3-9.   Table 3-10 presents the physical properties of resin systems cured with these compounds.

Some amine oxide adducts, in common with the ethylene oxide reaction products of ammonia, diethanolamine and triethanolamine, are classed as minimum-irritation-potential (MIP) curing agents.   These MIP curing agents are finding increasing industrial use in adhesive, laminating, and casting formulations, where the more irritating polyamines, because of their handling problems, are unsuited.

Cyanoethylation Products

In addition to reaction with epoxy resins and ethylene oxide groups, the amines may be modified by reaction with other organic compounds capable of addition to the amine groups through the active hydrogens.   A large number of such compounds have been suggested, but few give any advantage over the unmodified amines.   However, one type is promising. The reaction of amines with acrylonitrile produces curing agents with reduced reactivity.   Depending on the extent of modification, the degree of reactivity can be regulated rather markedly (3-1, 3-12).

The reaction which takes place involves the saturation of the double bond:

$$H_2N-R-NH_2 + CH_2\!\!=\!\!CH-CN \rightarrow H_2N-R-\overset{\overset{\displaystyle H}{|}}{N}-CH_2-CH_2-CN$$

Polyamine   Acrylonitrile

$$+ CH_2\!\!=\!\!CH-CN \rightarrow NC-CH_2-CH_2-\overset{\overset{\displaystyle H}{|}}{N}-R-\overset{\overset{\displaystyle H}{|}}{N}-CH_2-CH_2-CN$$

This reaction is known as cyanoethylation.   As in the case of the adducts discussed previously, there are no by-products formed during synthesis.

With polyfunctional amines such as diethylene triamine, cyanoethylation may take place at more than one amino group.   The formulation of bis-cyanoethyl diethylene triamine represents the limit for a useful product, since further reaction would lead to a compound of a functionality less than 3.   This would be unable to crosslink with the resin to produce a thermoset system, although catalytic cure might be possible.

Table 3-11 presents various parameters relative to the extent of cyanoethylation of diethylene triamine.   As the extent of modification is increased, the equivalent weight of the compound becomes greater.   The viscosity of the curing agent also increases with progressive modification,

but the viscosity of the resin–curing agent mixture remains fairly constant, because increasing amounts of curing agent are required to provide
stoichiometric ratios.

TABLE 3-11. Effect of Varying Degrees of Cyanoethylation of
Diethylene Triamine on Selected Properties (3-1)

Composition, molar ratios { Diethylene triamine	1	1	1	1
Acrylonitrile.......	0	1	1.33	2
Viscosity, 25°C, centipoises.................	7	30	50	110
Mixture by weight, resin/curing agent.........	9/1	5/1	4/1	3/1
Pot life, 25°C, min.:				
50 gram.....................................	40	80	150	240–300
1 lb..	20	40	90	120
Peak exotherm, °C:				
1-in. cube.................................	198	178	None	None
2-in. cube.................................	...	223	200	48
3-in. cube.................................	263	231	226	150

Unlike the resin and oxide adducts, the cyanoethylation products result
in curing agents which give improved pot lives. The pot life increases
and the peak exotherm decreases with the extent of modification. Two
typical cyanoethylation products
will be discussed to indicate the
effect of increasing modification.

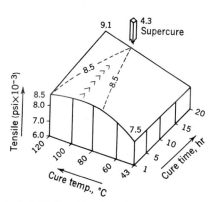

A typical cyanoethylation product formed from a ratio near equimolar has a room-temperature
viscosity of 30 to 40 centipoises.
It is used in stoichiometric ratios
of 22.5 phr with a typical commercial liquid resin, reducing the viscosity of the mix to the 100- to
800-centipoise range.

Such a compound provides for
room-temperature cures. In the
22.5-phr ratio it gives only a slight
improvement in pot life over the

FIG. 3-29. Tensile strength of cyanoethylation product cured system (3-5).

unmodified compounds, the range being 20 to 50 minutes. Peak exotherms fall in the 230 to 250°C range for both 50-gram and 1-lb batches.

The mechanical properties of the cured-resin system are presented as a
function of cure time in Figs. 3-29 to 3-31. Table 3-12 presents electrical
properties as a function of temperature. Table 3-13 presents the chemical resistance of the cured system.

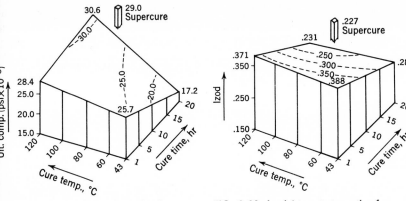

FIG. 3-30. Compressive strength of cyano-ethylation product cured system (3-5).

FIG. 3-31. Izod impact strength of cyano-ethylation product cured system (3-5).

TABLE 3-12. Typical Electrical Properties vs. Temperature of Resin Cured with Cyanoethylation Product (3-5)

Property	Frequency, cycles/sec		
	60	10^3	10^6
Power factor:			
23°C	0.0128	0.0195	0.0354
49°C	0.0107	0.0147	0.0408
66°C	0.0124	0.0135	0.0454
95°C	0.0481	0.0233	0.0503
Dielectric constant:			
23°C	4.22	4.11	3.55
49°C	4.39	4.32	3.75
66°C	4.55	4.47	3.94
95°C	5.21	4.95	4.33
Loss factor:			
23°C	0.054	0.080	0.127
49°C	0.047	0.064	0.153
66°C	0.056	0.060	0.179
95°C	0.251	0.115	0.218

D-C resistivity:	
23°C	Over 10^8 megohm-cm
49°C	Over 10^8 megohm-cm
66°C	$\sim$2 $\times$ 10^8 megohm-cm
95°C	9.4 $\times$ 10^5 megohm-cm

TABLE 3-13. Typical Chemical Resistance of Resin Cured with
Cyanoethylation Product (3-5)
(Test conditions: room temperature)

System tested in	Percentage weight gain, 7 days immersion
10% caustic	Negligible
Ethyl alcohol	Negligible
Kerosene	Negligible
Toluol	Negligible
Ethyl acetate	Negligible
30% sulfuric acid	2.05
Ethyl ether	1.32
Chloroform	17.30
Acetic acid	8.53
Acetone	5.91
Trichloroethylene	1.73

A more highly modified cyanoethylation product has a room-temperature viscosity in the 90- to 125-centipoise range. The stoichiometric ratio for a commercial resin is 37.5 phr, providing a mixed system with an initial viscosity of 800 to 1,600 centipoises.

The more highly modified products give a pot life, in 50-gram lots, in excess of 2½ hours at room temperature; in 1-lb batches, the pot life is

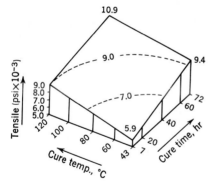

FIG. 3-32. Tensile strength of highly cyano-ethylated product cured system (3-5).

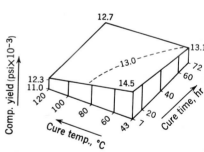

FIG. 3-33. Compressive yield strength of highly cyanoethylated product cured system (3-5).

60 to 80 minutes. Exotherm is negligible in smaller amounts; in 1-lb batches, it reaches about 180°C.

Postcure is required. An optimum cure cycle recommended for such curing agents is 2 hours at 70°C, 3 hours at 100°C, and 1 hour at 110°C.

Higher temperatures can be employed to provide a reduced cure time at the expense of somewhat higher exotherms.

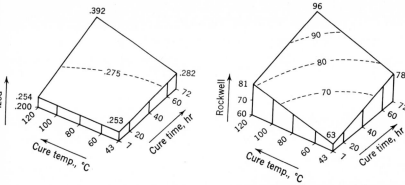

FIG. 3-34. Izod impact strength of highly cyanoethylated product cured system (3-5).

FIG. 3-35. Rockwell hardness (M) of highly cyanoethylated product cured system (3-5).

Typical physical properties for a cured system are presented in Figs. 3-32 to 3-36.   Electrical properties and chemical-resistance data are presented in Table 3-14.

The cyanoethylation products are particularly useful in laminating and adhesive formulations.   As the extent of the modification increases, the

TABLE 3-14. Typical Electrical Properties and Chemical Resistance of Resin Cured with Highly Cyanoethylated Product (3-5)

(Test conditions: room temperature)

Electrical properties	Frequency, cycles/sec		
	60	10^3	10^6
Power factor..................	0.019	0.025	0.054
Dielectric constant.............	5.1	4.9	4.0
Loss factor....................	0.095	0.12	0.22

Chemical Resistance

System tested in	Percentage weight gain, 7 days immersion
10% caustic.....................	Negligible
Ethyl alcohol....................	Negligible
Kerosene.......................	Negligible
Toluol.........................	Negligible
Ethyl acetate...................	Negligible
30% sulfuric acid...............	4.0
Ethyl ether.....................	0.68
Chloroform....	0.55
Acetic acid.....................	6.03
Acetone........................	0.03
Trichloroethylene................	0.03

wetting properties of the resin mix are improved.   The reduced exotherms of the more highly modified curing agents make them usefu
for casting applications.   The vapor pressure also is reduced as the

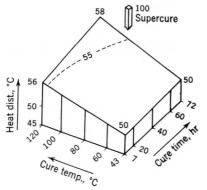

extent of modification proceeds
from 0.2 mm Hg at 25°C for diethylene triamine to less than 0.01 mm
Hg at 25°C for *bis* (cyanoethyl) diethylene triamine, making the modifications of value for vacuum casting.
Like the commercial polyamines, the
cyanoethylation products are skin
sensitizers and should be used with
caution.

FIG. 3-36. Heat-distribution temperature
of highly cyanoethylated product cured
system (3-5).

Amine Blends

It is possible to replace a portion
of one amine curing agent with a
proportion of a second in order to develop a compound having parameters somewhere between the two materials.   The primary amines or the
amine adducts may be blended with each other or, more commonly, with

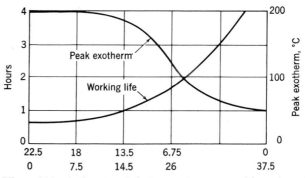

FIG. 3-37. Effect of blend of cyanoethylation products on pot life and exotherm (3-5).

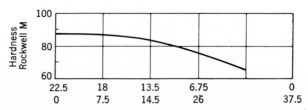

FIG. 3-38. Effect of blend of cyanoethylation products on hardness (3-5).

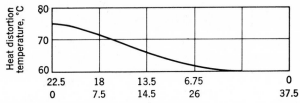

FIG. 3-39. Effect of blend of cyanoethylation products on heat-distortion temperature (3-5)

an aliphatic tertiary amine, and the variations possible by this technique are considerable.

Four examples will serve to illustrate the effect of blending amines: (1) blending an amine-resin adduct with a cyanoethylation product, (2) blending two cyanoethylation products, (3) blending DEAPA with varying amounts of a tertiary amine, and (4) blending a tertiary amine with a propylene oxide adduct of ethylene diamine.

1. When a cyanoethylation product synthesized from a 1:1 molar ratio of reactants is blended with a more highly modified cyanoethylation product, the effect is to increase the pot life of the mixture and decrease the exotherm over what

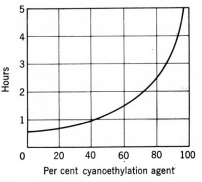

FIG. 3-40. Effect of blends of cyanoethylation and amine-resin adduct curing agents on pot life (3-5).

would be expected of the less modified compound. These data are presented in Fig. 3-37. The effect on the hardness and heat-distortion temperature is presented in Figs. 3-38 and 3-39.

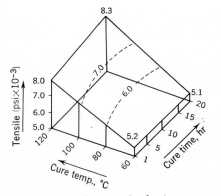

FIG. 3-41. Tensile strength of primary-tertiary amine blend, 5 phr/2 phr (3-5).

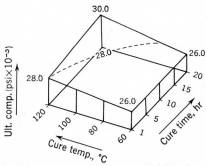

FIG. 3-42. Compressive strength of primary-tertiary amine blend, 5 phr/2 phr (3-5).

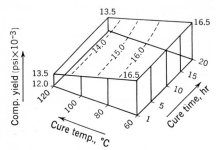

FIG. 3-43. Compressive yield strength of primary-tertiary amine blend, 5 phr/2 phr (3-5).

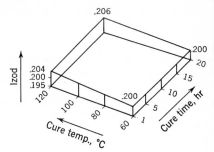

FIG. 3-44. Izod impact strength of primary-tertiary amine blend, 5 phr/2 phr (3-5).

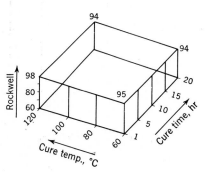

FIG. 3-45. Rockwell hardness (M) of primary-tertiary amine blend, 5 phr/2 phr (3-5).

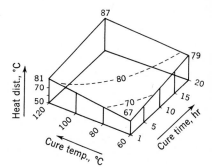

FIG. 3-46. Heat-distortion temperature of primary-tertiary amine blend, 5 phr/2 phr (3-5).

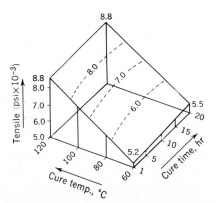

FIG. 3-47. Tensile strength of primary-tertiary amine blend, 3 phr/4 phr (3-5).

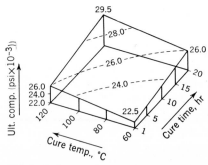

FIG. 3-48. Compressive strength of primary-tertiary amine blend, 3 phr/4 phr (3-5).

2. Similarly, to improve the pot life of an amine-resin adduct, a highly modified cyanoethylation product can be employed. Figure 3-40 presents the effect on pot life realized with increasing percentages of the cyanoethylation product.

3. The tertiary amines are particularly effective blending agents for the primary amines. Such blends may be formulated to reduce viscosity and to regulate the speed of the reaction. Care should, however, be

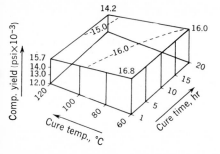

FIG. 3-49. Compressive yield strength of primary-tertiary amine blend, 3 phr/4 phr (3-5).

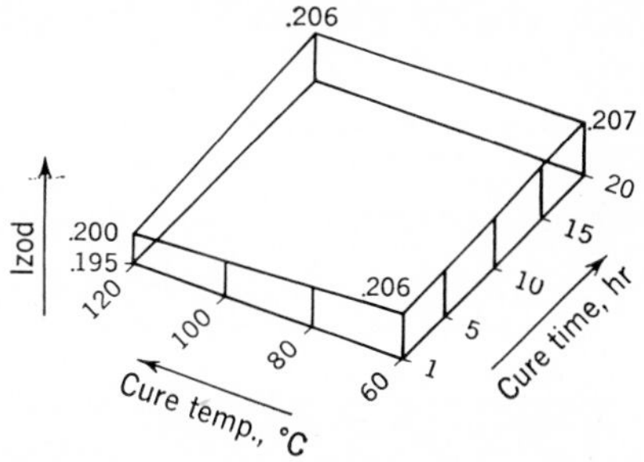

FIG. 3-50. Izod impact strength of primary-tertiary amine blend, 3 phr/4 phr (3-5).

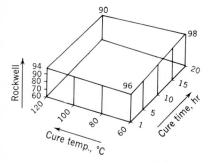

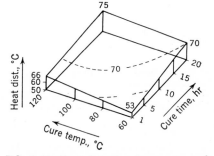

FIG. 3-51. Rockwell hardness (M) of primary-tertiary amine blend, 3 phr/4 phr (3-5).

FIG. 3-52. Heat-distortion temperature of primary-tertiary amine blend, 3 phr/4 phr (3-5).

taken to avoid reducing the reactivity of the curing agent to the point where ultimate properties of the cured system are affected. Physical properties for DEAPA in combination with 1-hydroxyethyl-2-heptadecenyl glyoxalidine at a 5 phr/2 phr ratio are presented in Figs. 3-41 to 3-46. The same compounds at 3 phr/4 phr ratio were used to cure the resin system presented in Figs. 3-47 to 3-52. These data indicate the range of systems that may be realized by the use of a single primary-tertiary amine blend.

4. Similar reductions in exotherm may be achieved by blending tertiary

amines with ethylene or propylene oxide adducts of polyamines.   Again, the reactivity of the mixture must not be cut back exceedingly lest the physical and chemical properties in particular be adversely affected.

CONCLUSION

The most widely used curing agents for the epoxy resins are the amines. The primary polyamines represent one class providing good room-temperature cures and highly versatile systems.   However, to improve handling properties, a number of modified compounds based on commercial amines have been introduced.

The modifications are of three sorts: amine-resin adducts, ethylene oxide adducts, and cyanoethylation products.   Amine blends also serve to give modified handling characteristics.   The amine-resin adducts provide more convenient stoichiometric ratios and extremely fast room-temperature cures.   They give properties similar to the unmodified amines.   The amine–ethylene oxide adducts provide amine curing agents with vastly reduced irritation potential but somewhat reduced mechanical and chemical properties.   The cyanoethylation products provide convenient mixture ratios and lower vapor pressures but reveal rather marked reduction in physical properties.   Amine blends are used to permit the regulation of pot life to a specific production situation and to modify selectively a generally suitable curing agent.

References

3-1. Allen and Hunter, Some Characteristics of Epoxide Resin Systems, *Journal of Applied Chemistry*, October, 1956.

3-2. Technical literature, The Epoxylite Corp.

3-3. Newey and Shokal, Curing Glycidyl Polyethers with N,N-Dialkyl-1, 3-Propanediamine, U.S. 2,642,412 (1953).

3-4. Charles F. Pitt, Bakelite Co., private communications and sales literature.

3-5. Bakelite Co., technical literature.

3-6. Wyandotte Chemicals Corp., technical literature.

3-7. Shell Chemical Corp., technical literature.

3-8. Applied Plastics Co., technical literature.

3-9. Ciba Company, Inc., technical literature.

3-10. Tucker, Cooperman, and Franklin, Dielectric Properties of Casting Resins, *Electronics Equipment*, July, 1956.

3-11. Lundsted, Ile, and Schulz, Totally Hydroxypropylated Alkylene Diamines, U.S. 2,697,118 (1954).

3-12. Farnham, Epoxy Resins Cured with Amines Having Cyanoethyl Groups, U.S. 2,753,323 (1956).

3-13. Technical data sheet, Amine ODT, Monsanto Chemical Co.
3-14. Delmonte, Electrical and Mechanical Properties of Epoxy Plastics, *ASTM Bulletin*, September, 1957.
3-15. Pitt and Paul, Low Toxicity Aliphatic Amines as Cross-linking Agents for Polyepoxy Resins, *Industrial and Engineering Chemistry*, July, 1957.

4

AMINES (CONTINUED), AMIDES, AND LATENT CURING AGENTS

In addition to the primary and secondary aliphatic polyamines discussed in Chap. 3 and their modifications and blends, cyclic aliphatic amines, tertiary amines, and aromatic amines may be used as curing agents. The aliphatic amines, as a class, impart similar properties to the cured resin, with the heat-distortion temperatures generally lying below 120°C, even when fully postcured. The primary aromatic (or aryl) diamines are used to provide systems having heat-distortion temperatures up to 175°C and somewhat improved chemical resistance and electrical properties. This chapter discusses the cyclic aliphatic amines, the tertiary amines, and the aromatic amines, together with the amides as typified by dicyandiamide and various latent catalysts, as typified by boron trifluoride amine complexes.

CYCLIC ALIPHATIC AMINES

Piperidine, a cyclic aliphatic amine, was one of the first amines to be used with epoxy resins on a commercially significant scale. Piperidine

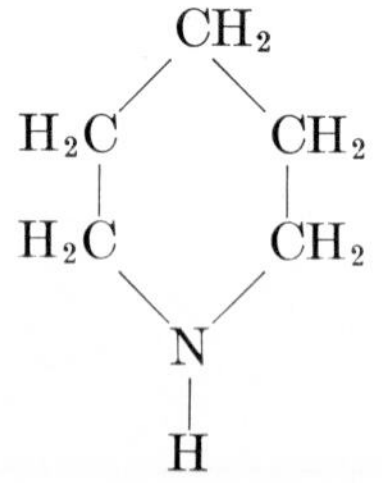

$$
\begin{array}{ccc}
 & CH_2 & \\
H_2C & & CH_2 \\
H_2C & & CH_2 \\
 & N & \\
 & H &
\end{array}
$$

has retained much of its popularity and can be considered representative of the class. Although other cyclic amines have been suggested, such as pyrrolidine, only menthane diamine appears to offer any commercial advantage over piperidine.

Piperidine is a colorless liquid with a molecular weight of 85.   It is a monofunctional secondary amine containing a single active hydrogen. To obtain crosslinking, therefore, cure must proceed by catalytic action arising from the exposed electron pair of the nitrogen atom.   Experimental data indicate that 5 to 7 phr should be employed with commercial resins to obtain optimum properties.   At this ratio, the viscosity of the resin mix will be reduced to about 6,000 centipoises and the pot life will be quite long.

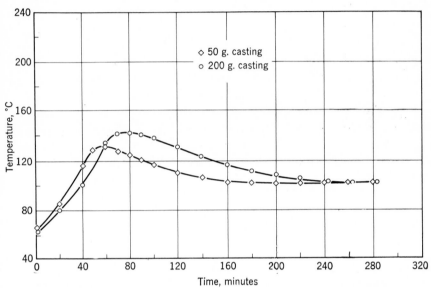

FIG. 4-1. Exotherm profile for epoxy resin and piperidine, 5 phr at 100°C (3-7).

If an appreciable bulk of resin is involved, upon mixing at 25°C there is a prompt rise in temperature to about 50°C.   The temperature then returns to ambient to provide a pot life on the order of 8 hours.   This temperature rise appears distinct from the exotherms which may occur during cure.   If allowed to gel at room temperature, there is no appreciable exotherm, and the mixture sets to a brittle solid in 24 to 48 hours. The properties of the system do not thereafter improve greatly with room-temperature aging, and postcure will be required.   Cure cycles ranging from 24 hours at 60°C to 3 hours at 100°C are adequate for thorough cure.   If the piperidine/resin system is cured at elevated temperatures prior to gelation, an exothermic rise will occur.   Figure 4-1 presents an exotherm profile for a 100°C cure.

Since exotherm control presents a problem with amine curing agents, it is frequently customary to gel the resin mix at lower temperatures prior

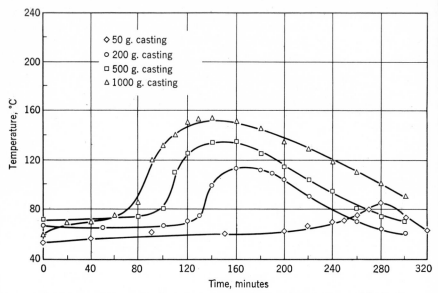

FIG. 4-2. Exotherm profile for epoxy resin and piperidine, 5 phr at 60°C (3-7).

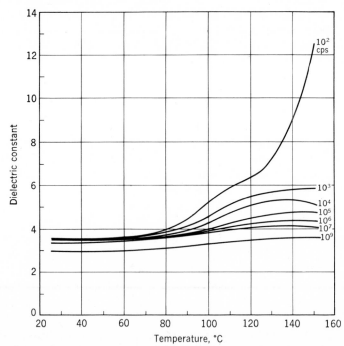

FIG. 4-3. Dielectric constant vs. temperature for various frequencies, piperidine cured resin (3-7).

to the final high-temperature cure. In the case of piperidine, if the initial temperature is moderate (Fig. 4-2), the exotherm, likewise, will be moderate. Once gelled, the temperature can then be elevated for post-cure without encountering significant exotherm (3-1).

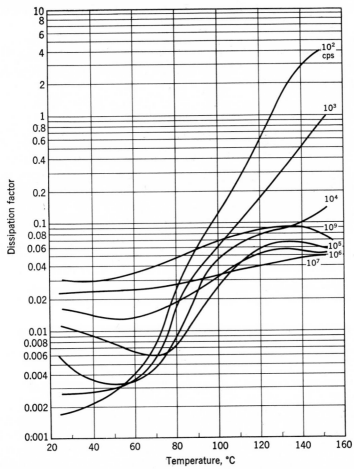

FIG. 4-4. Dissipation factor vs. temperature for various frequencies, piperidine cured resin (3-7).

The physical properties of a piperidine cured system fall into the same class as primary aliphatic polyamine cured systems. The Barcol hard-ness will be in the neighborhood of 35 to 40, with the heat-distortion temperature about 75°C for a moderately cured system. Tensile strength will be about 8,000 psi, compressive strength, 16,000 psi, etc. The electrical properties, likewise, are typical of a primary aliphatic poly-amine cured system. Figures 4-3 and 4-4 present the dielectric constant and dissipation factor at various frequencies as a function of temperature. The chemical resistance, as with most epoxy systems, is good.

Piperidine, like DETA and DEAPA, is a good general-purpose curing agent. Because of the longer pot life, it is popular (despite its significantly higher cost) in production situations where postcuring is possible. Because of the reduced exotherms, it can be used for the casting of somewhat larger masses than can either DETA or DEAPA. Typical of the class of unmodified amines, it is a skin-sensitizing agent—though somewhat less irritating than average—and due precautions should be exercised with its use.

TERTIARY AMINES

Tertiary aliphatic amines may be of various orders of reactivity, as indicated in Chap. 2. They may be either aliphatic in structure or aromatic substituted derivatives. With higher percentages and more reactive molecules, room-temperature cures may be obtained with rapidity. As is the case with the primary amines, postcuring will improve ultimate properties in most systems. As catalysts, the tertiary amines are used in amounts ranging from 5 to 15 phr, the amount being capable of some regulation to control pot life, curing conditions, and mixed viscosity. When used as accelerators for anhydride cures (Chap. 5), they are employed at amounts ranging from 0.1 to 3 phr.

The simplest of the tertiary amines, trimethylamine

$$
\begin{array}{c}
CH_3 \\
| \\
CH_3—N—CH_3
\end{array}
$$

is unsuitable for use as a curing agent, since it has a boiling point of 3.5°C, but the next higher compound in the series, triethylamine

$$
\begin{array}{c}
CH_2—CH_3 \\
/ \\
CH_3—CH_2—N—CH_2—CH_3
\end{array}
$$

has found use, particularly in adhesive formulations (4-1). When employed at the ratio of 10 phr, it gives a pot life of over 7 hours at room temperature and with a mixed resin system (containing equal parts of an aromatic and aliphatic-based polyglycidyl ether) gives a shear strength of 5,160 psi on bonded phenolic blocks after a 6-day room-temperature cure; at 15 phr, the same resin system gives shear strengths of 6,000 psi on aluminum blocks after a 6-day room-temperature cure.

The aromatic substituted derivatives of trimethylamine have become very popular in recent years. Chief among them are:

Benzyldimethylamine

$$\text{C}_6\text{H}_5-\text{CH}_2-\text{N} \Big\langle \begin{matrix} \text{CH}_3 \\ \text{CH}_3 \end{matrix}$$

Alpha-methylbenzyl dimethylamine

$$\text{C}_6\text{H}_5-\overset{\overset{\displaystyle\text{CH}_3}{|}}{\text{CH}}-\text{N} \Big\langle \begin{matrix} \text{CH}_3 \\ \text{CH}_3 \end{matrix}$$

Dimethyl amino methyl phenol (DMP-10*)

$$\text{OH}\cdots\cdots\quad \text{C}_6\text{H}_4-\text{CH}_2-\text{N} \Big\langle \begin{matrix} \text{CH}_3 \\ \text{CH}_3 \end{matrix}$$

Tridimethyl amino methyl phenol (DMP-30*)

$$\begin{matrix} \text{CH}_3 \\ \text{N}-\text{CH}_2- \\ \text{CH}_3 \end{matrix} \quad \text{OH}\cdots\cdots \quad -\text{CH}_2-\text{N} \Big\langle \begin{matrix} \text{CH}_3 \\ \text{CH}_3 \end{matrix}$$
$$\text{CH}_2$$
$$\text{N} \Big\langle \begin{matrix} \text{CH}_3 \\ \text{CH}_3 \end{matrix}$$

Benzyldimethylamine has proved valuable as a curing agent for room-temperature adhesive and coating formulations. The optimum amount was determined to be 15 phr with a mixed resin system similar to that employed with triethylamine (4-2). The workable pot life was on the order of 75 minutes, and the initial viscosity was extremely low. In about 24 hours at room temperature, the adhesive layer hardened sufficiently to permit handling; and at the end of 6 days at room temperature, shear strengths in excess of 3,500 psi were obtained on phenolic laminated blocks. A 48-hour cure at 60°C resulted in a shear strength of 4,600 psi on the phenolic blocks and 5,200 psi if the cure temperature was 80°C for the same period. In coating formulations, it is reported to provide clear films without the characteristic discoloration that results with most amine curing agents (4-2).

When percentages on the order of 5 to 15 phr are employed, the tertiary

* Rohm and Haas Chemical Co.

amines give cured systems similar to those obtained with the curing agents discussed in Chap. 3 and like the primary amines will, at these percentages, give high exotherms in larger masses. In some cases, such as with triethylamine, the pot life at room temperature will be considerably extended before the cure is initiated to an appreciable extent, and thereafter, cure will proceed rapidly. In other cases, such as with DMP-30, the pot life of a 1-lb batch, when 6 phr is employed, will be about 30 minutes; and if less than 5 phr is employed, cure will be inadequate. The increased reactivity of DMP-30 is attributed to the accelerating action of the phenolic hydroxyl.

Because of the short pot life of the more reactive tertiary amines and their more sensitive nature (in terms of reaction rate) to temperature, moisture present in the system, and percentage ratio employed, they have found only limited use in casting applications.   They are principally used in adhesive, laminating, and coating formulations.

As a secondary application, they are used as co-curing agents, particularly for the polysulfides, as discussed in Chap. 7, for which DMP-30 is usually preferred at a 5 to 10 phr ratio, and for the anhydride curing agents, in which case they are used in smaller amounts.

Like amines generally, the tertiary amines are skin-sensitizing agents and should be employed with care.

TERTIARY AMINE SALTS

Tertiary amine salts, such as DMP-30 triacetate and tribenzoate, have been introduced to provide tertiary amine curing agents which can be used at higher percentages and still provide relatively long pot lives. The tri-2-ethyl hexoate salt of DMP-30

is the most widely used of the tertiary amine salts as a curing agent for the epoxy resins.

It has been suggested (4-3) that the curing mechanism involves two steps, the first and rate-determining one being the removal of the fatty acids by esterification with some of the epoxy groups, the tertiary amines thereafter initiating polymerization through the mechanisms proposed in Chap. 2.

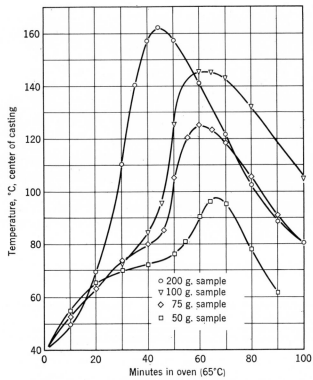

FIG. 4-5. Exotherm profiles for epoxy resins cured with 10.5 phr 2-ethyl hexoate salt of tridimethyl amino methyl phenol (3-7).

The DMP-30 salt can be used as curing agent for thin sections, as can DMP-30, itself. It is, however, higher in viscosity. The customary percentage is about 10 to 14 phr (as contrasted with 6 phr for DMP-30), which provides a pot life in the neighborhood of 3 to 6 hours at room temperature for a 1-lb batch. A moderate postcure will result in optimum properties for a laminating or adhesive formulation.

Figure 4-5 presents exotherm profiles for various sized castings employing the tri-2-ethyl hexoate salt of DMP-30 at the 10.5 phr ratio. Table 4-1 presents physical properties and chemical resistance. Table 4-2 presents selected electrical properties. Dielectric constant and dissipation

EPOXY RESINS

TABLE 4-1. Typical Physical Properties and Chemical Resistance of Resin Cured with Salt of DMP-30 (3-7)

(Test conditions: room temperature except as noted)

Physical Properties	
Tensile strength, psi	8,000
Elongation, %	1.6
Modulus, psi	0.66×10^6
Tensile strength, 54°C, psi	8,000
Elongation, %	1.5
Modulus, psi	0.53×10^6
Tensile strength, −57°C, psi	9,000
Elongation, %	1.7
Modulus, psi	0.65×10^6
Compressive strength, psi	18,400
Compression, ultimate, %	5.5
Flexural strength, psi	21,000
Modulus, psi	0.54×10^6
Impact strength, Izod	0.36
Hardness, Barcol	36

Chemical Resistance	
System tested in	*Percentage weight gain*
Ethyl alcohol, after 1 month immersion	0.75
Benzene, after 1 month immersion	0.26
Water absorption:	
After 24 hr immersion	0.07
After 1 week immersion	0.20
After 1 month immersion	0.47
Water-vapor transmission, g/sq m/24 hr	1.0

TABLE 4-2. Typical Electrical Properties of Resin Cured with Salt of DMP-30 (3-7)

(Test conditions: room temperature except as noted)

Surface resistivity, ohms	9.4×10^{13}
Surface resistivity after 24 hr in water, ohms	8.7×10^{13}
Volume resistivity, 50% relative humidity, ohm-cm	
25°C	8.7×10^{14}
100°C	5×10^{11}
150°C	1×10^9
200°C	1.3×10^8
Arc resistance, sec	120
Dielectric strength, volts/mil	400–500

factor are presented in Figs. 4-6 and 4-7.   The DMP-30 salt resembles DMP-30 as a sensitizing agent, with perhaps a slight reduction in irritation potential.

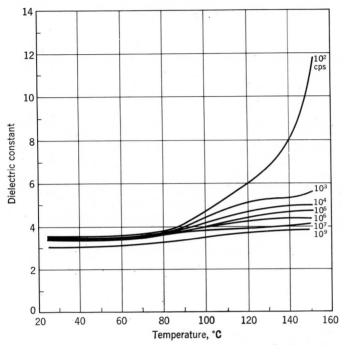

FIG. 4-6. Dielectric constant vs. temperature for various frequencies for resin cured with 10.5 phr 2-ethyl hexoate salt of tridimethyl amino methyl phenol (3-7).

AROMATIC AMINES

The principal advantage arising from the use of aromatic diamines is that they provide a significant increase (over the aliphatic amines) in heat-distortion temperature of the cured-resin system.   Certain aromatic diamines provide heat-distortion temperatures 40 to 60°C higher than obtained with even the most thoroughly postcured aliphatic amine. In these cases, the stable benzene ring is tightly crosslinked into the cured structure.   When the aromatic amine is monofunctional or tertiary in nature, as in the case of pyridine the heat-distortion temperature will be only equal to that of a tertiary aliphatic-amine cured system. Piperidine, the hydrogenated aliphatic derivative of pyridine, is an example.

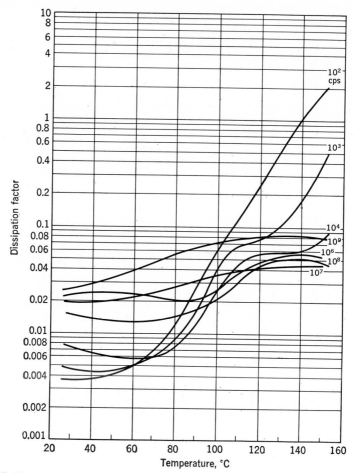

FIG. 4-7. Dissipation factor vs. temperature for various frequencies for resin cured with 10.5 phr 2-ethyl hexoate salt of tridimethyl amino methyl phenol (3-7).

As is the case of the aliphatic amines discussed in Chap. 3, the aromatic amines have been the object of research designed to improve their properties as curing agents for the epoxy resins. Although preferable to the anhydrides for higher-temperature work from the standpoint of chemical resistance, the unmodified commercial aromatic amines are capable of improvement. They produce high exotherms during cure and, if heat is required for mixing, increase the dermatitis potential by the release of irritating vapors.   A number of proprietary modifications of the aromatic amines are available, but, as was previously the case, none has proved superior in all respects to the unmodified compounds.   The unmodified compounds will be considered first, followed by a discussion of typical modified materials.

Unmodified Primary Aromatic Amines

Typical polyfunctional primary aromatic amines for curing epoxy resins are metaphenylene diamine, 4,4′ methylene dianiline, 2,6-diamino-pyridine, 4-chloro-ortho-phenylene diamine, and diamino diphenyl sulfone.   Metaphenylene diamine (MPDA)

4,4′ methylene dianiline (4,4′ MDA)

and diamino diphenyl sulfone (DADPS)

can be considered representative of the class.

Metaphenylene Diamine.   MPDA is a light amber crystalline solid with a molecular weight of 108 and a melting point of approximately 60°C.   Under humid conditions, it will darken noticeably, but this does not adversely affect its curing properties and, in some cases, appears to speed cure.

As will be seen from the structure, MPDA possesses four active hydrogens capable of linking into the epoxy-resin system.   The stoichiometric quantity required for commercial resins is 14 to 15 phr.

Two mixing procedures may be employed.   The first involves melting the MPDA at about 65°C and warming the resin to the same temperature. The two components may then be mixed.   The other procedure involves heating the resin to about 80°C and then, while continuously stirring, dissolving the curing agent into the resin.   After mixing, the compound may be allowed to return to room temperature in order to prolong pot

TABLE 4-3. Typical Physical Properties and Chemical Resistance of Resin
Cured with Metaphenylene Diamine (3-7)
(Test conditions: room temperature)

Physical Properties	
Tensile strength, psi	8,000
Compressive strength, psi	37,000
Compressive yield, psi	20,000
Flexural strength, psi	17,000
Impact resistance, Izod	0.207
Hardness, Rockwell M	108
Heat-distortion temperature, °C	150

Chemical Resistance (Measured on Laminates)

System tested in	*Percentage weight gain, 7 days immersion*
70% sulfuric acid	0.11
10% acetic acid	0.15
20% sodium chloride	0.13
50% sodium hydroxide	0.01
Acetone	0.29
Ethyl acetate	0.26
Butyl Cellosolve	0.04
Jet fuel	0.02
30% hydrogen peroxide	3.00
Distilled water	0.17

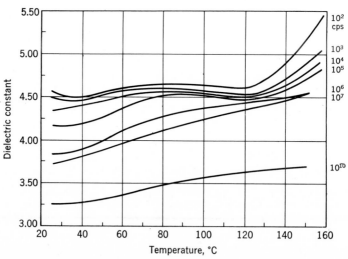

FIG. 4-8. Dielectric constant vs. temperature for various frequencies for resin cured with metaphenylene diamine (3-7).

life.   The pot life, in ½-lb batches, will be on the order of 6 hours at room temperature.

The curing process occurs in two easily recognizable stages.   The semicured or B-stage cure, in which the resin has set to an acetone-soluble, frangible semipolymerized solid, can be accomplished in about 12 hours at room temperature.   Complete cure requires 4 to 6 hours at 150°C.

Peak exotherms will be on the order of those expected from diethylene triamine and may be offset somewhat by lower-temperature gels.

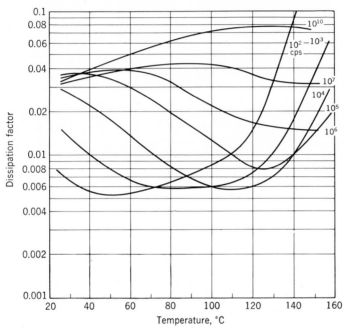

FIG. 4-9. Dissipation factor vs. temperature for various frequencies for resin cured with metaphenylene diamine (3-7).

The physical properties and chemical resistance of the cured system are presented in Table 4-3.   Figures 4-8 and 4-9 present the dielectric constant and dissipation factor.   Weight loss after 200 hours at 200°C will be on the order of 3 per cent.

Metaphenylene diamine can be used for casting applications, but the majority of industrial applications for the material is in laminating work.

Less irritating than the para isomer, metaphenylene diamine is still highly irritating and should be used in a well-ventilated area.   No unusual hazards, however, are presented in its industrial use, but if allowed to come in contact with the skin, MPDA will cause walnut-colored stains difficult to remove.

4,4′ Methylene Dianiline. 4,4′ MDA is a light amber solid. It has a molecular weight of 198 and a melting point of 85°C.

As will be seen from the structure, 4,4′ MDA possesses four active hydrogens capable of crosslinking. The stoichiometric quantity required for commercial resins is about 28.5 phr.

Although, like MPDA, 4,4′ MDA may be dissolved in hot resin, the recommended procedure is to heat the material to about 100°C and mix it into resin that has been warmed to about 90°C. It may then be allowed to return to about 60°C to prolong pot life. Pot life is short, a ½-lb batch, for instance, giving a pot life at 80°C of about 30 minutes. Peak exotherms may reach 260°C in this quantity. The recommended cure cycle is 4 to 6 hours at 165°C.

Heat-distortion temperatures may be improved over the value cited in Table 4-4 (4-6) by basing the stoichiometric calculations on determined epoxide equivalent and employing a long (16-hour) gel time at room temperature prior to postcure.

Amine used, % of equivalent	Heat-distortion temperature, °C	Hardness	
		Rockwell M	Barcol
94	152	111	42
97	153	111	41
100	162	109	40
103	162	108	38
106	159	108	32
109	152	108	28

However, when the 16-hour room-temperature gel is employed, long post-cures do not improve heat-distortion temperatures.

Cure time, hr	Heat-distortion temperature, °C	Hardness	
		Rockwell M	Barcol
4.5	158	108	39
5.0	155	107	36
5.5	156	108	38
6.0	154	108	36
7.0	154	108	38
7.5	155	109	40

Physical properties and chemical-resistance data for a system cured by 4,4' MDA are presented in Table 4-4. Electrical properties as a function of cure cycles and temperature are presented in Table 4-5. The low polarity of 4,4' MDA cured resins is evidenced by the low dielectric constant and power factor. The improved chemical resistance of the aromatic-amine cured resin over the aliphatic-amine cured resin is indi-

TABLE 4-4. Typical Physical Properties and Chemical Resistance of Resin Cured with 4,4' Methylene Dianiline (3-5)

(Test conditions: room temperature)

Physical Properties

Tensile strength, psi.....................	8,100
Compressive strength, psi...............	38,000
Flexural strength, psi...................	18,000
Impact strength, Izod..................	0.221
Hardness, Rockwell M..................	108
Heat-distortion temperature, °C..........	144

Chemical Resistance

System tested in	Percentage weight gain, 7 days immersion
Distilled water..........................	0.49
30% sulfuric acid.......................	0.54
10% caustic............................	0.42
10% ammonia (in water)...............	0.51
95% ethanol...........................	0.33
Glacial acetic acid.....................	0.13
Acetone...............................	2.45
Chloroform............................	1.21
Ethyl acetate..........................	0.36
Ethylene dichloride....................	0.85
Toluene...............................	0.41

cated in Table 4-4. In chlorinated solvents or acetic acid, the aliphatic-amine cured systems will disintegrate.

Like MPDA, 4,4' MDA provides high exotherms and must be stage-cured if employed in casting formulations. It is most useful in laminating work, and although not so irritating as MPDA, it is a skin irritant and must be used with care.

Diamino Diphenyl Sulfone. Diamino diphenyl sulfone is a solid aromatic amine used at a concentration of 30 phr to cure commercial liquid epoxy resins, usually with 1 per cent of an aliphatic amine or boron trifluoride monoethylamine as an accelerator. It is characterized by high mix viscosity and a pot life of 1 to 3 hours. It may be cured at 125 to 200°C in several hours. It gives heat-distortion temperatures as high as 175°C and is suitable for use in castings, laminates, and adhesives.

TABLE 4-5. Effect of Cure Cycles and Temperature on Typical Electrical
Properties of Resin Cured with 4,4′ Methylene Dianiline (3-5)

Property	Frequency, cycles/sec		
	60	10^3	10^6
Power factor:			
Cure A*			
23°C	0.0029	0.0075	0.0290
50°C	0.0014	0.0043	0.0525
100°C	0.0013	0.0035	0.0756
Cure B*			
23°C	0.0041	0.0086	0.0313
50°C	0.0015	0.0042	0.0525
100°C	0.0013	0.0040	0.0840
Cure C*			
23°C	0.0049	0.0107	0.0314
50°C	0.0017	0.0040	0.0412
100°C	0.0012	0.0034	0.0733
Cure D*			
23°C	0.0056	0.0124	0.0320
50°C	0.0015	0.0038	0.0490
100°C	0.0012	0.0033	0.0722
Dielectric constant:			
Cure A			
23°C	1.89	1.84	2.30
50°C	2.00	2.00	2.08
100°C	2.16	2.20	1.42
Cure B			
23°C	1.85	1.84	1.60
50°C	2.03	2.04	2.05
100°C	2.10	2.18	1.24
Cure C			
23°C	1.85	1.82	2.90
50°C	1.99	2.05	1.99
100°C	2.15	2.19	1.44
Cure D			
23°C	1.83	1.80	2.31
50°C	2.19	2.26	2.00
100°C	2.05	2.07	1.50
Loss factor:			
Cure A			
23°C	0.0053	0.0138	0.067
50°C	0.0029	0.0085	0.110
100°C	0.0027	0.0101	0.107
Cure B			
23°C	0.0077	0.0157	0.050
50°C	0.0030	0.0084	0.110
100°C	0.0035	0.0086	0.103

TABLE 4-5. Effect of Cure Cycles and Temperature on Typical Electrical Properties of Resin Cured with 4,4' Methylene Dianiline (3-5) (Continued)

Property	Frequency, cycles/sec		
	60	10^3	10^6
Cure C			
23°C...............	0.0040	0.0195	0.092
50°C...............	0.0035	0.0077	0.096
100°C.............	0.0027	0.0074	0.106
Cure D			
23°C...............	0.0102	0.0223	0.079
50°C...............	0.0037	0.0084	0.095
100°C.............	0.0024	0.0068	0.108

Property	Cure A	Cure B	Cure C	Cure D
Dielectric strength, volts/mil:				
23°C.............................	392	452	403	386
50°C.............................	401	464	466	440
100°C............................	495	518	543	480
Volume resistivity, megohm-cm $\times 10^7$:				
23°C.............................	6.7	6.3	6.1	6.8
50°C.............................	5.9	9.6	6.1	6.3
100°C............................	5.2	4.2	4.3	6.0
Surface resistivity, megohm $\times 10^5$:				
23°C.............................	4.7	4.5	4.3	4.7
50°C.............................	4.3	4.1	4.2	4.5
100°C............................	3.7	2.9	3.8	4.2

* Cure cycles: Cure A—2 hours at 100°C.   Cure B—24 hours at 100°C.   Cure C—2 hours at 130°C.   Cure D—24 hours at 130°C.

Modified Aromatic Amines

Modified proprietary aromatic amines are believed to be of two types, eutectic mixtures and chemical modifications of MPDA or 4,4' MDA. Table 3-6 presents the commercial designations of several of these materials.

Eutectic Mixtures.   Eutectic mixtures of aromatic amines provide compounds fluid at room (or only slightly elevated) temperatures.   These can be mixed with the resin without difficulty and provide somewhat extended pot lives.   The physical and electrical properties of a system cured by one such compound, employed at 19 phr, are presented in Table 4-6.   Chemical resistance is recorded in Table 4-7.

TABLE 4-6. Typical Physical and Electrical Properties of Resin Cured with Aromatic-amine Eutectic Mix (3-5)
(Test conditions: room temperature)

Physical Properties

Tensile strength, psi	13,000
Flexural strength, psi	15,400
Impact, Izod	0.216
Hardness, Rockwell M	110
Heat-distortion temperature, °C	140

Electrical properties	Frequency, cycles/sec		
	60	10³	10⁶
Power factor:			
25°C	0.0055	0.0133	0.0318
60°C	0.0335	0.0523	0.0352
100°C	0.0407	0.0627	0.0422
Dielectric constant:			
25°C	4.20	4.13	3.58
60°C	4.47	4.43	3.86
100°C	4.72	4.66	4.12
Loss factor:			
25°C	0.0219	0.053	0.116
60°C	0.149	0.234	0.148
100°C	0.189	0.292	0.174

TABLE 4-7. Typical Chemical Resistance of Resin Cured with Aromatic-amine Eutectic Mix (3-5)
(Test conditions: room temperature)

System tested in	Percentage weight gain, 7 days immersion
Distilled water	0.26
Toluene	0.07
Carbon tetrachloride	0.21
Chloroform	0.33
10% sodium hydroxide	0.19
Dichloroethylene	0.13
Kerosene	0.13
Ethanol	0.19
Ethyl acetate	0.05
Acetone	1.07
30% sulfuric acid	0.21
Ethyl Cellusol	0.04

TABLE 4-8. Typical Physical and Electrical Properties of Resin Cured with Modified Aromatic Amine (3-8)
(Test conditions: room temperature)

Physical Properties

Tensile strength, psi	9,200
Compressive yield, psi	18,000
Flexural strength, psi	19,000
Hardness, Rockwell M	118
Heat-distortion temperature, °C	154
Shrinkage during cure, %	<1
Coefficient of thermal expansion, in./in./°C	63×10^{-6}

Electrical properties	Frequency, cycles/sec	
	60	10^3
Power factor	0.007	0.025
Dielectric constant	4.0	3.6
Arc resistance, sec	90	
Dielectric strength, volts/mil	500	
Volume resistivity, ohm-cm	2.5×10^{14}	

TABLE 4-9. Typical Chemical Resistance of Resin Cured with Modified Aromatic Amine (3-8)
(Test conditions: room temperature)

System tested in	Percentage weight gain, 7 days immersion
Distilled water	0.20
10% caustic soda	0.19
10% ammonia	0.20
30% sulfuric acid	0.09
Glacial acetic acid	0.00
Kerosene	0.00
Toluene	0.00
Trichloroethylene	0.55
Chloroform	0.41
Acetone	1.35
Hydraulic fluid	0.05

The eutectic mixtures, since they are incorporated into the resin at lower temperatures, provide less of an irritation potential than the unmixed amines, but nonetheless they must be used with caution.

Chemical Modifications. The chemical modifications of the aromatic amines likewise provide compounds fluid at room (or only slightly elevated) temperatures. (See Table 3-6 for one such modification.) In pot life and peak exotherms, they are very similar to the unmodified compounds. The physical and electrical properties of a system cured by a proprietary chemically modified aromatic-amine curing agent employed at 16 phr are presented in Table 4-8. Chemical resistance is given in Table 4-9.

Although of reduced irritation potential, the chemical modifications of the aromatic amines should be used with caution.

AMIDES

Amides as a class are not curing agents for epoxy resins. So-called amide curing agents are effective only when free amines or amine decomposition products of the amides are present. Amide resins bearing primary amine groups, such as the compounds discussed in Chap. 7, may be used as curing agents to provide flexible and impact-resistant systems and also may be considered nonirritating curing agents for low (80°C) heat-distortion temperature systems.

Nonresinous amides which contain reactive amine groups give rigid resin products when used as curing agents for epoxy resins. The chief representative of the nonresinous amide-amine class is dicyandiamide (guanidine, 1-cyano)

$$H_2N-\overset{\overset{\displaystyle NH}{\|}}{C}-NH-CN$$

Dicyandiamide breaks down at 145 to 165°C to give good, rapid cures on the order of 30 minutes with solid resins. Because of the marked decrease in basicity of the monoalkyl substituted guanidines, arising from restricted molecular resonance (4-7), dicyandiamide–epoxy resin mixtures are very stable at room temperature.

Dicyandiamide is particularly useful for curing adhesive and laminating formulations based on solid resins. In laminating work, it is normally applied in solution coatings. It must first be dissolved in a solvent such as an acetone/water mix or dimethylformamide. It may then be added to the solution of solid resin. It provides good cure and extremely good laminating solution life.

When dicyandiamide is stirred into a liquid resin system, it will provide a pot life on the order of 24 hours, after which time it separates out. If milled into the system with sufficient thoroughness, it will provide a one-container system stable for at least 6 months. Being a room-temperature solid and mixed as a solid material, it has negligible irritation potential.

LATENT CATALYSIS

Because of the relatively short pot life (5 minutes to 4 days) available with most amines, considerable effort has been expended to develop a long or indefinite pot life curing agent other than dicyandiamide. The method of approach has been to block off the nitrogen or other reactive groups in a manner so that the reactivity at room temperature is destroyed. After application, heat may be applied to remove the chemical block, freeing the group and allowing the cure to be initiated. Three principal types have been employed: amine salts, boron trifluoride amine complexes, and amine-borate complexes. The first method, as represented by the tri-(2-ethylhexoic) acid salt of tridimethyl amino methyl phenol, presented earlier, does not result in indefinite pot life because of the esterification of the acid by the epoxy groups at room temperature, thus freeing the tertiary amines. The second is represented by the boron trifluoride complex of various amines. Approximately 15 have been suggested (4-5). In this case, higher temperatures disassociate the complex, and cure proceeds catalytically under the influence of the BF_3 and the amine. Boron trifluoride–amine complexes are tightly associated. The amine is inactivated and the boron satisfied, so that neither base nor acid is present. This accounts for the long pot life experienced with such compounds. While not providing indefinite pot life, the BF_3 complexes do prolong pot life considerably and are suitable for some applications. The use of BF_3 complexes in electrical systems, in particular, is to be avoided because of the corrosive effects of the liberated BF_3. Of the various BF_3 complexes suggested (4-4), only BF_3 monoethylamine has found much commercial use in liquid resin systems. However, complexes of BF_3 and such amines as piperidine, pyridine, diethylaniline, etc., may find commercial applications.

BF₃ Monoethylamine

BF₃ monoethylamine,

$$
\begin{array}{c}
\quad\text{F}\quad\text{H} \\
\quad|\quad\quad| \\
\text{F—B : N—CH}_2\text{—CH}_3 \\
\quad|\quad\quad| \\
\quad\text{F}\quad\text{H}
\end{array}
$$

may be considered a semilatent catalyst for the epoxy resins when used in small amounts (e.g., 1 part per 100 parts epoxy resin). However, optimum properties are obtained only when higher percentages are used. Cured properties compare favorably to those obtained with the standard epoxy resin/curing agent combination, but care is required in the measuring of the catalyst and in curing of the system.   BF₃ monoethylamine is very hygroscopic, which can lead to serious errors in weights, and the curing reaction is rapidly triggered and may be somewhat difficult to control.

The BF₃ monoethylamine must be classed as a slow rather than a latent catalyst, as can be seen in Fig. 4-10.   This figure, which plots viscosity

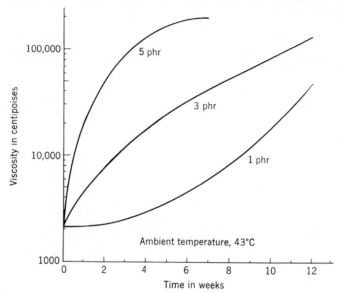

FIG. 4-10. Viscosity increase of boron trifluoride monoethylamine complex catalyzed resin (3-5).

against time, indicates that when using 1 part complex per 100 parts resin a viscosity increase of 2,000 to 50,000 centipoises occurs after 12 weeks at 43°C.   Using 3 parts complex the mix viscosity is 100,000 centipoises after 11 weeks, and with 5 parts a viscosity of 100,000 centipoises is reached in less than 4 weeks.

Specimens were prepared using 1, 3, and 5 parts of the BF₃ monoethylamine complex per 100 parts of resin by dissolving the complex in the resin at 80°C.   Bars were cast and then cured for 2 hours at 130°C plus 2 hours at 150°C.   The physical properties were (3-4) as shown in the accompanying table.

BF₃ monoethylamine complex, phr	Heat distortion, °C	Tensile strength, psi
1	45.0	2,300
3	121.0	7,900
5	147.0	4,900

If 2 phr of BF_3 monoethylamine is employed and the resin gelled at 105°C for 2 hours, good color will be obtained; if temperature is increased by as little as 10°C, however, dark castings will result. Compounds containing 2 phr BF_3 monoethylamine gelled at the lower temperatures will yield heat-distortion temperature values dependent on the postcuring temperature—with 4 hours appearing to be optimum postcure time. With a postcure of 150°C, the heat-distortion temperature is 125°C; at a postcure of 175°C, the heat-distortion temperature is 150°C; and at 200°C, the heat-distortion temperature is 175°C.

Borates

Materials such as triethanolamine borate have also found limited use as latent curing agents. In order to achieve ultimate properties with triethanolamine borate, fairly long cures are required and gelation is slow, even at high temperatures. Gelation may be hastened by using chromium acetylacetonate at 0.5 phr as an accelerator (4-8).

CONCLUSION

In addition to the aliphatic polyamines and their modifications, representative of the secondary amines, as discussed in Chap. 3, the cyclic aliphatic amines, the tertiary aliphatic amines, and the aromatic amines may also be used for curing agents.

Piperidine, typical of the cyclic aliphatic amines, provides the advantage of relatively long pot life and finds application in a variety of casting, adhesive, and laminating formulations.

The aliphatic tertiary amines are somewhat more restricted as to their value, being used in room-temperature or low-temperature curing adhesive formulations, where they provide strengths superior to that obtained with the class of compounds discussed in Chap. 3. They also, as a class, find widespread use in laminating and coating formulations because of their ability to give good cures (with adequate cure time) in thin sections.

To improve the pot life of the tertiary amines, amine salts have been introduced. These compounds extend the versatility of the tertiary amines and permit their convenient use in casting formulations.

The aromatic diamines provide somewhat better electrical properties in the cured system than the aliphatic amines, but they are principally valuable in extending the heat-distortion temperatures of the cured materials and in obtaining improved chemical resistance. They are principally useful in laminating formulations and find limited use as casting curing agents.

The amides, when containing reactive amine groups, are also used for the curing of epoxy resin. Dicyandiamide is used in adhesive and laminating formulations and is particularly valuable for the long life it affords the resin mix. Temperatures on the order of 145°C are, however, required to break down the dicyandiamide and to effect cure. At room temperature, dicyandiamide can be considered a latent curing agent.

A semilatent curing agent, the boron trifluoride–monoethylamine complex, has been proposed and finds use in a limited number of applications. Although it provides a high heat-distortion temperature, the other physical properties are less satisfactory than those obtained with the aromatic amines.

The material presented in Chaps. 3 and 4 has considered, in terms of classes, the most widely used curing agents for the epoxy resins.

References

4-1. Newey and Shokal, Glycidyl Ether Compositions and Method of Using Same, U.S. 2,575,558 (1951).
4-2. Newey and Shokal, Glycidyl Ether Compositions, U.S. 2,553,718 (1951).
4-3. Bondi and Parry, A Mechanism for the Curing of Epoxide Resins by Amine Salts, paper presented at 128th Meeting American Chemical Society, 1955.
4-4. Greenlee, Compositions, U.S. 2,717,885 (1955).
4-5. The Epoxylite Corp., unpublished reports.
4-6. Conners, Dow Chemical Co., private communication.
4-7. Pauling, "The Nature of the Chemical Bond and the Structure of Molecules and Crystals," Cornell University Press, 1945.
4-8. Langer and Elbling, Triethanolamine Borate—Epoxy Resin Catalyst, *Industrial and Engineering Chemistry*, July, 1957.

5

ORGANIC ACIDS AND ACID ANHYDRIDES
AS CURING AGENTS

Organic dibasic and polybasic acids and acid anhydrides are the second chief class of curing agents for epoxy resins. They give good over-all physical, electrical, and chemical properties, and they are not skin-sensitizing agents, although some release irritating vapors. As a class, they provide moderate-to-high heat-distortion temperatures, with some anhydrides exceeding, by a considerable extent, the best values of aromatic diamines. Liquid anhydrides are comparable in handling ease to the aliphatic amines. The solid materials—when not employed in solution—must be incorporated into the system with considerable stirring, and the system must generally be worked hot.

Acid anhydrides have found widespread use in Europe as curing agents for the epoxy resins since the beginning of epoxy-resin technology. Such use was first described in the patent literature by Castan (5-1), and for a number of years, their use in this connection in the United States was restricted. A cross-licensing arrangement consummated in the middle of 1956 by most of the basic resin suppliers, however, opened the acid anhydride curing agents to widespread exploitation in this country.

The cured epoxy-acid structure contains ester-type bonds

$$\text{Epoxy chain—O—}\overset{\displaystyle O}{\overset{\displaystyle \|}{C}}\text{—acid chain}$$
Ester linkage

which are more susceptible to caustic attack than amine-cured systems, but otherwise the systems are generally very stable thermally and chemically.

Because the anhydrides have a reduced water content and are more readily soluble in the liquid epoxy resins, they are preferred to the acids for curing epoxy resins in casting and laminating formulations. Organic acids find use primarily in surface coatings.

DIBASIC ACIDS

Among the various acids listed in the literature for possible reactants for surface coatings, oxalic acid can be considered typical, and inasmuch as it has been suggested for use in casting formulations, it will be discussed as representative. Although a number of other dibasic and polybasic acids have been suggested, drawbacks such as a tendency to foam the resin (5-2) or to be too insoluble in it to provide suitable handling characteristics have prevented their adoption.

Oxalic Acid

$$O{=}C{-}OH{\cdot}H_2O$$
$$O{=}C{-}OH{\cdot}H_2O$$

Oxalic acid is a white crystalline powder with a molecular weight of 126 and a melting point of 99°C. It is normally available in the ortho form which contains two molecules of water of hydration, as shown in the molecular formula. It is a very strong organic acid.

Oxalic acid is employed in amounts ranging from 60 to 170 per cent of stoichiometric (determined by allowing one carboxyl group per epoxy group). In the case of a resin having an epoxide equivalent in the 650 range, about 6.9 phr would be employed. If the epoxide equivalent is in the 750 to 800 range, about 5.2 phr would be used. With the dihydrate just shown, slightly larger amounts are required, on the order of 7.3 phr in the latter case.

Oxalic acid, used in stoichiometric amounts, gives a pot life of several days in a liquid resin system and is cured at 125 to 175°C for 1 hour or longer.

In solution coatings, oxalic acid does not exhibit a tendency to discoloration upon high-temperature aging, such as is the case with diethylene triamine and most other amines (5-3).

ACID ANHYDRIDES

The anhydrides (5-1) are characterized by low peak exothermic values, but correspondingly, they must be cured for long periods at elevated temperatures, with, in some cases, the consequent risk of vaporization and loss of curing agent. However, the introduction of amine accelerators to reduce cure times, and the use of new liquid anhydrides with their ease of mixing, has offset many of the former disadvantages of the acid anhydride curing agents. The anhydrides generally are somewhat hygroscopic and should not be allowed to remain exposed to the air for extended periods.

As was indicated in Chap. 2, it is necessary to open the anhydride ring by esterification with a hydroxyl in order for crosslinking of the epoxy resin to be initiated. The commercial-grade diglycidyl ether of bisphenol A may be used, in order to obtain mixes of lower viscosity, since higher-weight hydroxyl-containing species are inevitably present in small amounts.

The anhydrides are customarily used at amounts providing 0.85 to 1.1 mols of anhydride carboxyl per epoxy equivalent. However, amounts down to 0.5/1 may be employed with some anhydrides to produce excellent cured systems. Preliminary data indicate that the competing reactions may be directed by temperature, one reaction predominating at lower temperatures, one at higher (Chap. 2). This can be seen from pot-life studies, which indicate, at least in some cases, that pot life decreases with increasing temperature to a given point, at which time the trend is temporarily reversed. Because of this temperature dependence, the initial cure temperature will affect—perhaps strongly—the ultimate properties and may, in fact, dictate the optimum amount of curing agent.

Amine accelerators are employed in catalytic amounts—0.5 to 3 per cent—and serve to speed gel times and cure. Tertiary amines are most commonly used, several—among them alpha-methylbenzyl dimethylamine and n-butyl amine—being given in the literature. To an extent, the specific amine selected governs the speed of cure. It is reported (3-14) that the optimum amine proportion is critical—above or below that value, properties at high temperature will be markedly reduced.

The commercially available anhydrides may be considered to fall into three classes: room-temperature solids, room-temperature liquids, and chlorinated derivatives. Phthalic anhydride (PA), maleic anhydride (MA), hexahydrophthalic anhydride (HHPA), and pyromellitic dianhydride (PMDA) may be considered representative of the first class; a methylated maleic adduct of phthalic anhydride (MNA—known commercially as Methyl Nadic®* Anhydride) and dodecenyl succinic anhydride (DDSA) may be considered representative of the second; and dichloromaleic anhydride (DCMA), tetrachlorophthalic anhydride, and chlorendic anhydride, of the third.

The liquid anhydrides, in addition to possessing the advantage of easy mixing, also are used at weight ratios that are extremely convenient, permitting the formulation of 1/1 systems. Long pot life, low viscosity of the room-temperature mix, and relative freedom from sensitizing action and irritating effects are other inherent advantages.

Chlorinated anhydrides, in common with other chlorinated compounds proposed for use with epoxy resins, possess certain disadvantages. In

* ® Registered trade-mark of National Aniline Division, Allied Chemical and Dye Corporation.

some cases, they pose handling problems and require considerable attention to ventilation for their successful use in hot mixing procedures. In all cases they are subject to thermal degradation at higher temperatures, with the subsequent release of chlorine gas. This breakdown point, beyond which occurs the liberation of free chlorine, may, in fact, be below the heat-distortion temperature of the material. Chlorinated compounds, however, possess the advantage of flame resistance, and other of their properties make them suitable in specific applications.

Phthalic Anhydride

Phthalic anhydride (PA) is a powdery white solid having a molecular weight of 148 and a melting point of 128°C. PA imparts low exotherms, has a long pot life, and has reasonably simple handling properties. The heat-distortion temperature falls in the range of the aliphatic amines.

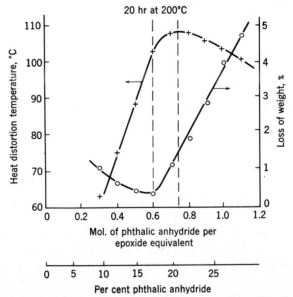

FIG. 5-1. Effect of phthalic anhydride curing agent content on heat-distortion temperature and high-temperature weight loss (2-5).

The amount of PA employed with the epoxy resins is determined by the resin species involved, inasmuch as it can be used with lower- and higher-molecular-weight resins.   In general, 0.60 to 0.90 equivalent of PA is used per epoxy group, giving values of 30 to 45 phr for the lower homologs of diglycidyl ether of bisphenol A.   The effect of anhydride percentage on heat-distortion temperature and weight loss after 200 hours at 200°C is shown in Fig. 5-1.

The resin is usually heated to 120 to 140°C prior to adding the anhydride.   The mixture is stirred until homogeneous, a constant temperature being maintained during mixing.   The anhydride will sublime somewhat during these operations.   Once the anhydride is thoroughly dissolved, the resin mix may then, in the case of the lower-weight resins, be allowed to return to about 60°C to prolong pot life.   At temperatures below this, PA will precipitate but can be returned to solution upon reheating.   The higher-weight resins are usually applied at higher temperatures because of their tendency to solidify upon cooling.

PA-catalyzed resins must be cured at high temperatures and for relatively long periods of time.   Pot life and minimum curing-time data (3-9) for two resins (A and B) having epoxide equivalents of 210 to 230 and 380 to 450, respectively, are given in the accompanying table.

Cure temperature, °C	Gel time, hr		Minimum cure time, hr	
	Resin A	Resin B	Resin A	Resin B
100	14	. . .	48	
120	7	3	24	18
150	3	1.5	8	4
160	1.5	1	4	3
200	0.75	0.5	2	1.5

The effect of higher temperatures on curing rates is shown by yield temperature (similar to standard heat-distortion temperature) measurements in Fig. 5-2.   The effect of higher-temperature cures on linear shrinkage is shown in Fig. 5-3.   It will be seen that long cures are required: 24 hours at 120°C, 8 hours at 150°C, and 2 hours at 200°C being typical values.

The physical and electrical properties of typical PA-cured resin systems are presented in Table 5-1.   From this table it will be seen that the physical and electrical properties are comparable to those of an amine-cured system.   Dielectric constant and power factor are unaffected by temperatures up to 100°C (Figs. 5-4 and 5-5).   Dielectric strength is also preserved over a wide range of temperatures (Fig. 5-6).

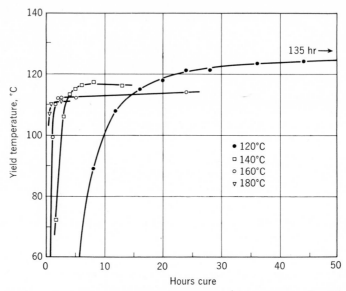

FIG. 5-2. Effect of cure time and temperature on yield temperature for 30 per cent phthalic anhydride cured epoxy (5-13).

A PA-cured system may be considered to provide chemical resistance typical of the anhydride-cured systems; it is therefore presented in detail. Table 5-2 provides chemical-resistance data for a system cured 4 hours at 150°C in terms of weight gain after 1 year immersion at room temperature in various chemicals.

The following discussion of chemical resistance of the cured PA system is based on data presented by Meyerhans (5-5).

When a postcured test sample was immersed in distilled water at varying temperatures, the following results were obtained: (1) At the end of 1 year at 40°C, the weight increase was 1 per cent, with no effect on flexural strength. (2) At the end of 1 year at 70°C, the

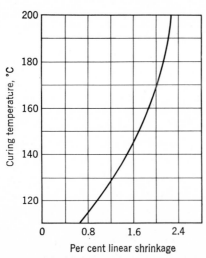

FIG. 5-3. Linear shrinkage as a function of cure temperature for 30 phr phthalic anhydride cured resin (3-9).

weight increase was 1 5 per cent, with a 25 per cent reduction in flexural strength.   (3) At 100°C, the weight increase was 3 per cent at the end of 2 months immersion, and at the end of 3 months, the sample was swollen and the flexural strength had declined by 80 per cent.

The resistance of a PA-cured system to mineral acids is generally a function of temperature and acid concentration.   Although concentrated

TABLE 5-1. Typical Physical and Electrical Properties of Resin Cured with Phthalic Anhydride (3-9)

(Test conditions: room temperature)

Physical properties	Resin A *	Resin B†
Tensile strength, psi	5,000–7,000	11,500–12,500
Compressive strength, psi	21,000–22,000	15,000–16,000
Flexural strength, psi	15,000–16,000	18,000–19,000
Impact strength, Izod	0.46	0.70
Hardness, Rockwell M	100	100
Heat-distortion temperature, °C	. . . .	109
Modulus of elasticity in tension, psi	0.48×10^6	0.45×10^6
Thermal conductivity, cal/(sec)(sq cm)(°C)(cm).	4.0×10^{-4}	4.0×10^{-4}
Water absorption, 24-hr immersion, %	0.053	0.08

Electrical properties	Frequency, cycles/sec			
	Resin A		Resin B	
	60	10^3	60	10^3
Power factor	0.007	0.002	0.0012	0.026
Dielectric constant	3.64	3.65	3.89	3.50

	Resin A	Resin B
Dielectric strength, volts/mil	415	400–410
Surface resistivity, ohms	5.7×10^{12}	$>5.7 \times 10^{12}$
Volume resistivity, ohm-cm	$>8.0 \times 10^{13}$	$>8.0 \times 10^{13}$

* Epoxide equivalent 190 to 200.
† Epoxide equivalent 390 to 450.

sulfuric acid destroys a sample within a few days at room temperature, a 50 per cent concentration has little effect below 60°C.   A 50 per cent solution of nitric acid, at room temperature, will cause spongy swelling at the end of a few days, although a 10 per cent solution will little affect it. Concentrated hydrofluoric acid, on the other hand, will provide for only a slight weight increase at the end of 6 months submersion at room temperature.

The resistance of a PA-cured system to organic acids, likewise, is generally a function of temperature and acid concentration. When a sample

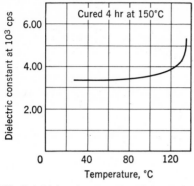

FIG. 5-4. Dielectric constant vs. temperature for 30 phr phthalic anhydride cured resin (3-9).

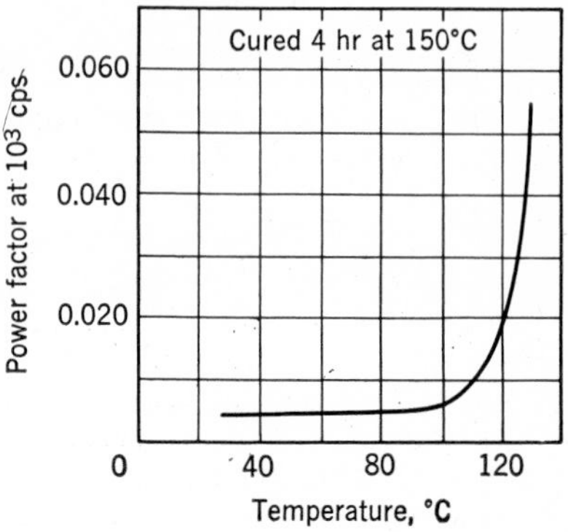

FIG. 5-5. Power factor vs. temperature for 30 phr phthalic anhydride cured resin (3-9).

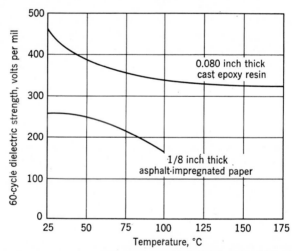

FIG. 5-6. Effect of temperature on dielectric strength of phthalic anhydride cured resin (5-4).

is immersed in concentrated formic acid, for example, the weight gain in 6 months at room temperature is about 2 per cent. In the same medium over the same period at 60°C, the weight gain is about 13 per cent. In the same medium at 100°C, the weight gain is 15 per cent at the end of 1 month. On the other hand, with concentrated stearic acid, there will be a slight decrease in weight after prolonged submersion at 60°C.

When samples of a PA-cured system are immersed in strong alkalies, chemical resistance is poor.   In a 30 per cent solution of aqueous ammonia at 20°C, the weight increase is about 13 per cent at the end of 3 months. In lower concentrations, resistance is better—with weight gain on the order of 1.5 per cent after 6 months immersion at 20°C in a 20 per cent solution.   The poor alkali resistance of the anhydride-cured system compared to the amine-cured system is explained by the presence of hydrolyzable ester linkages.   In this regard, the anhydride-cured epoxies resemble the polyesters.

TABLE 5-2. Typical Chemical Resistance of Resin Cured with Phthalic Anhydride (3-9)

(Test conditions: room temperature)

System tested in	Percentage weight gain, 1 year immersion	System tested in	Percentage weight gain, 1 year immersion
30% H_2SO_4....	0.614	H_2O.........	0.887
3% H_2SO_4.....	0.879	10% HNO_3....	0.835
10% NaOH....	0.800	10% HCl......	0.753
1% NaOH.....	0.878	5% acetic acid.	0.960
95% ethanol...	1.500	Oleic acid......	0.078
50% ethanol...	0.985	10% NH_4OH..	0.938
10% NaCl.....	0.782	3% H_2O_2......	0.923

The solvent resistance of a PA-cured system is varied.   Castings will resist hydrocarbon and aliphatic alcohols but are nonresistant to the chlorinated hydrocarbons.   Once again, resistance is a function of temperature and concentration.   When a sample is immersed in ethyl alcohol at 20°C for 6 months, the weight increase is about 1 per cent; at 40°C, about 15 per cent, with cracking in evidence at the third month.   At 78°C, there is complete destruction after 10 days.   In acetone at 20°C (1 to 10 per cent solution), the weight gain is less than 1 per cent after 6 months.   In acetone at 20°C (50 per cent solution), the weight gain is over 15 per cent in 6 months.   In undiluted acetone, complete disintegration occurs after 3 days.

Resistance to weathering is good.   A sample of a PA-cured system was exposed 1 year in an industrial atmosphere containing considerable sulfur dioxide, and at the end of exposure, there was no change in flexural strength and about 0.6 per cent moisture absorption.   A sample subjected to 3,500 hours of an artificial weathering cycle involving heat, moisture, ultraviolet, and freezing temperatures showed no damage at the end of the series, and the flexural strength of the sample remained unchanged.

PA is used chiefly in intermediate-temperature laminates and castings. Because of the low exotherm it can be employed for larger casting work than the amine curing agents can.

PA should be handled with care. As an organic acid, it will cause burns to the skin if prolonged contact is allowed. Taken orally, it will cause systemic injury.

Maleic Anhydride

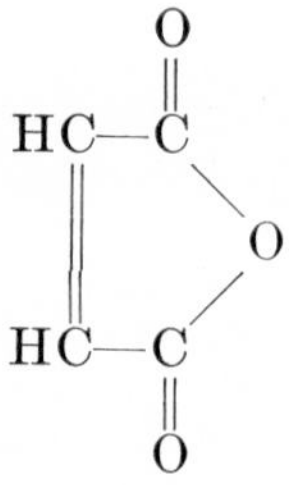

$$
\begin{array}{c}
\text{HC-C} \\
\quad \| \quad \backslash \\
\quad \quad \quad \text{O} \\
\quad \| \quad / \\
\text{HC-C}
\end{array}
$$

Maleic anhydride (MA) is a white crystalline solid with a molecular weight of 98.06 and a melting point of 52.8°C (5-6). Because of brittleness in the cured resin and toxic properties, it is used chiefly as a secondary anhydride in anhydride mixtures. A discussion of such use is presented under the section on PMDA.

Hexahydrophthalic Anhydride

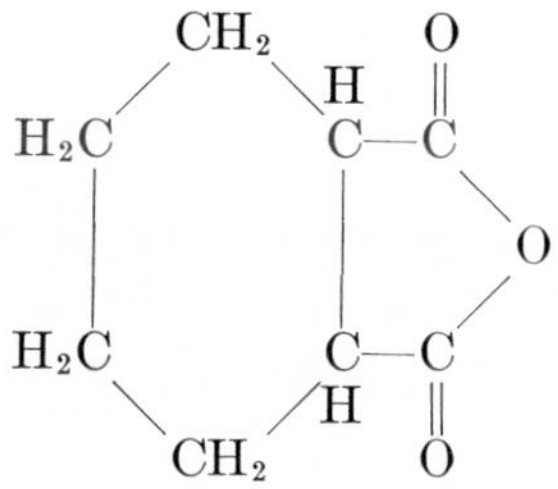

Hexahydrophthalic anhydride (HHPA) is a glassy solid having a molecular weight of 154 and a melting point of 35 to 36°C (5-6). Its higher cost, compared to PA, has limited its application as a curing agent for epoxy resins, but the low melting point of the anhydride permits its convenient use where the increased cost can be tolerated. HHPA provides long pot life, since it is soluble in the liquid epoxy resins and may be worked at room temperature. When using 0.5 per cent of benzyl-dimethylamine, cure cycles are on the same order as with PA systems. With a commercial diglycidyl ether of bisphenol A resin, about 80 phr of

HHPA is required.   When 90 parts HHPA are blended with 10 parts tetra-hydrophthalic anhydride, a room-temperature-liquid eutectic is obtained. Data on HHPA-cured systems indicate that heat-distortion temperatures in the 125 to 130°C range may be expected, with Barcol hardness of

TABLE 5-3. Typical Properties of Glycerol- and Bisphenol-based
Resins Cured with Low-melting Anhydrides (3-7, 5-6)
(Test conditions: room temperature)

Physical properties	Curing agent* and resin			
	Glycerol-based resin		Bisphenol-based resin	
	HHPA	DDSA	HHPA	MNA
Compressive strength, ult, psi.......	15,500	8,570	16,800	18,800
Compressive modulus, psi $\times$ 10^{-5}....	6.6	4.0	3.6	4.8
Flexural strength, psi..............	17,500	7,770	15,200	11,200
Flexural modulus, psi $\times$ 10^{-5}........	5.5	2.6	3.3	3.6
Heat-distortion temperature, °C.....	57	38	124	122
Color of casting...................	Colorless	Straw	Amber	Amber
Amount of curing agent required, phr	107	186	80	80

Chemical Resistance

System tested in	Percentage weight gain	
	Glycerol-based resin	
	HHPA	DDSA
Water, 25°C, 1 month............	1	0.8
Acetone, 25°C, 1 month.........	Disintegrated	
Water, boiling, 3 hr..............	2.7	0.8
Acetone, boiling, 3 hr............	4.9	Disintegrated

* 1 per cent benzyldimethylamine, based on total formulation, was used as an accelerator.

about 30.   Impact strength is 0.30.   Dielectric constant at 60 cycles is 3.28; at 10^6 cycles, 3.03.   Power factor at 60 cycles is 0.008; at 10^6, 0.014 (5-6).   Table 5-3 lists physical properties of a bisphenol and a glycerol-based resin cured with HHPA.

With glycerol-based resins, clear, colorless castings of good mechanical strength may be achieved if the cure is conducted at lower temperatures.

Although the chemical resistance (Table 5-3) of the glycerol-based system is low compared to the aromatic-based resin system, values are significantly better than obtained with other clear plastics such as polystyrene and acrylics (3-7).

HHPA may be blended with chlorendic anhydride at a 70/30 ratio to obtain a reduced-reactivity, chlorine-containing, room-temperature-liquid eutectic.

HHPA is not known to be toxic, but due caution should be employed in its use.

Pyromellitic Dianhydride

Pyromellitic dianhydride (PMDA) is a white powder with a molecular weight of 218 and a melting point of 286°C (5-7). It is a comparatively

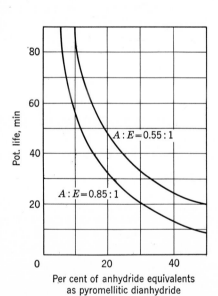

Per cent of anhydride equivalents
as pyromellitic dianhydride

FIG. 5-7. Pot life at 120°C as a function of pyromellitic dianhydride/phthalic anhydride ratio (5-7).

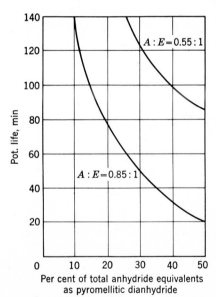

Per cent of total anhydride equivalents
as pyromellitic dianhydride

FIG. 5-8. Pot life at 90°C as a function of pyromellitic dianhydride/phthalic anhydride ratio (5-7).

reactive curing agent, insoluble in the liquid epoxy resins at room temperature and, hence, somewhat difficult to incorporate. Three systems for mixing are presently being employed: the first involves dissolving the PMDA into the resin at higher temperatures, using a second anhydride to reduce reactivity; the second involves dissolving the PMDA in solvent, such as acetone, and using the PMDA-solvent-resin mix in solution coatings; and the third involves suspending the PMDA in the liquid resin at room temperature, subsequent cure temperatures being sufficient to promote substantially complete reaction.

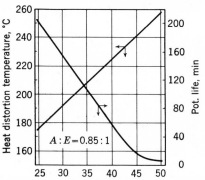

FIG. 5-9. Pot life at 90°C and heat-distortion temperature as a function of pyromellitic dianhydride/maleic anhydride ratios (5-7).

An examination of the PMDA molecule reveals that the PMDA is potentially capable of linking the rigid aromatic ring into the epoxy resin at four reactive points, and from this one would expect what in fact occurs: PMDA-cured compounds yield heat-distortion temperatures substantially above those obtainable with the monoanhydride curing agents.

When using mixed anhydrides (the first mixing procedure above), the total anhydride is maintained at the optimum value (about 85 per cent of stoichiometric) by allowing for the differences in the equivalent weight of the anhydride involved. The higher the concentration of the PMDA in the PMDA–monoanhydride mix, the more difficult the mixing and the shorter the pot life. The anhydride mixture is added separately or as a solid mix to the resin which is preheated to about 70°C. Heating is continued with agitation until a temperature of 120°C is reached. Once the anhydrides are completely dissolved, temperature may be returned to about 90°C to prolong the pot life. Pot-life data on PMDA/PA and PMDA/MA blends are presented in Figs. 5-7 to 5-9.

The chief advantages of PMDA are the high heat-distortion temperature, high thermal stability, and extreme radiation resistance (5-15) it affords. In the hot-mix procedure, the heat-distortion temperature is a function of the modifying anhydride and its percentage, as well as the cure cycle employed (Table 5-4, Figs. 5-9 to 5-11). The higher the per cent of PMDA, the higher the heat-distortion temperature of the system. MA is, in terms of this parameter, superior to PA as a modifying anhydride. This superiority is also in evidence when considering weight loss at 200°C over a period of 500 hours. A PMDA/PA system at 20 phr/28 phr gives a value of 23.7 per cent; a PMDA/MA system at 21 phr/19 phr gives a value of 2.3 per cent.

PMDA–anhydride mix cured resins have very high compressive strengths but low tensile and flexural strengths compared to amine-cured

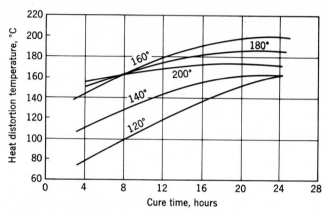

FIG. 5-10. Heat-distortion temperature vs. cure time at various curing temperatures for pyromellitic dianhydride/phthalic anhydride casting (5-14).

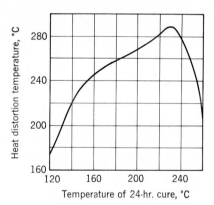

FIG. 5-11. Effect of curing temperature on pyromellitic dianhydride/maleic anhydride casting (5-7).

systems. It should be noted, however, that the retention of strengths at higher temperatures, even above the heat-distortion temperature, is outstanding (Fig. 5-12, Table 5-4). Chemical resistance of PMDA/PA and PMDA/MA cured systems are presented in Table 5-5. As will be seen, the chemical resistance is markedly superior to that obtained with PA.

TABLE 5-4. Typical Physical and Electrical Properties of Resin Cured with Pyromellitic Dianhydride in Combination with Phthalic Anhydride and Maleic Anhydride (5-7)

Formulation	Maleic anhydride		Phthalic anhydride	
	A	B	C	D
Anhydride equivalents/ epoxide equivalents........	0.85/1	0.85/1	0.85/1	0.55/1
Percentage of total anhydride as pyromellitic dianhydride	50	40	50	50
Weight ratios:				
Epoxy resin (epoxide equivalent 216)..............	100	100	100	100
Pyromellitic dianhydride...	21	17	20	14
Second anhydride.........	19	23	28	20
Pot life at 90°C, min........	10	56	20	90

Physical Properties (Test conditions: room temperature)

Tensile strength, psi.........	3,830	3,670	4,500	6,000
Tensile modulus, psi.........	0.42×10^6	0.40×10^6	0.54×10^6	0.54×10^6
Compressive strength, psi....	41,600	46,000	43,000	
Flexural strength, psi........	11,100	10,940	13,000	13,000
Flexural modulus, psi........	0.40×10^6	0.42×10^6	0.53×10^6	0.56×10^6
Impact strength, Izod.......	0.30	0.34	0.30	0.25
Hardness, Rockwell.........	M109	M109	E84.2	M119
Heat-distortion temperature, °C......................	290	255	207	150
Coefficient of thermal expansion, in./in./°C..........	5.2×10^{-5}	5.37×10^{-5}	4.5×10^{-5}	2.46×10^{-5}

Physical Properties (Test conditions: elevated temperature)

Flexural strength, psi:				
150°C....................	4,600	5,100	3,660	
200°C....................	3,900	3,800		
Flexural modulus, psi $\times 10^{-6}$:				
150°C....................	0.24	0.18	0.13	
200°C....................	0.18	0.13		
Weight loss at 230°C, %:				
7 days...................	1.7			
15 days..................	2.4			
22 days..................	3.4			

TABLE 5-4. Typical Physical and Electrical Properties of Resin Cured with
Pyromellitic Dianhydride in Combination with Phthalic Anhydride and
Maleic Anhydride (5-7) (Continued)

Formulation	Maleic anhydride		Phthalic anhydride	
	A	B	C	D

Electrical Properties (Test conditions: room temperature)

	A	B	C	D
Power factor:				
60 cycles/sec..............	0.0129	0.00706	0.0078	
10^3 cycles/sec.............	0.0144	0.01030	0.0077	0.0025
10^6 cycles/sec.............	0.0295	0.02690	0.0325	
Dielectric constant:				
60 cycles/sec..............	4.06	3.73	3.75	
10^3 cycles/sec.............	3.98	3.67	3.70	4.12
10^6 cycles/sec.............	3.56	3.34	3.39	
Dielectric strength, volts/mil	324	349	398	400
Volume resistivity, ohm-cm...	1.59×10^{15}	8.10×10^{15}	1.27×10^{16}	1.8×10^{14}
Surface resistivity, ohm......	5.66×10^{15}	5.66×10^{15}	2.51×10^{15}	2×10^{12}

Electrical Properties (Test conditions: elevated temperature)

	A	B		
Power factor at 10^3 cycles/sec:				
23°C.....................	0.0095	0.0098		
100°C.....................	0.0057	0.0058		
150°C....................	0.0052	0.0053		
200°C....................	0.0057	0.0083		
Dielectric constant at 10^3 cycles/sec:				
23°C.....................	3.65	3.66		
100°C.....................	3.83	3.90		
150°C....................	3.86	3.86		
200°C....................	3.88	3.88		

The second method of using PMDA involves dissolving the material in
hot acetone and resin at reflux temperatures. The mix is stable for
1 week. The solvent system is principally useful in laminating formulations, and details on properties of PMDA laminates are presented in
Chap. 10.

The third method of mixing PMDA involves suspending the PMDA in
the liquid resin by room-temperature mixing. Catalytic amounts of an
amine or other agent may be employed to maintain the suspension.

When such a technique is used, amounts of PMDA considerably below normal stoichiometric may be used (about 26 phr appears best) to provide heat-distortion temperatures higher than obtainable with the more complicated procedures.   This composition of matter has been made the subject of a patent application by the authors.   Table 5-6 presents physical

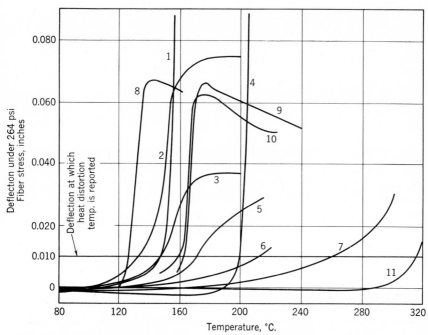

1. Resin A + amine curing agent.
2. Resin A + 50% PMDA/50% PA at A/E = 0.55/1.
3. Resin A + 40% PMDA/60% PA at A/E-0.85/1.
4. Resin A + chlorendic anhydride.
5. Resin A + 50% PMDA/50% PA at A/E = 0.75/1.
6. Resin A + 50% PMDA/50% PA at A/E = 0.85/1.
7. Resin A + 50% PMDA/50% MA at A/E = 0.85/1.
8. Resin B + TETA.
9. Resin B + MPDA.
10. Resin B + 4,4′-MDA.
11. Epoxylite #812-9. Proprietary filled high-temperature compound based on Resin C.

FIG. 5-12. Heat-distortion test deflection vs. temperature for various curing agents (5-7, 4-5, 1-15).

properties of such a system; Table 5-7 presents electrical properties. Cure cycles employed for these data were 20 hr at 220°C.   Pot life is quite long, as might be expected, but settling poses a problem.   In general, it will be noted with PMDA formulations, as with other anhydrides, that the cure cycles are relatively long.

PMDA finds principal use in laminating formulations for higher temperatures. It is also employed to a limited extent as an adhesive and in casting formulations. Its use is expected to increase as the price decreases.

TABLE 5-5. Typical Chemical Resistance of Resin Cured by Pyromellitic Dianhydride/Phthalic Anhydride and Maleic Anhydride Mixes (5-7)
(Test conditions: room temperature)

System tested in	% weight gain (or loss)			
	PMDA/PA			PMDA/MA
	7 days immersion	30 days immersion	90 days immersion	90 days immersion
95% H_2SO_4...........	....	....	−51.5	−37.8
3% H_2SO_4...........	0.18	0.35	0.53	1.42
70% H_2SO_4...........	−0.06	−0.09	−0.11	−0.05
35% HCl...........	0.12	0.20	0.38	0.49
10% HCl...........	0.12	0.12	0.47	1.24
50% HNO_3...........	0.20	0.15	1.23	2.20
30% HNO_3...........	0.10	0.24	0.40	1.10
Water (distilled)...........	0.16	0.33	0.40	1.51
1% NaOH...........	0.18	0.37	0.56	1.45
50% NaOH...........	0.04	−0.049	−0.04	0.01
30% Na_2SO_4...........	0.18	0.34	0.47	1.35
20% NaCl...........	−0.06	0.08	0.21	1.19
88% H_3PO_4...........	0.07	0.09	−0.09	0.08
10% H_3PO_4...........	0.18	0.38	0.54	1.68
Glacial acetic acid...........	−0.01	0.06	0.21	0.32
10% acetic acid...........	0.20	0.70	5.44	1.45
Oxalic acid (sat.)...........	0.17	0.37	0.56	1.44
Acetone...........	0.77	1.82	4.04	0.98
Ethyl acetate...........	0.16	0.54	1.54	
Ethylene glycol...........	−0.045	−0.07	−0.05	−0.04
Ethylene dichloride...........	0.70	2.51	1.73	0.61
Butyl Cellosolve...........	0	0.08	0.20	0.47
30% H_2O_2...........	0.10	0.34	0.61	1.67

The PMDA/PA combination is of a lower order of toxicity than the PMDA/MA blend and may be preferred where the hot-mix procedure is employed and when optimum properties are not required. PMDA is of a low order of toxicity, but should be handled with care in order to prevent acid burns or irritation of the skin and respiratory tract.

TABLE 5-6. Typical Physical Properties of Dispersed PMDA–Epoxy-resin System (5-6)

Physical properties	Unfilled casting	Filled* casting
Heat-distortion temperature, °C	280–290	265
Tensile strength, psi	2,810	4,740
Tensile modulus $\times 10^{-6}$ psi	0.42	0.55
Flexural strength, psi:		
Room temperature	8,100	9,500
150°C	4,100	5,900
200°C	3,100	
Compressive strength, psi ult	41,700	42,300
Hardness, Rockwell M	112	105
Shrinkage during cure, %	1.63	1.81

* 25 phr hydrated aluminum silicate.

TABLE 5-7. Typical Electrical Properties of Dispersed PMDA–Epoxy-resin System (5-6)

Electrical properties at 10^3 cycles/sec	Unfilled casting	Filled* casting
Dielectric constant:		
Room temperature	3.47	4.22
100°C	3.91	4.52
150°C	3.81	4.31
200°C	3.77	4.12
Dissipation factor:		
Room temperature	0.0080	0.0231
100°C	0.0042	0.0254
150°C	0.0043	0.0228
200°C	0.0055	0.0168
Surface resistivity, ohm:		
Room temperature	1×10^{13}	1×10^{13}
100°C	1×10^{13}	1×10^{13}
150°C	1×10^{13}	1×10^{13}
200°C	3×10^{12}	3×10^{12}

* 25 phr hydrated aluminum silicate.

Methylated Maleic Acid Adduct of Phthalic Anhydride

The methylated maleic acid adduct of phthalic anhydride (MNA) is a light-yellow liquid having a melting point below 12°C and a molecular weight of 178 (5-6). It may be incorporated in the liquid epoxy resin at about 80 phr and gives cured properties very similar to those obtained with HHPA. It possesses, even when used with 0.5 per cent of an accelerator, an unusually long pot life at room temperature, periods of up to 2 months being reported. Cure cycles, as might be expected, are relatively long. After a cure of 16 hours at 120°C, and 1 hour at 180°C, a diglycidyl ether of bisphenol A system will yield a Barcol of 37 and an impact strength of 0.30. Dielectric constant at 60 cycles is 3.39; at 10^6 cycles, 3.20; power factor at 60 cycles is 0.006; at 10^6 cycles, 0.0188 (5-6). Physical properties are reported in Table 5-3.

MNA is not a primary skin irritant but is a strong organic acid and should be handled with care.

Dodecenyl Succinic Anhydride

Dodecenyl succinic anhydride (DDSA) is a light-yellow viscous oil (300 entipoises) at room temperature, having a molecular weight of 266 (5-6). DDSA is chiefly interesting for its long aliphatic chain, which imparts flexibility in the cured casting. The use of glycerol-based epoxy resins with DDSA (at 186 phr) has revealed casting compositions of good pot life (8.5 days), low viscosities (300 to 1,000 centipoises), short cure times (2 hours at 100°C followed by 2 hours at 150°C), and good clarity. Physical properties and chemical resistance of a glycerol-based system cured with DDSA are presented in Table 5-3.

Although not known to be toxic, dodecenyl succinic anhydride should be handled with caution.

Dichloromaleic Anhydride

$$
\begin{array}{c}
\quad\quad\quad\quad O \\
\quad\quad\quad\quad \| \\
Cl-C-C \\
\quad\quad\quad\quad\quad \searrow \\
\quad\quad\quad\quad\quad\quad\quad O \\
\quad\quad\quad\quad\quad \nearrow \\
Cl-C-C \\
\quad\quad\quad\quad \| \\
\quad\quad\quad\quad O
\end{array}
$$

Dichloromaleic anhydride (DCMA) is a white solid having a molecular weight of 167.   It may be incorporated into the liquid epoxy resin either by dissolving it at elevated temperature or by dispersing it into the resin at room temperature.   If it is dissolved at 70 to 80°C the pot life is short, but with room-temperature procedures, involving grinding the DCMA into the resin with a ball-mill or heavy-duty agitator, pot lives on the order of 8 hours may be obtained.   Approximately 38 phr of DCMA is employed with the liquid epoxy resins.

Cure temperatures, even without accelerators, are reasonably low and short, 4 hours at 85°C being adequate.   Longer and higher temperature cures are, however, necessary to obtain the best heat-distortion values. Using an epoxy resin with an epoxide equivalent in the 225 to 290 range, for instance, a heat-distortion temperature of 105°C can be achieved with a 1-hour cure at 120°C.   An additional cure at the same temperature will increase this value about 15°C (5-12).

Cured castings give tensile strengths of 12,500 psi, with compressive strengths on the order of 15,500 psi.   Flame resistance is improved over the anhydrides previously discussed because of the chlorine present.

As an organic acid, DCMA should be handled with care.   Inhalation of vapors and skin contact should be avoided.

Chlorendic Anhydride

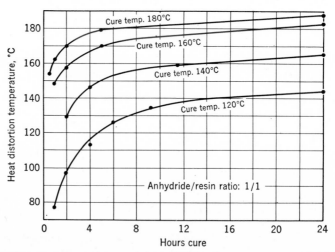

Chlorendic anhydride (hexachloro endomethylene tetrahydro phthalic anhydride) is a white powder, having a molecular weight of 370 and a melting point of 239°C (5-8, 5-9).   Stoichiometric quantities, based on calculating one carboxyl group in the anhydride for one epoxy group in the resin, are 185 phr for a commercial liquid epoxy resin.   It has been

FIG. 5-13. Effect of cure temperature and time on heat-distortion temperature of chlorendic anhydride cured resin (5-8).

ound, however, that substantially less chlorendic anhydride is required, the actual value being in the neighborhood of 100 phr (5-11).

In order to mix the chlorendic anhydride into a liquid epoxy resin, the resin is first warmed to 120°C. The temperature is maintained at 100 to 110°C during mixing. At the temperature required for mixing, the pot life is very short, on the order of ½ hour.

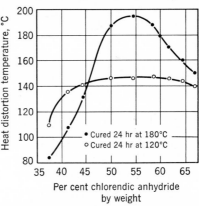

FIG. 5-14. Effect of chlorendic anhydride ratio on heat-distortion temperature (5-8).

The heat-distortion temperature and the physical properties obtained in the cured system will be sharply dependent on the cure cycle employed. The heat-distortion temperature will be somewhat improved by the use of amounts of curing agent slightly in excess of 100 phr. Figure 5-13 illustrates the effect of cure cycles on heat-distortion temperatures, when employing a weight ratio of 1/1 chlorendic anhydride to epoxy resin (molecular weight 400). Figure 5-14 illustrates the effect of varying percentages of chlorendic anhydride in terms of heat-distortion temperature

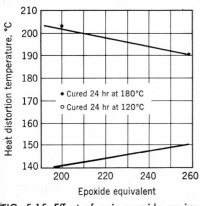

FIG. 5-15. Effect of resin epoxide equivalent on heat-distortion temperature of chlorendic anhydride cured system at 54 per cent by weight chlorendic anhydride (5-8).

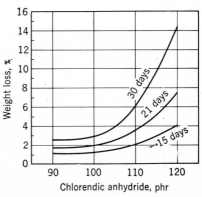

FIG. 5-16. Effect of chlorendic anhydride ratio on high-temperature (200°C) weight loss of system cured 24 hours at 120°C (5-8).

for two cure cycles. Likewise, as might be expected from the discussion of PA, the functionality of the resin employed will also affect the heat-distortion temperature. The heat-distortion temperatures for cured sys-

TABLE 5-8. Typical Physical Properties of Resin Cured with
Chlorendic Anhydride (5-8)
(Test conditions: room temperature)

Tensile strength, psi	12,000
Tensile modulus, psi	4.6×10^5
Compression strength, psi	20,500
Flexural strength, psi	17,000
Flexural modulus, psi	5.2×10^5
Heat-distortion temperature, °C	168

tems with 54 per cent chlorendic anhydride are presented in terms of
epoxide equivalent of the resins in Fig. 5-15. Although slightly more
than 100 phr of chlorendic anhydride is required to achieve maximum
heat-distortion temperatures, the use of lesser amounts results in lower
weight loss at elevated temperatures (Fig. 5-16).

Physical properties for a system cured with a 1/1 chlorendic anhydride/
epoxy-resin weight ratio at 140°C for 24 hours are presented in Table 5.8

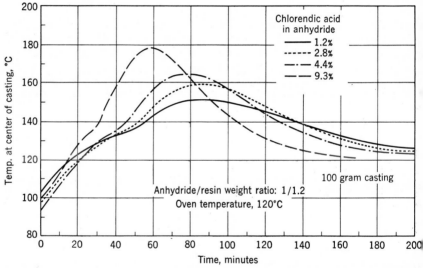

FIG. 5-17. Effect of chlorendic acid on exotherm of chlorendic anhydride cured system (5-8)

At room temperature, the dielectric constant for a system cured at 120°C
is 3.4 at 10^2 cycles and 3.0 at 10^8 cycles; for a system cured at 180°C,
the values are 3.2 and 2.9. The loss factor for a 120°C cure is 0.003 at
10^2 cycles and 0.021 at 10^8 cycles; for a 180°C cure, 0.003 at 10^2 cycles and
0.016 at 10^8 cycles.

The presence of chlorendic acid in the anhydride decreases solubility,
accelerates the rate of cure, and also produces higher exotherms (Fig.

5-17). It should, therefore, be stored in tightly closed containers. If the acid concentration is greater than 5 per cent, it will reduce the heat-distortion temperature (Fig. 5-18). Similarly, traces of impurities such as dichlorobenzene in production lots can seriously retard cure.

Chlorendic anhydride is particularly useful in applications where flame resistance is of significance. A moderately cured system has a burning rate of 0.15 in. per minute, a time to ignite of 65 seconds, and a time to flame out of 115 seconds (5-10).

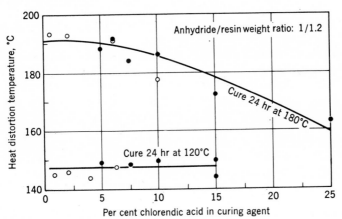

FIG. 5-18. Effect of chlorendic acid on heat-distortion temperature of chlorendic anhydride cured system (5-8).

Because of its nonflammability, chlorendic anhydride is useful in casting and laminating formulations.

Like organic acids generally, chlorendic anhydride will produce burns if allowed to contact the skin. Caution should therefore be exercised in its handling.

CONCLUSION

Except for the amines, the organic acids and anhydrides comprise by far the largest class of commercial curing agents for the epoxy resins. The acids are used primarily in coating applications and the anhydrides in casting and laminating work.

Providing cured systems somewhat less chemically resistant than the amines, the anhydrides offer the advantage of less toxicity and lower exotherms during cure. The liquid anhydrides and some of the lower-melting-point compounds offer very considerable pot lives, with physical properties falling in the range of the amine-cured systems. Several of the anhydrides, pyromellitic dianhydride and chlorendic anhydride in particular, offer heat-distortion temperatures above the range of that pro vided by the aromatic amines.

References

5-1. Castan, Process of Preparing Synthetic Resins, U.S. 2,324,483 (1943).

5-2. Koroly, Expanded Cellular, Resinous Products Containing Polyepoxide and Aconitic Acid, U.S. 2,623,023 (1952).

5-3. Bradley, Compositions of Matter Containing Glycidyl Ethers and Oxalic Acid, U.S. 2,500,449 (1950).

5-4. Farneth and Gallousis, Versatility Cast into New CT's, *Allis-Chalmer Electrical Review*, Third Quarter, 1955.

5-5. Meyerhans, Chemical Resistance of Ethoxyline Resins, *Kunststoffe*, vol. 44 No. 4 (1954).

5-6. National Aniline Division, Allied Chemical and Dye Corp., sales literature

5-7. E. I. duPont de Nemours and Co., Inc., sales literature.

5-8. Hooker Electro–Chemical Co., sales literature.

5-9. Velsicol Corp., sales literature.

5-10. Robitschek and Nelson, Flame and Heat Resistant Epoxy Resins, *Indus trial and Engineering Chemistry*, October, 1956.

5-11. Rudoff, Chlorinated Maleic Adduct–Ethoxyline Resinous Composition, U.S. 2,744,845 (1956).

5-12. Westvaco, Chloro-Alkali Division Food Machinery and Chemical Corp., sales literature.

5-13. Dearborn, Fuoss, Mackensie, and Sheppard, Epoxy Resins from Bis, Tris, and Tetrakis-glycidyl Ethers, *Industrial and Engineering Chemistry*, **45** 2715–2721 (1953).

5-14. Feild and Robinson, Pyromellitic Dianhydride in Curing of Epoxy Resins *Industrial and Engineering Chemistry*, **49**: 369–373 (1957).

5-15. Colichman and Strong, Effect of Gamma Radiation on Epoxy Plastics, *Modern Plastics*, October, 1957.

6

DILUENTS, FILLERS, AND RESINOUS
MODIFIERS

The properties of cured epoxy resins may be varied over a wide range by the selection of curing agent and cure cycles. They may be varied over even a wider range by incorporating into the uncured system liquid diluents, organic and inorganic fillers, and other synthetic resins.

In commercial practice, in fact, seldom is the unmodified resin employed except in laminating. The formulation of commercial compounds is a highly complex and specialized field, often involving considerations unique to each particular application. This and subsequent chapters outline the principles of formulating and compounding.

DILUENTS

Diluents are free-flowing liquids used to reduce the viscosity of the resin so that better penetration in casting and better wetting ability in laminate and adhesive formulations may be achieved and so that higher filler contents may be employed.

At one extreme of the scale, a low-viscosity glycerol-based resin can be considered a diluent for more viscous resins based on bisphenol A. When using such a diluent, amounts as high as 33 phr are required to achieve a significant reduction in viscosity. At the other extreme, propylene oxide will effect a considerable reduction in viscosity even when used in percentages on the order of 5 phr. Glycerol-based resins are normally used in conjunction with a second diluent in aromatic-based resin mixes; and propylene oxide, because of its low boiling point, will not prove satisfactory at higher-temperature cure cycles. Most diluents fall between the two extremes. The following diluents are employed commercially or have been suggested:

1. CH_2——CH—CH_2—$O\left[-CH_2-\underset{\underset{R}{|}}{CH}-CH_2-O\right]_n-CH_2-CH$——$CH_2$ (with epoxy O groups)
   Glycerol-based resin (mol. wt 300)

2. ⬡—O—CH_2—CH——CH_2 (with epoxy O)
   Phenyl glycidyl ether (mol. wt 150)

3. CH_3—CH_2—CH_2—CH_2—O—CH_2—CH——CH_2 (with epoxy O)
   Butyl glycidyl ether (mol. wt 130)

4. CH_3—CH_2—CH_2—CH_2—CH_2—CH——CH—CH_3 (with epoxy O)
   Octylene oxide (mol. wt 128)

5. ⬡—CH——CH_2 (with epoxy O)
   Styrene oxide (mol. wt 120) (little used, toxic)

6. CH_2=CH—CH_2—O—CH_2—CH——CH_2 (with epoxy O)
   Allyl glycidyl ether (mol. wt 114)

7. ⬡—CH_3 (with CH_3)
   Xylene (mol. wt 98) (nonreactive)

8. CH_2——CH—CH_2—Cl (with epoxy O)
   Epichlorohydrin (mol. wt 92) (little used)

9. CH_3—CH——CH_2 (with epoxy O)
   Propylene oxide (mol. wt 56) (little used, volatile)

As may be seen from the above formulas, the diluents may be either reactive (i.e., may contain epoxy groups or other reactive groups) or nonreactive. The reactive diluents are preferred over the nonreactive (6-1). Figure 6-1 relates several diluents in terms of their effect on viscosity as a function of percentage employed. Because of the availability of peracetic acid, making possible the oxidation of olefin groups to epoxy groups (Chap. 1), the number of commercially available reactive diluents is

xpected to increase. Dipentene monoxide and α-pinene oxide are two
uch.

Use of a reactive diluent will somewhat decrease the tendency of the
:uring agent to volatilize during cure, and particularly in room-tempera-
ure curing adhesive formulations it is employed for this purpose.   How-
:ver, when diluents are used in connection with vacuum casting tech-
iiques, there is considerable risk of volatilizing them during the vacuum

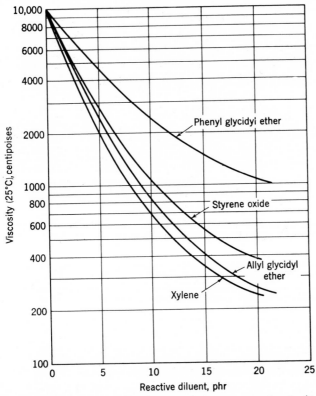

FIG. 6-1. Effect of reactive diluent concentration on resin viscosity (3-7).

cycle.   Since most diluents have some solvent power, their compatibility
with any foreign material in contact with the fluidized resin should be
established prior to use.

Quantities Used

Diluents should be used sparingly if the properties of the cured system
are to be preserved.   An amount of 5 to 10 phr is best, and at these percentages they effect a sharp reduction in viscosity.   Up to 20 phr may be

tolerated in some applications, but it is usually recommended that no
more than 15 phr be employed.   For reactive diluents, additional curing
agent is required (Fig. 6-2), the amount being based on the number of
reactive groups in the diluent; this is easily calculated on the basis of
molecular weight.

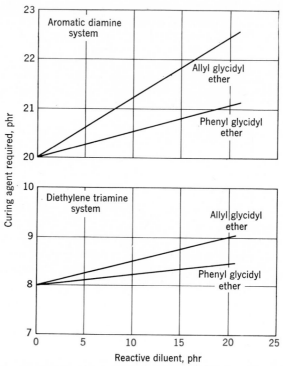

FIG. 6-2. Relationship between diluent concentration and curing agent concentration (3-7).

Pot Life and Exotherm

Most diluents decrease the reactivity of the curing agent, primarily
because of the dilution of the resin; consequently, the pot life is longer.
If reactive epoxy-containing diluents are used, the peak exotherms,
although somewhat delayed, will be higher than in the unfluidized resin
system because of the heat release of the high number of epoxy groups per
gram in the diluent.   However, organic diluents containing alcoholic
hydroxyl groups accelerate the curing rate in the presence of amine
curing agents (see Chap. 2).   When lower percentages of diluents are
employed, these effects are of little significance with regard to pot life and
exotherm but may, of course, adversely affect other properties of the resin.

Properties

Diluents, in general, degrade the physical properties of cured epoxy resins. When the diluents are reactive, they tend to inhibit chain building (because their functionality is lower than that of the resin) and thus interfere with development of ultimate properties; however, if they form no vulnerable linkages, the effect on chemical resistance is slight. When inert diluents are employed, a portion may be driven off during cure,

TABLE 6-1. Effect of Diluents and Diluent Concentrations on Physical Properties of Cured Resin (3-5)
(Test conditions: room temperature)

Diluent and amount	Flexural strength, psi	Flexural modulus, psi $\times 10^{-6}$	Work to break, ft-lb	Hardness, Rockwell M	Impact strength, Izod	Heat-distortion temperature, °C
None............	18,500	0.53	2.6	100	0.2	100
Butyl glycidyl ether, 12.8 phr..	18,600	0.46	4.5	91	0.2	75
Styrene oxide:						
12.8 phr........	18,000	0.47	4.4	96	0.2	90
14.8 phr........	18,800	0.51	4.0	96	0.2	80
16.8 phr........	17,700	0.60	3.5	95	0.2	79
Phenyl glycidyl ether, 12.8 phr..	18,000	0.47	4.9	95	0.2	89
Xylene:						
6 phr..........	17,900	0.47	4.1	94	0.2	74
12.8 phr.......	13,900	0.42	3.7	79	0.2	62

consequently increasing the shrinkage and reducing the adhesion. Entrapped inert diluents will modify the denseness of the crosslinked structure and, to some extent, inhibit the chain-building process. Volatilization of the diluent during exothermic heating, prior to gelling, can entrap diluent bubbles throughout the casting.

Diluents decrease heat-distortion temperatures and hardness; however, in the case of longer-chain reactive diluents, some improvement in flexural strength may be realized together with a slight increase in impact resistance because of the plasticizing effect of the aliphatic chains.

Table 6-1 presents the effect of various diluents on the physical properties of a cured resin and indicates, as well, the effect of increasing percentages of the diluent on these properties. Table 6-2 presents the same information in terms of electrical properties.

With regard to mechanical properties, the effect of diluent on the coefficient of thermal expansion is important. Diluents tend to raise by a considerable value the coefficient of thermal expansion of a resin system (6-2). A cured resin with no diluents or filler will have a coefficient of thermal expansion of about 50 to 60 $\times$ 10^{-6} in./in./°C; this value is increased to about 75 to 80 $\times$ 10^{-6} in./in./°C by the use of a diluent.

TABLE 6-2. Effect of Diluents and Diluent Concentrations on Electrical Properties of Cured Resin (3-5)

(Test conditions: room temperature)

Diluent and amount	Frequency, cycles/sec		
	10	10^3	10^6
No diluent:			
Power factor..............	0.009	0.019	0.032
Dielectric constant...........	4.4	4.2	3.7
Loss factor.................	0.03	0.08	0.11
Butyl glycidyl ether, 12.8 phr			
Power factor..............	0.0072	0.0146	0.0327
Dielectric constant...........	4.16	4.9	3.57
Loss factor.................	0.03	0.060	0.116
Styrene oxide, 12.8 phr			
Power factor..............	0.0052	0.0144	0.0277
Dielectric constant...........	3.76	3.75	3.16
Loss factor.................	0.019	0.054	0.088
Styrene oxide, 14.8 phr			
Power factor..............	0.00561	0.0147	0.0273
Dielectric constant...........	3.65	3.58	3.35
Loss factor.................	0.0205	0.0526	0.0913
Styrene oxide, 16.8 phr			
Power factor..............	0.00526	0.0133	0.0260
Dielectric constant...........	3.58	3.53	3.39
Loss factor.................	0.0188	0.0469	0.0881

The effect of allyl glycidyl ether together with a glycerol-based resin on the adhesive properties of a system cured at room temperature with diethylene triamine is presented in Table 6-3.

Diluents are skin-irritants and should be used with care.

FILLERS

Fillers may be added to epoxy resins to reduce cost, lower the coefficient of thermal expansion, reduce shrinkage, increase thermal conductivity, alter surface hardness, reduce exotherms, improve adhesive properties, and/or change the handling characteristics of the resin system to impart the desired flow or thixotropic properties.

Fillers may be either organic or inorganic, metallic or nonmetallic. As is rather obvious, fillers containing a high percentage of chemically combined water should be avoided. Aside from this, the principal restriction is that the filler should be neutral or only slightly basic and in general nonreactive* with either the resin or the curing agent; when this is not

TABLE 6-3. Effect of Diluents on Adhesive Properties of Cured Resin (6-1)
(Test conditions: room temperature.   Cure: 144 hours at 25°C.)

Formulation	Parts by weight	Shear strength, psi		
		At 25°C	After 1 hr in water at 100°C	After 1 month in water at 25°C
Formulation *A*:		250	410	Soaked apart
Resin, epoxide equivalent 249	100			
Formulation *B*:		4,020	4,280	3,990
Resin, epoxide equivalent 249	80.9			
Resin, epoxide equivalent 150*	14.3			
Allyl glycidyl ether	3.6			
Formulation *C*:		1,590	Boiled apart	2,090
Resin, epoxide equivalent 325	70			
Resin, epoxide equivalent 150*	30			
Formulation *D*:		4,175	4,580	2,725
Resin, epoxide equivalent 325	68			
Resin, epoxide equivalent 150*	17			
Allyl glycidyl ether	12.8			

* Glycerol-based resin.

the case, stoichiometric calculations for the amount of curing agent to employ must consider their effect. Bentonites and other clays, for example, are highly alkaline and can accelerate—or even catalyze—the curing reaction. The most widely used fillers, however, conform to these restrictions, and the curing agent/resin ratio is based solely on the resin content of the filled compound. Synthetic resins, likewise, may be used as fillers, but for the purpose of this text, they will be considered generically as resinous modifiers rather than fillers. As such, they are discussed subsequently in this chapter and in Chap 7.

Since fillers are available from a number of commercial suppliers and since they are offered in a range of particle sizes from 0.1 μ upward, the

* It is possible that some hydroxyl-bearing fillers may be used advantageously.

proper selection has become a specialized science practiced by the formulators.   It is necessary to select not only the correct filler, particle size
shape, and absorption characteristics, but also the optimum loading
volume.

Quantities Used

The loading volumes of the filler will depend on (1) handling characteristics, i.e., upper limits of permissible viscosity; (2) system limits, i.e.

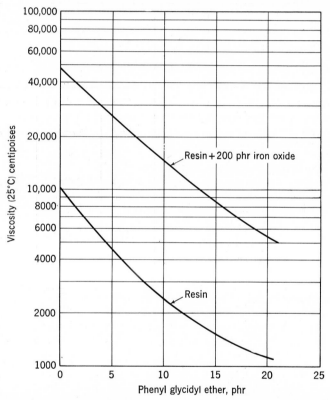

FIG. 6-3. Effect of reactive diluent concentration on viscosity of filled resin (3-7).

each particle must be thoroughly wetted; and (3) ultimate properties
desired, i.e., the particular improvements to be expected of the filler in the
cured system.   In general, the lightweight fillers such as asbestos and
uncompressed silica will bring about great increases in viscosity at ratios
below 25 phr; the medium-weight fillers, such as talc and powdered
aluminum, may be conveniently used in ratios up to 200 phr; and the

heavier fillers may be loaded in volumes up to 300 phr, with ratios as high as 900 phr sometimes being employed. The smaller the particle size, likewise, the more easily the filler will be to incorporate and the less tendency for it to settle; conversely, with larger particles and heavier materials, there will be pronounced settling, unless lightweight secondary fillers are employed as antisettling agents, or unless the filler is thoroughly milled into the resin in advance of application. In some instances, a reactive diluent may be employed to accommodate higher loading volumes. Figure 6-3 presents viscosity of a filled and unfilled resin as a function of percentage of phenyl glycidyl ether.

Pot Life and Exotherm

Fillers slow the curing reaction and reduce the exotherm because of their diluting effect and, in some cases, because of the increase in thermal conductivity they impart to the system. The effect of various fillers on these parameters is presented in Table 6-4. The combined action of the filler, of which the reduced exotherm is only one facet, serves to permit an increase in permissible casting size.

Properties

Although heat resistance may be somewhat improved by the incorporation of fillers, there is no evidence to indicate that the heat-distortion temperature can be increased significantly by their use and some evidence to indicate that, in many cases, it will be slightly reduced.

Metallic and oxide fillers will, however, increase hardness and improve machineability. For this purpose, they are usually used in loading volumes on the order of 200 to 300 phr. Aluminum powder appears to be a particularly good filler in this respect.

Although most fillers will reduce impact resistance, fibrous fillers such as short-fiber asbestos will somewhat improve impact resistance. Both fibrous and nonfibrous fillers will improve compressive yield strength but will reduce tensile strength, ultimate compressive strength, and compressive fatigue strength.

Good dielectric materials, such as mica, asbestos, and powdered glass (in nonhumid environments), will somewhat improve electrical properties, particularly arc resistance. Oxidizing-type fillers which volatilize any electrically ruptured organic materials can increase arc resistance even more significantly (6-3). Fillers such as silicon dioxide and oxides of such metals as aluminum, titanium, and zirconium are effective in con-

TABLE 6-4. Effect of Fillers on Viscosity, Exotherm, Modulus of Rupture, and Shrinkage (3-5)

Filler	Viscosity, 25°C			
	20% filler	35% filler	50% filler	65% filler
Unfilled...............	1,100 centipoises			
Asbestos...............	3,850	23,650	100,000	
Albalith...............	2,700	9,600	95,000	
Silica.................	2,750	6,800	51,500	
Mica..................	2,100	4,800	54,500	
Surfex MM............	2,200	3,500	22,600	100,000
Flint powder...........	2,200	4,300	39,500	
Quartz................	2,100	3,750	13,150	100,000
Kryolite...............	1,900	2,750	6,150	20,900
Portland cement.	1,950	2,400	4,100	19,300
Limestone.............	1,700	3,250	10,000	31,700
Atomized aluminum 101.........	2,100	3,100	4,600	34,500
Barytes...............	1,700	2,450	4,200	17,200
Atomized aluminum 100.........	1,900	2,950	5,500	33,500
Atomized aluminum 120.........	1,800	3,000	5,900	35,000

Filler	Peak exothermic temperature rise, °C				Working life, min.				Modulus of rupture, psi	Shrink-age, %
	% filler				% filler				20% filler	20% filler
	20	35	50	65	20	35	50	65		
Unfilled...............	223°C				48 min				18,174	0.91
Asbestos...............	158	122	55	...	53	60	73	...	10,920	0.48
Albalith...............	169	133	76	...	47	66	85	...	6,896	0.59
Silica.................	170	115	53	...	52	72	95	...	16,875	0.77
Mica..................	159	111	51	...	50	71	94	...	12,358	0.66
Surfex MM............	186	125	55	33	49	57	70	80	11,970	0.64
Flint powder...........	178	113	53	...	52	75	96	...	17,566	0.41
Quartz................	178	113	51	34	49	74	107	130	14,100	0.67
Kryolite...............	166	113	56	36	54	71	107	120	15,483	0.54
Portland cement........	183	147	77	41	52	62	89	102	14,370	0.69
Limestone.............	179	128	59	37	49	71	90	95	12,433	0.47
Atomized aluminum 101...	174	127	47	37	56	68	100	105	13,710	0.80
Barytes...............	179	152	83	38	49	60	84	116	17,417	0.71
Atomized aluminum 100...	176	115	52	35	53	70	99	105		
Atomized aluminum 120...	178	128	53	33	52	67	100	105	14,790	

centrations as low as 1 per cent in interrupting the continuous path of an electric arc.

Most fillers will reduce the coefficient of thermal expansion because of their bulk effect, but unless they have a negative coefficient of thermal expansion, as is the case of certain ground ceramics, the reduction will be more dependent on the loading volume than the specific filler. This is indicated in Fig. 6-4.

Metallic fillers and coarse sand, in particular, will improve thermal conductivity but, in the latter case, only at the expense of mechanical properties. A cured system highly filled with aluminum powder, for instance, will give a value for thermal conductivity on the order of

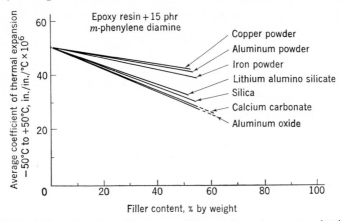

FIG. 6-4. Effect of various fillers on coefficient of thermal expansion (3-7).

$5,000 \times 10^{-6}$ cal/(sec)(sq cm)(°C)(cm)—about ten times higher than the range for unfilled epoxies. It is generally not possible, however, to employ sufficiently large loading volumes to match exactly the thermal conductivity of metals. Metallic fillers may, also, act as inhibitors of cure, and some will catalyze depolymerization at elevated temperatures.

Fillers are particularly effective in decreasing shrinkage due to the reduced peak exotherm temperature and by bulk replacement, the amount of decrease being more a function of loading volume than the particular filler employed, although modest differences between the various materials can be noted (Table 6-4).

Because of a combination of several of the foregoing factors, fillers are useful in adhesive formulations, particularly in increasing performance at high temperatures. An effective adhesive filler, if ground or suspended into the resin properly, is aluminum oxide (6-4). Table 6-5 presents a comparison of the shear strength of a fluidized resin unfilled and filled with 100 phr of aluminum oxide.

Fillers can also be used for a variety of miscellaneous purposes, such as to increase or decrease cured weight, reduce flammability, increase electrical conductivity, regulate flow properties, etc.

TABLE 6-5. Effect of Filler on Shear Strength of Adhesive Formulation (6-4)
(Resin system: fluidized.   Cure: room temperature for 144 hours.)

Filler	Shear strength, psi			
	At 25°C	At 105°C	After 1 hr in water at 100°C	After 1 week in water at 25°C
No filler....................	2,760	450	2,740	2,840
100 phr aluminum oxide.......	3,750	1,650	3,930	2,890

Fillers may affect the moisture resistance, the moisture-vapor transmission, and the solvent resistance either adversely or advantageously. Glass, as a filler, for instance, has a strong tendency to promote surface-water absorption.   The effects of several fillers on these properties are presented in Figs. 6-5 to 6-7.

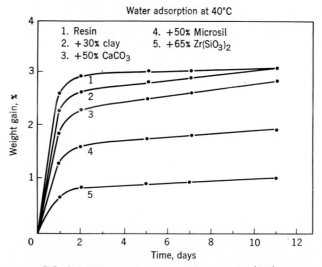

FIG. 6-5. Water resistance of filled epoxies (6-9).

Fillers, as dyes and pigments, are used to color resins.   Since the liquid epoxy resin is a good wetting agent, it is frequently possible to incorporate the coloring agent by mechanical stirring; although with some compounds, it is necessary to grind them into the system with a ball mill or

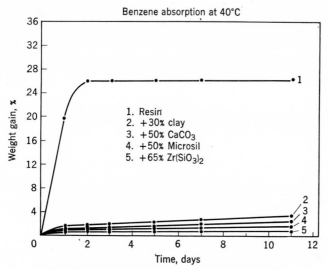

FIG 6-6. Benzene resistance of filled epoxies (6-9).

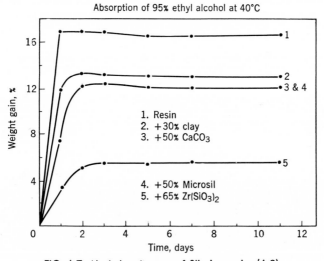

FIG. 6-7. Alcohol resistance of filled epoxies (6-9).

other grinding device. Titanium dioxide is frequently employed in connection with the colorant to provide a whiting agent with the necessary hiding power suitable for tinting. In order to facilitate the determination of thorough mixing of the curing agent, it may be advisable to incorporate the coloring material into the curing agent rather than the resin.

The following colorants have been used successfully with the liquid epoxies (3-5):

Pigments:
White........... Titanium dioxide
Red............. Cadmium Red Medium (Chemical and Pigment Co.)
Yellow.......... Cadmalith Golden (Chemical and Pigment Co.)
Black........... Hytherm Black (Patent Chemicals)
Gray............ Aluminum powder
Dyes:
Red............. National Fast Red (National Aniline)
Green........... Calco Condensation Green AY (American Cyanamid)
Yellow.......... Calco Condensation Yellow BTC (American Cyanamid)
Blue............ Calco Condensation Blue (American Cyanamid)
Brown.......... Bismark Brown (National Aniline)

The list, of course, is representative, and suitable dyes and pigments are available from a number of other commercial suppliers.

Incorporation into Resin

In order to obtain best results with fillers, they should be heated in order to drive off moisture and adsorbed gases prior to incorporation into the resin. Once thoroughly dry, they may then be stirred directly into the resin, preferably warmed to facilitate mixing. In some cases, it will be necessary to employ a grinding device to accomplish the mixing with sufficient thoroughness. Unless complete mixing is accomplished, the compound will not possess maximum properties.

RESINOUS MODIFIERS

Epoxy resins are compatible with many other synthetic resins. Because of the toughness and high adhesive properties of the epoxies, they are being used in increasing amounts as upgrading agents for coatings of all types—phenolics, polyesters, ureas, furanes, melamines, vinyls, fluorocarbons, and asphaltic materials.

On the other hand, various of these resins are used in epoxies to modify the properties of the cured system. Thus, phenolic resins may be used to increase heat-distortion temperatures of some systems. Still other resins (Chap. 7) are used to impart flexibility, high impact strength, and greater thermal shock resistance. Lower-priced synthetic resins may be used in fairly high percentages to reduce the over-all cost of the epoxy-resin system, etc.

In general, the best results are obtained with resins which actually react, at least to some degree, with the epoxies rather than acting as inert organic fillers.

Typical formulas for the more important of these modifiers, together with the reaction mechanisms with the epoxies, are presented below.

Phenolic Monomers and Resins

Various phenolic resins and intermediates will react with the epoxies and cure them, usually in the presence of an acid or base catalyst such as phosphoric acid, caustic, or dicyandiamide. The patent literature contains a comprehensive investigation of these polyfunctional phenols (6-5) and phenolic resins (6-6 and 1-14).

Among those suggested as crosslinking agents for epoxy resins are: Bisphenol A

and trimethylolallyloxy phenol

Phenolic resins

and butylated epoxidized phenolic resins

Crosslinking of these substances with epoxy resins occurs through the phenolic hydroxyls and, when present, the methylol and/or epoxy groups (see Chap. 2).

Commercial use of the monomeric phenols has been suggested for castings, but they find their chief use in solution coatings (Chap. 10).

Phenolic resins, on the other hand, are of commercial significance in coatings, castings, and adhesives.

One proprietary phenolic-epoxy blend can be described as typical. The compound is a very viscous material at lower temperatures but rapidly becomes fluid with temperature increase. At 80°C it provides a viscosity of 400 centipoises. It may be catalyzed with about 0.5 per cent alpha-methylbenzyl dimethylamine to give a pot life of 1 hour at 80°C. It cures with but moderate exotherm and thereby permits the casting of larger shapes than are possible with unmodified epoxy systems. High-temperature weight loss in the cured system is surprisingly low: on the order of 0.5 per cent after aging for 200 hours at 200°C. Most of this

TABLE 6-6. Typical Mechanical Properties of Epoxy-Phenolic Blend Catalyzed with 0.5 Per Cent Alpha-Methylbenzyl Dimethylamine (3-5)
(Test conditions: room temperature)

Mechanical properties	Curing cycle	
	40 min at 150°C	9 hr at 160°C
Tensile strength, psi.............	11,100	11,000
Compressive strength, psi........	46,000	40,600
Compressive yield, psi...........	16,100	14,500
Flexural strength, psi............	18,700	19,000
Flexural modulus, psi............	0.50×10^6	0.48×10^6
Flexural yield strength, psi.......	16,500	15,500
Impact strength, Izod...........	0.268	0.334
Hardness, Rockwell M...........	82	84
Heat distortion, °C..............	68.3	79.5

Effect of Heat Aging on Mechanical Properties

Mechanical property	Control	After 200 hr at 200°C
Flexural strength, psi............	18,000	14,000
Impact strength, Izod...........	0.21	0.22
Hardness, Rockwell M...........	89	91
Heat distortion, °C..............	79	84

TABLE 6-7. Chemical Resistance of Epoxy-Phenolic Blend Catalyzed with
0.5 Per Cent Alpha-Methylbenzyl Dimethylamine (3-5)
(Test conditions: room temperature)

System tested in	Percentage weight gain, 7 days immersion	System tested in	Percentage weight gain, 7 days immersion
Distilled water......	0.33	Chloroform........	11.9
5% Soap solution...	0.37	o-Dichlorobenzene..	0.08
30% H_2SO_4........	0.22	Ethyl ether........	0.35
10% NaOH........	0.27	Ethyl acetate......	0.95
10% NH_4OH.......	0.30	Ethylene dichloride.	4.90
Ethanol...........	0.30	Toluene...........	0.01
Glacial acetic acid...	0.67	Trichloroethylene...	0.43
Acetone...........	9.1		

loss occurs during the first 25 hours of aging; thereafter, the material is stable.

The physical properties of a cured casting of such a phenolic–epoxy-resin blend are presented in Table 6-6. The chemical resistance is given in Table 6-7.

Aniline Formaldehyde Resins

Aniline formaldehyde (A/F) resins may be of varying molecular weights, depending on the degree of polymerization. They are synthesized by reacting the two intermediates in a strongly acid medium to produce a polymer of the structure

$$\left[\begin{array}{c} H \\ | \\ -N- \end{array} \!\!\!\!\!\bigcirc\!\!\!\!\!- CH_2 - \begin{array}{c} H \\ | \\ N- \end{array} \!\!\!\!\!\bigcirc\!\!\!\!\!- CH_2 - \begin{array}{c} H \\ | \\ N- \end{array} \!\!\!\!\!\bigcirc\!\!\!\!\!- CH_2 - \right]_n$$

As in the case of the synthesis of epoxy resins, the length of the polymer may be controlled by the regulation of reactants. When an A/F ratio of 1/0.75 is employed, for instance, a low-melting-point (60°C) solid is formed; used in an equimolar ratio, a high-melting-point partially crosslinked solid results.

To date, only the lower-melting A/F resins have been investigated as curing agents for the epoxy resins (6-7), the higher-melting-point materials being too inconvenient to incorporate as hot melts.

The reactions of A/F resins and epoxy resins involve crosslinking through the primary or secondary amine groups present on the A/F chain. The process is analogous to that which occurs during cure of an amine/epoxy-resin system.

The low-melting-point A/F resins can be incorporated into the liquid epoxy resin at about 100°C. At that temperature, the pot life will be about 30 minutes. The mix may be cooled to increase the pot life, but it will necessitate reheating to obtain sufficiently low viscosities. Exotherms are low, and a recommended cure cycle is 16 hours at 120°C.

An A/F resin of 1/0.75 construction will provide heat-distortion temperatures in the same range of the aromatic amines, such as metaphenylene diamine. When used at a stoichiometric ratio (empirically determined) of approximately 35 phr, the heat-distortion temperature will be about 155°C. Solvent and chemical resistance appear to be equal to that provided in aromatic-amine cured systems.

Use of the higher-melting-point A/F resins in solution coatings for high-temperature laminates appears to be a distinct possibility.

Ureas and Melamines

Urea formaldehyde and melamine formaldehyde resins have been investigated extensively and find wide application in coating formulations.

Crosslinking with the epoxy resins is mostly accomplished through methylol groups. In coating formulations, the epoxies can be used in connection with the ureas and melamines to provide increased chemical resistance and improved mechanical strength and adhesion. Melamine can be employed for curing higher-weight epoxy resins when used on the order of 4 phr, but because of insolubility, powder techniques are required for mixing.

Furfurals

Furfural resins containing methylol groups may be used as resinous modifiers for the epoxy resins similar to methylol-bearing phenol and melamine resins: (1) to improve flexibility (when used on the order of 25 phr); (2) to improve chemical resistance (6-8), particularly resistance to acids, and specifically to hydrofluoric acid (when used on the order of 65 phr, at which ratio there will be some loss in mechanical properties); and (3) to reduce cost. A furfural–epoxy-resin coating has served as the exterior lining of oil-well tubing with excellent results.

Polyesters

Polyesters, based on a variety of polybasic acids and polyhydroxyl alcohols, may contain free carboxyl groups and/or aliphatic hydroxyls capable of reacting with the epoxy resins. The wide range of molecular structures possible for the polyester resins, together with the possibility of co-curing reactions occurring when they are combined with the epoxies, indicates that their potentialities as resinous modifiers are quite promising. Certain of the polyesters can be used as flexibilizers (Chap. 7) to provide properties similar to those offered by the polysulfides, while others can be used in rather high loading volumes as extenders without markedly influencing the cured properties of the system (6-10). The effect of the polyester on the properties will be dependent on the acids and alcohols employed in synthesis and on the number of members in the resin chain. If other reactive elements are introduced, the properties may be varied even more widely. One example of a specialized epoxy-polyester formulation is magnet wire insulation using both polyester and polyester amide compositions (6-11).

Vinyls

The principal use of epoxies in vinyl-resin systems is as a heat stabilizer. Vinyl chloride resins, in the presence of heat, lose HCl. The presence of the evolved HCl catalyzes further and more rapid degradation. By employing the epoxy as an antioxidant and scavenger of HCl

$$R-\underset{\displaystyle \diagdown\!\!\diagup}{\overset{O}{CH}}\!-\!CH_2 + HCl \rightarrow R-\underset{\displaystyle |}{\overset{Cl}{CH}}-CH_2-OH$$

the degradation can be retarded appreciably.

Various solution coating systems of the epoxies and vinyl chloride and vinyl chloride acetate resins have been suggested. Small percentages of vinyl formal and vinyl acetate resins are used in epoxy adhesives to improve peel and impact strengths (6-15).

Isocyanates (Polyurethanes)

The field of isocyanates is even newer than that of the epoxy resins. Isocyanates are characterized by the extremely reactive $-N\!=\!C\!=\!O$ radical, which reacts with hydroxyl groups present in the epoxy-resin chains to provide crosslinking. The isocyanate groups will also react with primary and secondary amines

and, consequently, are capable of co-curing not only with the epoxies but with any amine curing agent present to provide tightly crosslinked structures.

Monomeric diisocyanates such as tolylene diisocyanate, diphenylmethane 4,4'-diisocyanate, and 3,3'-butolylene 4,4'-diisocyanate give promise of application in epoxy adhesive formulations and have been suggested for use in casting formulations to provide lower moisture-vapor transmission and increased resistance to water absorption. Higher molecular weight diisocyanates such as the reaction product of tolylene diisocyanate and polybutanediol are available as flexibilizers for epoxy resins. Epoxy resins, as cross-linking agents for the isocyanates, are used to provide foams of increased resistance to hydrolysis aging.

Fluorocarbons

Various fluorinated resins are commercially available. These are insoluble in the liquid epoxy resins and do not react with them, but solution coatings have been suggested as offering cured compounds combining the adhesion of the epoxies and the low water transmission of the fluorinated materials.

Silicone Resins

Combinations of silicone and epoxy resins offer considerable promise of unusual casting and coating materials. The epoxy resins possess good all around electrical and mechanical properties together with ease of handling. Silicone polymers are usually very weak and soft mechanically, but they possess the high thermal stability imparted by the presence of the silicon atom. Hence, a combination which couples the good properties of both should offer much in the way of improved high temperature electrical insulation.

Considerable effort has been expended on this difficult problem. Early work involved the development of materials containing both the silicon atom and the epoxy group for use in treating glass cloth. The goal was to secure a bond to the glass by reacting the silicon with oxygen in the glass, and to secure a bond between the epoxy group in the resin and the epoxy group in the treating agent, thereby improving the adhesion and wet strength in epoxy glass laminates. These treating reagents were achieved by reacting allyl glycidyl ether, methallyl alcohol, crotonyl alcohol, beta-chloroallyl alcohol, or glycidyl methoerylate with silanes such as methyltrichlorosilane, vinyl trichlorosilane, and allyltrichlorosilane (6-12). Silane finishes have subsequently been introduced for glass cloth used with epoxy resins. See Chap. 10.

Work in Europe has involved the preparation of epoxy-silicone electrical coatings (6-13). These have been based on the reaction in solvent media of diglycidyl ether of bisphenol A with slightly condensed silanols obtained by hydrolysis of diethyldichlorosilane in aqueous butanol-xylene mixtures and curing with metal soaps. These coatings have shown marked reduction in brittleness over unmodified epoxy coatings.

Modifications of silicone adhesives with 10 to 40 per cent of epoxy resins (usually with epoxy resins having a degree of polymerization of 1) have resulted in a marked increase in shear strength at 500 F (6-14).

The commercial availability of silanes containing primary amines facilities still further epoxy-silicon combinations.

The peracetic acid process offers means of epoxidizing vinyl containing silicone polymers, thereby achieving still further improved resins.

CONCLUSION

Simple epoxy resin–curing agent systems are seldom used commercially, because advantageous modifications are nearly always needed to lower cost, improve handling characteristics, and modify selected properties.

A large number of chemical compounds can be used in the development of specific formulations.

Diluents are employed to regulate the viscosity of the resin to the particular application, to improve wetting ability of adhesive and laminating formulations, and to increase the convenient loading volume of fillers.

In general, fillers are employed to achieve selected improvement in one or more parameters of a resin system—to reduce shrinkage, lower the coefficient of thermal expansion, improve thermal conductivity, increase hardness, etc. These modifications will usually be achieved at the expense of other properties in the system, so that it can be said that most fillers will somewhat reduce over-all mechanical, electrical, and/or chemical properties.

In addition to fillers, a variety of resinous modifiers may be employed in the epoxy system, among them being the phenolic resins, the aniline formaldehyde resins, and the polyesters.

Each particular resin formulation will exhibit its own specific properties, and through the judicious selection of components, it is possible to design systems exactly suited to highly specialized industrial applications.

References

6-1. Wiles and Newey, Compositions Containing Glycidyl Ethers, U.S. 2,528,932 (1950).

6-2. Brown, Casting Resin Investigation at Naval Ordnance Plant, *Electronic Equipment*, July, 1956.

6-3. Chemical Agents Prevent Formation of Carbon Tracks in Organic Insulation, *Electrical and Electronics Insulation*, November, 1955.

6-4. Wiles, Adhesive Compositions Containing Glycidyl Ethers and Alumina, U.S. 2,528,933 (1950).

6-5. Bender, Farnham, and Guyer, Thermosetting Resins from a Diphenol and a Diglycidyl Ether of a Diphenol, U.S. 2,506,486 (1950).

6-6. Bradley and Newey, Epoxy Resins from Alkyl Phenol Novolac Resins, U.S. 2,716,099 (1955).

6-7. Bishop, The Use of Aniline–Formaldehyde Resins as Curing Agents for Epoxide Resins, Symposium of British Society of Chemical Industry, April, 1956.

6-8. Brenner and Singer, Epoxy Furane Blends, *Materials and Methods*, June, 1955.

6-9. Formo and Bolstad, Where and How to Use Epoxies, *Modern Plastics*, July, 1955.

6-10. Cranker, The Chemistry of Modifiers for Epoxy Resins and Their Effect on Properties, paper presented at Society of Plastic Engineers (Southern California Section) Symposium, Los Angeles, Calif., November, 1956.

6-11. Sattler, Synthetic Resins and Insulated Products Produced Therewith, U.S. 2,626,223 (1953).

6-12. Erickson and Silver, Chemical Finishes for Glass Fiber Reinforcement, Govt. Report PB-121165, 1953.

6-13. Preparation of Dissolved Epoxy Resins Modified with Organosilicon Compounds, German Patent Application G 13463 (39c, 30), 1954.

6-14. Kidwell and McHugh, Investigation of High-temperature Structural Adhesives, Govt. Report PB-121657, 1956.

6-15. Wiles and Elam, Compositions Containing Glycidyl Polyethers of Dihydric Phenols and Polyvinyl Acetate, U.S. 2,602,785 (1952).

7
PLASTICIZERS AND FLEXIBILIZERS

The generally excellent properties of the epoxy resins, combined with their compatibility with a wide range of modifying agents (Chap. 6), made inevitable the development of epoxy compounds which, when cured, possess greater impact resistance and flexibility, while retaining the valuable properties of the rigid system: excellent chemical resistance, good electrical properties, ease of cure, etc.

For convenience, the class of materials used to impart higher flexibility to the cured resin may be divided into two types: the plasticizers and the flexibilizers. The plasticizers, in this connection, are defined as those compounds which are nonreactive when combined with the epoxy resin and may be considered as inert resinous or monomeric "fillers"; the flexibilizers—which may be either mono- or polyfunctional—are those compounds which react with the epoxy resin and become an integral part of the cured system.

PLASTICIZERS

Considerable work has been directed toward developing suitable plasticizers for the epoxy resins but has met with little success. The more common monomeric plasticizers for rubbers and vinyls, such as dioctyl phthalate or tricresyl phosphate, for example, are generally incompatible with epoxies; they tend to separate out of the system during cure and subsequent aging and, even when retained, result in only a slight reduction in rigidity. Depolymerized rubber, likewise, is unsatisfactory. When as little as 10 phr is used, viscosities of a liquid resin will increase markedly. The rubber can be milled into an epoxy-solvent system in larger volumes, but the physical properties of the cured resin are not outstanding.

A few nonreactive monomeric plasticizers have been employed in adhesive formulations, but they are not of general utility.

MONOFUNCTIONAL FLEXIBILIZERS

Monofunctional flexibilizers are somewhat more effective than plasticizers when used with epoxy resins. These materials generally contain, as the reactive point, a single epoxy group. Epoxidized vegetable oils, for instance, and similar compounds represented by the formula

$$R—CH \overset{O}{\overset{/ \ \backslash}{———}} CH_2$$

(where R can be any aliphatic chain over 12 carbons long) can be used to impart modest flexibility to cured-resin systems. The flexibility is achieved by the action of the long-chain floating radical, which forces the molecules of the cured system somewhat further apart than would normally be the case, thus permitting freer movement of the crosslinked structure under imposed loads. These compounds, being at one point reactive, do not separate out during cure. Such materials, like reactive diluents which they resemble, sharply reduce the viscosities of the mix and, when used in higher percentages, degrade the ultimate properties of the cured resin. In lower volumes (on the order of 20 phr), they find use in adhesive and laminating formulations and, in some cases, in casting formulations to improve low-temperature impact resistance.

POLYFUNCTIONAL FLEXIBILIZERS

It follows from the preceding discussion that long aliphatic-chain epoxy resins may be employed as flexibilizers for the epoxy resins based on the diglycidyl ether of bisphenol A, but the greatest success in imparting impact resistance and flexibility to epoxy-resin systems has been accomplished through the use of other resins or semiresinous materials capable of direct reaction with the epoxy groups.

The most important of these materials are: (1) thermoplastic polyamide resin, (2) polysulfides, and (3) certain of the polyesters. These, along with the fatty diamines, are discussed as representative. Also in limited use are certain of the glycols, isocyanates, polymerized fatty acids, etc.

As will be expected, the number of considerations involved in the formulation of an optimum epoxy compound containing a polyfunctional flexibilizer is far larger than involved in the formulation of a rigid system. It is necessary to select not only the best curing agent and/or resin, but additionally the proper flexibilizer or combination of flexibilizers, together with the optimum epoxy/flexibilizer ratio. As with rigid systems, a variety of fillers and filler loading volumes may be employed and diluents and other modifiers may be incorporated.

When higher percentages of the flexibilizers are used (100 phr and higher), extremely flexible rubberlike compounds result. With ratios below 100 phr, resilient impact-resistant materials are achieved. Within the possible range, a number of unique adhesives, coatings, castings, and laminates can be formulated for applications where the unmodified epoxies are unsuited. For example, waterproofing compounds can be formulated so flexible that they will not interfere with the stress readings of sensitive strain gages, others so tough that they cannot be indented by a fingernail yet, in thin 30–40 mil coatings, will withstand up to 12 ft-lb of impact without damage.

Some flexibilizers reduce exotherms (compared to the values obtained with aliphatic amines) and, in some cases, shrinkage. They reduce internal strains during cure, thereby making possible castings of larger volumes and more complex configurations. Addition of flexibilizers improves adhesive properties of the unmodified epoxies, in terms of room temperature shear strengths, peel strengths, lower-temperature performance, and adhesion to flexible plastics.

Low tear strength at higher mixture ratios, embrittlement with aging, and severe loss of strength at higher temperatures pose problems still not overcome. In this latter case, however, it will be recognized that the requirements for flexibility are opposed to those for higher heat-distortion temperatures and that one parameter can be achieved only at the expense of the other. Extremely flexible materials, for instance, can be considered as having heat-distortion temperatures lower than ambient. The effect on heat-distortion temperature, and more importantly, performance at elevated temperatures, depends on the amount of flexibilizer employed. At lower percentages, the reduction is not severe compared to values obtained with modified aliphatic polyamine cured systems.

Polyamide Resins

Although arbitrarily classed here as flexibilizers, primarily on the basis of their structure and the increased impact resistance they impart to cured epoxy-resin systems, the polyamide resins may be considered as nonirritating polyamine curing agents, which impart cured properties as subsequently indicated.

The polyamide resins of interest as flexibilizers for epoxy resins are markedly different from the common Nylon-type polyamides. Instead of being condensations of adipic acid and hexamethylene diamine, they are condensation polymers of dimerized (and trimerized) vegetable oil, unsaturated fatty acids, and aryl or alkyl polyamines. The structure of these polymers is exceedingly complex but may be approximated by the following equations:

$$
\begin{array}{ccc}
\text{COOH} & \text{COOH} & \\
| & | & \\
(\text{CH}_2)_7 & (\text{CH}_2)_7 & \\
| & | & \\
\text{CH} & \text{CH} & \\
\| & \| & \\
\text{CH} & \text{CH} & \\
| & | & \text{Diels-Alder} \\
\text{CH}_2 \quad + & \text{CH} & \xrightarrow{\text{reaction}} \\
| & \| & \\
\text{CH} & \text{CH} & \\
\| & | & \\
\text{CH} & (\text{CH}_2)_5 & \\
| & | & \\
(\text{CH}_2)_4 & \text{CH}_3 & \\
| & & \\
\text{CH}_3 & &
\end{array}
$$

9,12-Linoleic acid   9,11-Linoleic acid (isomerized)

$$
\begin{array}{c}
\text{COOH} \\
| \\
(\text{CH}_2)_7 \\
| \\
\text{CH} \\
\diagup \quad \diagdown \\
\text{HC} \qquad \text{CH}-(\text{CH}_2)_7-\text{COOH} \\
\| \\
\text{HC} \qquad \text{CH}-\text{CH}_2-\text{CH}=\text{CH}-(\text{CH}_2)_4-\text{CH}_3 \\
\diagdown \quad \diagup \\
\text{CH} \\
| \\
(\text{CH}_2)_5 \\
| \\
\text{CH}_3
\end{array}
$$

Linoleic acid dimer

Linoleic acid dimer $+ H_2N$—CH_2—CH_2—$NH_2 \rightarrow$
Ethylene diamine

$$
\begin{array}{l}
\overset{O}{\overset{\|}{C}}\overset{H}{\overset{|}{-N}}-CH_2-CH_2-\overset{H}{\overset{|}{N}}-R \\
\overset{|}{(CH_2)_7} \\
\overset{|}{CH}
\end{array}
$$

$$
HC \underset{HC}{\overset{\diagup}{\diagdown}} \overset{\diagdown}{\diagup} \overset{\begin{array}{c}CH-(CH_2)_7-\overset{O}{\overset{\|}{C}}-\overset{H}{\overset{|}{N}}-CH_2-CH_2-\overset{H}{\overset{|}{N}}-R\\ CH-CH_2-CH=CH-(CH_2)_4-CH_3\end{array}}{}
$$

$$
\begin{array}{l}
CH \\
\overset{|}{(CH_2)_5} \\
\overset{|}{CH_3}
\end{array}
$$

where R may be hydrogen or another linoleic acid dimer group (7-1).

When amines having higher functionality than ethylene diamine are used, the resinous product will have active amine hydrogens (rather than amide hydrogens) capable of reacting with epoxy resins (Chap. 4) just as do ordinary polyamines.

The commercial polyamides are amber-colored thermoplastic resins with molecular weights up to 10,000 and melting points ranging up to 190°C. The higher-melting-point polyamides can be reacted at only about 10 phr with the epoxies and, consequently, have elicited little interest from the epoxy-resin formulators. Properties of the three grades of lower-weight polyamides which are useful as flexibilizers are presented in Table 7-1. The amine number, as given by the supplier, is a useful indication of the degree of reactivity to be expected.

TABLE 7-1. Properties of Typical Polyamides (7-2)

Property	Versamid* 100	Versamid 115	Versamid 125
Amine value†	83–93	210–230	290–320
Melting point, °C	43–53	Fluid	Fluid
Viscosity, centipoises:			
25°C			40,000–60,000
40°C		80,000–120,000	
150°C	10,000–15,000		

* Registered trade-mark, General Mills, Inc.

† Amine value is milligrams of KOH equivalent to base content of 1 gram of polyamide as determined by titration with HCl.

The free amine groups remaining in the condensed resin provide adequate focal points for epoxy crosslinking and catalytic polymerization. Flexibility is imparted by the presence of the aliphatic polyamide chains which separate the rigid benzene rings of the epoxy molecules and provide greater degrees of freedom for the chains to assume under stresses and impact loadings. It will also be recognized that the actual structure of the polyamides is quite complex, consisting of numerous isomeric products, and that steric hindrances may be expected to complicate the reactions.

Since the polyamide is the curing agent, the extent to which the mixture ratios can be varied without loss of properties is limited by chemical as well as physical considerations. Calculations based on heat-distortion temperatures indicate that, for the commercial polyamides having amine values in the 200 range, approximately 80 phr provides stoichiometric amounts for a typical epoxy resin. For polyamides having amine values in the 300 range, approximately 45 phr provides stoichiometric amounts. Actual optimum values will vary from resin to resin, depending on the exact epoxide equivalent. These ratios can be increased to achieve more flexible materials. Within acceptable limits, the higher the ratio of polyamide to epoxy, the greater the flexibility. The effect of composition is expressed generally:

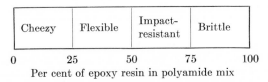

Cheezy	Flexible	Impact-resistant	Brittle

```
0        25        50        75        100
```
Per cent of epoxy resin in polyamide mix

At the lower concentrations, cure can be accomplished by the addition of a second curing agent, to provide rigid systems with some degree of impact resistance.

As is seen from Table 7-1, the room-temperature viscosity of the polyamides is high. For this reason, they are often used in connection with fluidized resins or worked at elevated temperatures. Figure 7-1 presents viscosity as a function of temperature for two typical polyamides.

At room temperature, it is possible to obtain pot lives in excess of 4 hours with production quantities of polyamide/epoxy blends (7-2). The pot lives at room temperature are longer than when an epoxy resin is cured with an amine such as diethylene triamine, and the exotherms are lower. Table 7-2 presents pot life and exotherm data for two polyamides in combination with a fluidized resin. From this it can be seen that the polyamides with higher amine values are more reactive and provide higher peak exotherms. Pot lives at higher temperatures are correspondingly shorter (Table 7-3), as would be expected from the discussion of amine curing agents, and fall in the same general range as that expected from diethylene triamine at room temperature.

Typical cure cycles for thin sections vary from 20 minutes at 150°C to 3 hours at 65°C. Larger masses, containing 5 lb or more, require no external heat for cure.

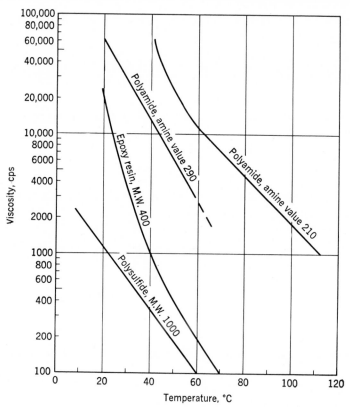

FIG. 7-1. Viscosity vs. temperature for typical liquid polyamides (7-2) and typical liquid polysulfides (7-6).

Physical properties of the polyamide-cured system will be sharply dependent on the amount of polyamide employed. The range of hardness obtained with a fluidized resin and a polyamide with an amine value of about 300 is presented in Table 7-4. The effect of varying ratios likewise influences the heat-distortion temperatures of the cured systems. In stoichiometric amounts, the heat-distortion temperature will be higher with the polyamides having lower amine values than with those having higher values. Similarly, fluidized resins will provide heat-distortion temperatures about 25°C lower than nonfluidized resins. If higher heat-distortion temperatures are desirable, a portion of the polyamide may be replaced by an aromatic amine. For instance, if 50 phr of polyamide (200 amine value) is employed in connection with 3.8 phr metaphenylene diamine, the heat-distortion temperature of the cured system is about 104°C as contrasted with 80°C for a system cured by stoichiometric amounts of the polyamide.

Tensile strengths for typical impact-resistant polyamide-cured systems fall in the 4,500- to 7,000-psi range, with flexural strengths being from

TABLE 7-2. Pot Life and Exotherm Data for Epoxy-Polyamide Blends (7-2)

Blend	Batch size	Peak exotherm, °C	Pot life at 25°C, min
Polyamide (amine value 210–230), 100 phr...... {9 lb.....		151	90
{200 g....		34	260
Polyamide (amine value 290–320), 66 phr...... {9-lb.....		150	90
{200 g....		116	90

TABLE 7-3. Effect of Temperature on Pot Life of Epoxy Resin Cured with 100 Phr Polyamide (7-2)

	Temperature, °C		
	40	50	60
Pot life, min............	66	50	20

TABLE 7-4. Effect of Varying Ratios of Polyamide on Hardness of Cured Resin (7-2)

Polyamide (amine value 290–320), phr	Hardness	
	Barcol*	Shore A
66	60–65	
100	20–25	
150	.....	90
185	.....	85
234	.....	50
300	.....	30
400	.....	<5

* Impressor Model GYZJ-935.

7,000 to 9,600 psi. Flexural modulus will be 0.2 to 0.3 $\times$ 10^6 psi, elongation about 9 per cent, and compressive strengths in the 7,000- to 12,000-psi range. Impact resistance (Izod) will be 0.2 to 0.3 ft-lb per in. or by falling-ball tests, approximately 9 ft-lb. Linear shrinkage will be about 1 per cent. Linear coefficients of thermal expansion are increased (over unmodified epoxy-resin systems cured with the simpler polyamines) by the use of polyamides even in nonfluidized systems.

Electrical properties of the cured system fall in the range expected of the epoxies, and typical values are presented in Table 7-5.

TABLE 7-5. Electrical Properties for Typical Polyamide-cured Systems (3-5)
(Test conditions: room temperature)

Polyamide and concentration	Frequency, cycles/sec		
	10	10^3	10^6
Polyamide (amine value 210–230), 100 phr:			
Power factor	0.0090	0.0108	0.0170
Dielectric constant	3.20	3.14	3.01
Loss factor	0.0357	0.0339	0.0572
Dielectric strength, volts/mil	470		
Volume resistivity, ohm-cm	1.5×10^{14}		
Arc resistance, sec	76		
Polyamide (amine value 290–320), 66 phr:			
Power factor	0.0085	0.0108	0.0213
Dielectric constant	3.37	3.32	3.08
Loss factor	0.0285	0.0359	0.0656
Dielectric strength, volts/mil	430		
Volume resistivity, ohm-cm	1.1×10^{14}		
Arc resistance, sec	82		

Chemical resistance of polyamide-cured systems is lower than obtained with aliphatic-amine curing agents.

The polyamides, in their own right excellent thermoplastic adhesives, find limited use as epoxy flexibilizers in adhesive, laminating, casting, and coating formulations (7-3). In adhesive formulations they provide excellent shear strengths to temperatures as low as $-76°C$ and good resistance to impact loads. In higher percentages, 200 to 250 phr, they can be used for bonding Mylar film and other difficult-to-bond materials.

Unlike unmodified amine curing agents, the polyamides do not appear to be skin-sensitizing agents.

Polysulfides

A number of polysulfide polymers useful as flexibilizers for epoxy resins are available commercially (Table 7-6). They are viscous, colorless to clear liquids. The general formula for the materials can be given as:

$$HS—(C_2H_4—O—CH_2—O—C_2H_4—S—S)_n— \atop C_2H_4—O—CH_2—O—C_2H_4—SH$$

The commercial resins differ primarily in molecular weight, crosslinking, and viscosities.

TABLE 7-6. Properties of Typical Polysulfides (7-6)

	LP-3*	LP-8*	LP-33*
Physical state....................	Mobile liquid	Mobile liquid	Mobile liquid
Molecular weight.................	1,000	500–700	1,000
Per cent crosslinking..............	2.0	2.0	0.5
Pour point, °C.................. ...	−20	−32	−12 to −15
Specific gravity, 20°/4°C...........	1.27	1.27	1.27
Viscosity, at 27°C, centipoises.......	700–1,200	250–350	1,300–1,550
Flash point (open cup), °C.........	214	182	205
Fire point (open cup), °C...........	240	205	240
Moisture content, %..............	0.1	0.2	0.1
pH (water extract)................	6.0–8.0	6.0–8.0	6.0–8.0
Color........................	Clear amber	Clear amber	Clear amber

* Thiokol Corporation.

Epoxy resins, with the following structure, based on the polysulfide chain have been synthesized (7-4):

$$\overset{O}{\overset{/\backslash}{CH_2}}{—}CH—CH_2—S{\sim\!\sim\!\sim\!\sim}S—CH_2—\overset{O}{\overset{/\backslash}{CH}}{—}CH_2$$

but the mercaptan terminated materials are more commonly used. The polymer with a degree of polymerization of 6, having a molecular weight in the 1,000 range, can be considered typical of the class, and subsequent data will be based on this compound.

The reactivity of the mercaptan (SH) groups in the presence of a catalyst and the nature of the polysulfide molecules make the polysulfides good flexibilizers for the epoxy resins, particularly when high orders of flexibility are requisite.

Polysulfide liquid polymers may, by themselves, cure by oxidation condensation or addition to firm rubbery solids. When used in combination with epoxy resins, the curing reactions between the polysulfide and epoxy is by addition:

$$R-\underset{\Large \diagdown\!\diagup}{CH}\!\!-\!\!\overset{O}{\underset{}{CH_2}} + HS-R' \rightarrow R-\underset{\overset{|}{OH}}{CH}-CH_2-S-R'$$

The reaction of the epoxy group with the mercaptan group is not so vigorous as with an amine or amide group. Uncatalyzed, the reaction will gel the epoxy resin within a few days, leaving it unworkable, but the cure will be inadequate. Hence curing agents are required.

Upon addition of a curing agent—primary, secondary, or tertiary aliphatic polyamines or anhydrides are used—crosslinking is prompt. Discounting the random number of mercaptans along the chain, approximately 250 phr of a typical polysulfide is required to provide a mercaptan group for each epoxy group of a commercial resin. The usual formulation involves 100 phr or less of polysulfide—leaving well over one half of the epoxy groups available for reacting with a crosslinking agent or by self-polymerization. In actual practice, the amount of curing agent is usually based on epoxy resin content and is calculated by ignoring the mercaptan groups.

The curing mechanism is quite specific, even when large amounts of polysulfide are employed. For example (7-5), when using 10 phr of triethylene tetramine as a curing agent for a 2/1 polysulfide/epoxy blend, it was found on the basis of toluene-extraction data that less than 8 per cent of the mercaptans remained unreacted at room-temperature cures. When a tertiary amine, such as DMP-30, was used as a curing agent, the reaction was even more specific. After room-temperature cure, less than 1 per cent of the mercaptans remained unreacted at the 2/1 ratio. When postcuring is employed, some of the excess curing agent subsequently reacts with or catalyzes self-polymerization of the remaining epoxy groups. Since the excess does not cause end stopping of the chains and embrittlement, the effect on ultimate properties of any entrapped unreacted materials is slight. Some differences in properties will, however, be experienced between compounds cured by crosslinking and by catalytic-type curing agents. For example, tertiary-amine cured materials will give better tensile strengths at room temperature; primary-amine cured materials will give more stable properties at temperature aging. To improve selected parameters and regulate pot life, it is possible to use lesser amounts of curing agents than would be indicated for the unmodified epoxy resins. Likewise, of course, the curing agent may, within limits, be selected on the basis of handling characteristics without seriously affecting the properties of the cured system. An amine such as piperidine, for example, may be employed in place of DMP-30 to provide longer pot life. The unmodified aliphatic amines are preferred as curing agents for epoxy-polysulfide blends rather than their adducts. Cure may be accomplished at room temperature with the more reactive curing agents; postcuring, however, will improve impact resistance, chemical resistance, electrical properties, etc., as is the case with unmodified epoxy systems.

With larger amounts of polysulfides, peak exotherms are reduced to the 38°C range and pot lives are correspondingly extended, even when using a highly reactive curing agent. However, with lower concentrations, the reaction proceeds at an accelerated rate (Table 7-7).

TABLE 7-7. Effect of Polysulfide Concentration on Rate of Cure of Epoxy-resin Compounds (7-6)
(Test conditions: room temperature.   Samples: 50 grams.   Curing agent: tridimethyl amino methyl phenol.)

Polysulfide concentration, %................	0	33	50	67
Gel time, min...............................	41	15	21	72
Tack free, min..............................	225	27	38	1,000
Max temperature, due to reaction exotherm, °C	45	107	103	61

TABLE 7-8. Effect of Per Cent Polysulfide on Properties of Cured Resin (7-6)
(Test conditions: room temperature)

	Polysulfide/epoxy ratio					
	100/0	300/100	200/100	100/100	100/200	0/100
Elongation, %...............	200	100	50	30	10	
Hardness, Shore A..........	35	50	70	95	98	100
Volume shrinkage, %........	5	2.5	2.8	3.5	4.5	6
Dielectric constant, at 10^3 cps.	7.5	6.5	5.5	4.0	3.8	3.5
Volume resistivity, ohm-cm...	10^9	10^{10}	10^{11}	10^{12}	10^{13}	10^{14}

It will be seen from Table 7-6 that the viscosity of the polysulfides is low. The viscosity may further be reduced by temperature, as is indicated in Fig. 7-1. If, of course, blends of epoxy polysulfide are worked at higher temperatures, there will be a consequent reduction in pot life.

The amount of polysulfide employed determines cured properties (Table 7-8). Typical properties for various epoxy–polysulfide resin blends are presented in Table 7-9. The data indicate the effect of both crosslinking and catalytic amines on cured properties. Figure 7-2 presents volume resistivity as a function of temperature for typical poly-

TABLE 7-9. Typical Properties of Cured Epoxy Resin
Flexibilized with a Polysulfide (7-5)

Formulation, parts by weight:				
Epoxy resin	100	100	100	100
Polysulfide, mol. wt 1,000, 2% crosslinked	50	100	50	100
Tridimethyl amino methyl phenol	10	10		
Triethylene tetramine	....	....	10	10
Working properties, 50-gram mass:				
Viscosity at 25°C, centipoises...	2,650	2,000	2,650	2,000
Pot life at 25°C, min	20	35	20	40
Peak exotherm, °C	151	129	154	121
Stress-strain properties:				
After 5 days at 25°C				
Tensile strength, psi	4,800	2,800	4,580	1,785
Elongation, %	10	30	0–5	30
Hardness, Shore D	78	63	60	41
After 70 hr at 100°C				
Tensile strength, psi	4,200	900	5,000	1,800
Elongation, %	0–5	80	0–5	30
Hardness, Shore D	76	40	65	43
Impact strength, ft-lb:				
At 25°C	1.1	78	47	110*
At −34°C	0.5	1.3	2.5	3.5
Electrical properties at 25°C and 10³ cycles/sec:				
Dielectric constant	4.5	5.5	3.5	6.0
Loss factor	0.009	0.012	0.012	0.020
Volume resistivity, ohm-cm	6.1×10^{12}	6×10^{11}	2×10^{12}	1.5×10^{11}
Surface resistivity, ohm	1.5×10^{13}	1.5×10^{13}	4×10^{13}	3.3×10^{12}
Chemical resistance, after 30 days immersion at 25°C, swell volume, %:				
Hydrochloric acid, 10%	2	4		
Sulfuric acid, 20%	2	4		
Ammonium hydroxide, conc....	3	7		
Sodium hydroxide, 10%	1	2		
Sodium hydroxide, 50%	−1	−1		
Sodium chloride, satd. soln	1	1		
Benzene	38	27		
Carbon tetrachloride	−2	12		
Methyl ethyl ketone	35	20		
Ethyl acetate	26	17		
Water absorption, %:				
After 24 hr	0.2	0.4	0.3	0.4
After 7 days	0.6	1.2	0.8	0.9
After 24 days	1.3	1.5	0.8	1.2

* Limit of test equipment.

sulfide blends. Because of the reaction mechanisms involved, fluidized resins or reactive diluents should not be employed when using the polysulfide at higher (200 phr) ratios.

The polysulfides are widely used in casting formulations, in coatings, in laminates, and in adhesives (7-8). Used in higher loading volumes, they make possible the formulation of uniquely flexible materials.

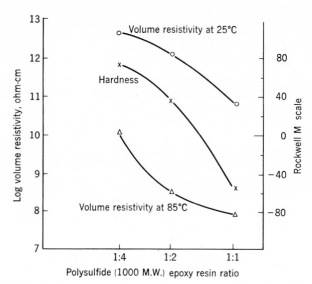

FIG. 7-2. Hardness and resistivity of epoxy-polysulfide blends (7-7).

The polysulfides, like the polyamides, are not believed to be skin-sensitizing agents; however, they have a strong characteristic odor, which with familiarity becomes less unpleasant.

Fatty Diamines

Fatty diamines, as flexibilizers for the epoxy resins, offer an interesting combination of long free-floating chains, characteristic of the monofunctional flexibilizers, and reactive hydrogen groups, characteristic of the polyfunctional flexibilizers. A typical fatty diamine having the following formula

$$R_{soya}-\overset{\overset{\text{H}}{|}}{N}-CH_2-CH_2-CH_2-NH_2$$
Duomeen S*

may be considered typical of the class useful in epoxy-resin formulations.

* Trade-mark of Armour & Co., Inc.

The fatty diamines react with the epoxy resins as do the other aliphatic amines. Stoichiometric quantities for this typical fatty diamine are on the order of 70 phr for a typical commercial epoxy resin. The melting point of the compound is just above room temperature, and consequently it must be mixed hot; once melted, it is very fluid. At room temperature, the material has the appearance of a yellow soapy paste.

Mixing temperatures on the order of 50°C are adequate, but thorough stirring is required. After mixing, the compound may be allowed to

TABLE 7-10. Physical Properties of Typical Fatty-diamine Cured System (3-5)
(Test conditions: room temperature, except as noted)

Clash-Berg torsion stiffness, psi:	
23°C.	2,500
0°C.	82,000
−25°C.	180,000
−50°C.	285,000
Brittleness, °C.	14
Tear resistance, lb/in.	279
Hardness, Durometer A.	74
Scott tensile:	
Strength, psi.	1,380
Elongation, %.	110
Tensile, stress-strain:	
Strength, psi.	1,320
Elongation, %.	71
Modulus of elasticity, psi.	237,000

return to room temperature to prolong pot life. In 100-gram batches, it provides a pot life on the order of 1 hour at room temperature. At 40°C, the pot life is 20 minutes. Peak exotherms are as high as 170°C in small batches. Postcures of 150°C may be employed without affecting flexibility.

The fatty diamines do not appear to give good castings when used in less than stoichiometric quantities. When stoichiometric quantities are employed, a thermoset compound with a heat-distortion temperature lower than room temperature results. The physical properties give the cured system handling characteristics and texture similar to a plasticized vinyl chloride. Table 7-10 presents physical data for a typical system. The electrical properties of the fatty-diamine cured system are in the lower range expected of aliphatic-amine cured systems. Table 7-11 presents typical values.

At the stoichiometric ratio of 70 phr, there will be a large number of soya chains present in the cured resin, and as might be expected, the chemical resistance will be low compared to a system containing only

15 phr of a monofunctional flexibilizer. Chemical-resistance data for a typical cured system are presented in Table 7-12.

By replacing a portion of the fatty diamine with a secondary curing agent, it is possible to achieve wide gradations in flexibility and physical properties. Table 7-13 presents data for two possible variations.

TABLE 7-11. Electrical Properties of Typical Fatty-diamine Cured Systems (3-5)

Property	Frequency, cycles/sec		
	60	10^3	10^6
Power factor:			
23°C	0.0540	0.0422	0.0366
50°C	0.0775	0.0675	0.0538
100°C	0.0875	0.0717	0.0660
Dielectric constant:			
23°C	3.62	3.32	2.81
50°C	5.25	4.65	3.16
100°C	9.09	9.55	4.06
Dielectric strength, volts/mil			
23°C		448	
50°C		406	
100°C		392	

TABLE 7-12. Chemical Resistance of Typical Fatty-diamine Cured System (3-5)
(Test conditions: room temperature)

System tested in	Percentage weight gain, 7 days immersion
Distilled water	0.73
30% sulfuric acid	1.73
10% Caustic	0.58
95% Ethanol	11.8
Acetone	Disintegrated
Ethyl acetate	1.97
Acetic acid (glacial)	Disintegrated
Chloroform	Disintegrated
Ethylene dichloride	Disintegrated
Toluene	Disintegrated

The fatty diamines provide good performance at lower temperatures, under conditions of thermal shock, and under vibration; they may be used in casting and laminating formulations where high temperatures are not encountered. Their room-temperature adhesive strength is good.

TABLE 7-13. Physical Properties of Typical Systems Flexibilized with
Fatty Diamine and Second Curing Agent (3-5)

Property	Cure*	Aromatic amine	0.8 aromatic amine, 0.2 fatty diamine	Aliphatic amine	0.8 aliphatic amine, 0.2 fatty diamine
Compressive strength, psi........	A	32,300	27,100	31,200	27,900
	B	30,800	30,400	32,800	25,400
Compressive yield, psi...........	A	19,200	13,900	16,100	12,100
	B	19,000	14,300	16,900	12,700
Flexural strength, psi...........	A	19,500	15,500	18,400	12,500
	B	15,470	15,700	16,000	14,400
Flexural modulus of elasticity, psi $\times$ 10^{-5}.................	A	5.4	4.2	5.4	4.0
	B	4.8	4.4	5.4	4.3
Impact strength, Izod...........	A	0.214	0.209	0.203	0.209
	B	0.192	0.211	0.198	0.180
Hardness, Rockwell M..........	A	109	92	100	72
	B	112	94	103	88
Heat-distortion temperature, °C..	A	100	66	75	56
	B	141	71	85	61

* Cure A: ½ hour at 70°C plus 1 hour at 100°C. Cure B: same as A plus 8 hour at 150°C.

Like the unmodified amines, the fatty diamines are skin-sensitizing agents and caution should be exercised in their handling.

Polyester Flexibilizers

Potentially, the polyester flexibilizers (7-9) appear to be the most versatile. Unlike the flexibilizers previously discussed, it is possible to formulate polyesters which are virtually nonreactive with the epoxies at the lower temperatures and yet which can link into the system when a curing agent is added. Other formulations can, themselves, act as curing agents (7-10).

The long-chain polyesters useful as flexibilizers have chain lengths of at least 14 members, with longer chains providing increased flexibility. The chains may be terminated either with carboxyl or alcoholic hydroxy groups, depending on the ratio of reactants employed in their synthesis. The carboxylic-terminated polyesters cure the epoxy resins in a fashion similar to the anhydrides; the alcoholic-hydroxyl-terminated polyester will link into the molecule by esterification during anhydride cure o etherification during amine cure; although uncatalyzed, they will not react.

An example of each (7-9) will serve to describe the materials more fully. A carboxy-terminated polyester may be formulated by reacting 5 mols of adipic acid with 4 mols of glycerol. This reaction product will have an acid equivalent per 100 grams of about 2.5, corresponding to a mixture of compounds having an average molecular weight of about 800 and an average of about 44 members in the chain. It can be reacted at stoichiometric ratio with an epoxy resin to produce a highly elastomeric product under cure conditions suitable to an anhydride, and if desired, an amine accelerator may be employed to reduce cure time. Lower orders of flexibility may be obtained by using the material in conjunction with an anhydride, the degree of flexibility being governed by the amount of flexibilizer present.

A hydroxyl-terminated polyester may be synthesized by using 3 mols of adipic acid and 4 mols of glycerol. This reaction product will have 3.4 mols of end hydroxyls per 100 grams and about 32 members in the chain. It will not react with the epoxy resin unless temperatures on the order of 200°C are used, but it will react readily in the presence of a curing agent. It can be packaged into the resin at the percentage desired to impart the impact resistance or flexibility required for the specific formulation, such as, for example, low-temperature shock resistance. By substituting an amine such as ethyl diethanolamine in the foregoing reaction, a composition containing catalytic tertiary amines will be produced capable of independent cure.

A typical hydroxyl-terminated long-chain polyester, when used at 100 phr with an epoxy resin/amine curing agent system, will give a compound having a Shore D hardness of 60, a 40 per cent elongation, a tensile strength of 1,650 psi, and an impact resistance in excess of 78 ft-lb at room temperature. Electrical properties and chemical resistance of this particular formulation are somewhat below the values obtained with an unmodified epoxy system.

A typical carboxyl-terminated long-chain polyester is recommended for use with anhydrides (3-9) when impact resistance and flexibility are required. The specific material is solid at room temperature and must be dissolved into the hot resin, temperatures above 60°C being required. As in the case with the hydroxyl-terminated materials, amounts can be varied to meet the application requirements. Chemical resistance and electrical properties will be lower than expected of the unflexibilized compound.

As indicated in Chap. 6, other polyesters can be employed as extenders, these materials having fewer members in the resin chain and, consequently, imparting less flexibility to the cured system.

CONCLUSION

Flexibilizers for the epoxy resins are particularly useful where the high adhesion and low shrinkage of the unmodified resins cause strains in the system during cure.   The flexibilizers impart increased impact resistance to the cured system and improved performance at lower temperatures, and somewhat offset the effect of differing coefficients of thermal expansion during temperature cycling.

Agents used to impart impact resistance to cured epoxy resins may be classed as plasticizers, which are nonreactive, and flexibilizers, which are reactive.   Their use provides the formulator with compounds capable of accommodating a number of specific impact and flexible requirements not obtainable with the unmodified epoxy systems.   Specific applications will be suggested in subsequent chapters.

References

7-1. Floyd, Peerman, and Wittcoff, Characteristics of the Polyamide–Epoxy Resin System, Symposium of British Society of Chemical Industry, April, 1956.
7-2. General Mills, Inc., sales literature.
7-3. Floyd, Ward, and Minarik, Polyamide–Epoxy Resins, *Modern Plastics*, **33**:10 (1956).
7-4. Bender, Farnham, and Guyer, Diglycidyl Thio Ethers of Dithiols Containing Oxygen, U.S. 2,731,437 (1956).
7-5. Cranker and Breslau, Epoxy Casting Resins Modified with Polysulfide Liquid Polymer, *Industrial and Engineering Chemistry*, vol. 48, January, 1956.
7-6. Thiokol Corp., technical literature.
7-7. Nadler, Mallard, and Bowen, Potting Aircraft Electrical Connectors, *Electronics Equipment*, July, 1956.
7-8. Jorczak and Dworkin, Flexible Epoxy Plastics, *Plant Engineering*, September, 1954.
7-9. Fisch, Elastic Infusible Products from Epoxy Compounds and Crosslinking Agents, U.S. 2,712,535 (1955).
7-10. Cass, Acidic Polyester-Ethoxyline Resinous Compositions, U.S. 2,683,131 (1954).

8

CASTING, POTTING, ENCAPSULATION, SEALING, AND LIGHTWEIGHT FOAMS

The properties of the epoxy resins make them almost ideally suited for casting, potting, encapsulation, and sealing. They are also well suited to the formulation of lightweight foams for use by these techniques.

The term casting refers to the manufacture of individual solid shapes by pouring a hardenable liquid into a prepared mold and subsequently transforming the liquid into a dimensionally stable component. The terms potting, encapsulation, and sealing are three somewhat overlapping designations having to do with the protection of components or component systems by the application of an exterior resinous sheath. The terms, as used subsequently, are defined more explicitly in Fig. 8-1. Considered as a generic class, the four processes involve a number of common considerations, not only as to formulation but as to application techniques.

In casting applications, the structural properties are generally of the most consequence: hardness, toughness, dimensional stability, machinability, etc.

In potting, encapsulation, and sealing, the insulation properties are generally of the most consequence: moisture, impact, and chemical and electrical resistance.

The general range of properties for a number of cured epoxy resins is given in Chaps. 3 to 7. These data will suggest potential uses for the resins.

COMMERCIAL APPLICATIONS

Epoxy-resin castings can be used for patterns, molds, and finished products. Since shrinkage is slight and dimensional stability good, the castings require little machine time, and in ease of handling, the epoxy liquid systems surpass most conventional materials.

Epoxy patterns (8-1) are particularly convenient duplicates when mass-production runs are required.   They can be cast and cured quickly, and the smooth, void-free surfaces will give excellent draws.   Epoxy molds are useful for short production runs, custom-designed parts, and prototype models.   Minor design changes can be incorporated by building up additional formations and remachining.   The use of epoxies in such situations, where previously expensive metallic components were required, has

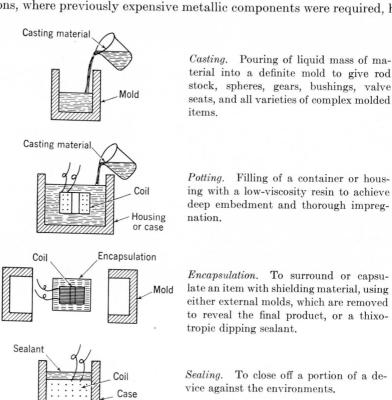

Casting. Pouring of liquid mass of material into a definite mold to give rod stock, spheres, gears, bushings, valve seats, and all varieties of complex molded items.

Potting. Filling of a container or housing with a low-viscosity resin to achieve deep embedment and thorough impregnation.

Encapsulation. To surround or capsulate an item with shielding material, using either external molds, which are removed to reveal the final product, or a thixotropic dipping sealant.

Sealing. To close off a portion of a device against the environments.

FIG 8-1. Definition of terms: casting, potting, encapsulation, and sealing.

effected significant cost savings in the industry.   The epoxies are particularly valuable for use in cast tooling, where the cost of the complete unit is often less than the material cost of metal tooling.

Finished cast-epoxy products are used as bobbins, gears, metalworking hobs, lightweight machine stock, caps for drop-hammer dies, etc.   Foam-in-place castings are valuable in the aircraft industry, where lightweight structural materials are essential.

Because of the high degree of fill obtainable in production situations, and the uniquely resistant nature of the cured resin, the epoxies are widely used for potting all sizes of electrical coils—from miniature transformers (8-2) to the random windings of 200 hp motors (8-3).   The tough, durable construction of the potted unit frequently eliminates the necessity for an exterior totally enclosing case, with the consequent savings of space,

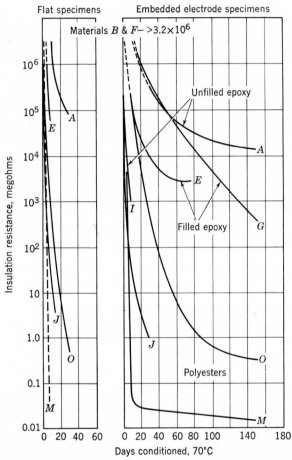

FIG. 8-2. Effect of moisture on insulation resistance of epoxy and polyester resins (8-4).

weight, and money.   The advantage of potting electrical equipment against severe environments as encountered in chemical manufacturing plants, in humid coastal areas, and in the military services is manifest. The fungus-resistant nature of the insulation is particularly valuable in moist tropical climates.   A typical compound, for example, successfully withstood 16 cycles of the fungus-resistance requirement of specification

MIL-5272, at which time the test was terminated. Weathering and aging tests have been conducted on epoxy-resin insulated electrical equipment in the arctic, in the Mojave Desert, and in the tropics. These natural environmental extremes do not adversely affect the electrical properties. The chemical resistance, coupled with the extreme resistance to rough handling and mechanical and thermal shocks, combine to provide apparatus of greatly increased service life.

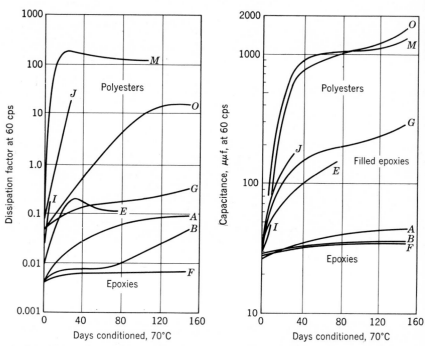

FIG. 8-3. Effect of moisture on dissipation factor of epoxy and polyester resins (8-4).

FIG. 8-4. Effect of moisture on capacitance of epoxy and polyester resins (8-4).

Components of electronics systems can be integrated in a single cast block to eliminate individual mounting attachments and to provide systems insensitive to handling. Such systems are easily replaceable in service upon failure of an integral component. They can be plugged in as easily as a vacuum tube. The number of components thus incorporated into one cast block is dependent primarily on economic considerations, since failure of a single item requires in many cases scrapping the complete unit if chemical strippers are not completely satisfactory. Such potted systems, only slightly heavier than equivalent unpotted systems, will occupy considerably less volume, and the integral insulator will retain constant electrical characteristics throughout considerable pressure and temperature variations. The unique moisture resistance of the epoxy resins is particularly valuable in this work. Figures 8-2 to 8-4 compare the effect of high humidity on the electrical properties of epoxy (specimens

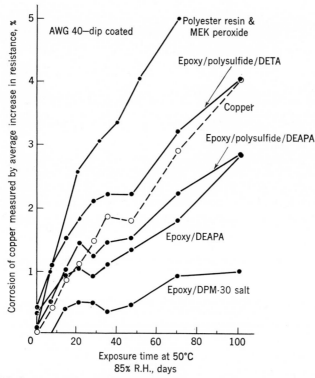

FIG. 8-5. Corrosive effects of various casting compositions on copper wire (8-5).

A to I) and polyester (specimens J to M) systems (8-4). Figure 8-5 indicates the comparative corrosive effects on embedded components for epoxy and polyester systems (8-5).

Commercial electrical applications for epoxy-resin potting compounds are summarized in Table 8-1. Because of the polar nature of the epoxy resins, the electrical properties of cured systems are dependent on frequency. The power factor, for example, is lowest at about 50 cycles/sec and remains fairly constant up to about 55×10^3 cycles/sec. It then increases as frequency is raised to 10^6 cycles/sec (8-6). Because of this frequency dependence, the epoxies require full engineering for high frequency applications.

Encapsulating and sealing techniques provide exterior shields over components or component systems wherever the thorough impregnation of deep embedment is not required. Such techniques, however, do not provide for sufficiently dense fill for many electrical applications. For example, indifferent success is obtained by sealing over the ends of the windings of large electrical motors with a paste to provide protection

TABLE 8-1. Electrical Casting, Encapsulating, Potting, and Sealing Applications for Epoxy Resins

Electrical equipment:
  Small aircraft armatures and stators
  Large random-, form-, and field-coil type motors
  Transformer bushing manufacture and repair
  Magnetic chucks
  Circuit-breaker components
  Commutator and slip-ring repair
  Bus-bar insulation
  Power, distribution, and high-voltage transformers
Electronics equipment:
  Multivibrators as timing circuits for computers, amplifiers, and power supplies
  Selenium rectifiers
  Metallized, paper, and ceramic capacitors
  Antenna-matching and torroidal transformers
  Ferrite pot cores
  Radio-frequency chokes
  Inductors
  Vacuum-tube and magnetic amplifier circuits
  Germanium diodes and transistors
  Miniature and subminiature vacuum tubes
  Printed circuits
  Hermetically sealed relays
Cables:
  Cable splices for mineral, lead, and rubber cables
  Dams for gas-filled cables
  Conduit sealing
  Hull fitting and cable terminal sealing

from environmental extremes. The apparatus will run hot and be subject to cracking during thermal cycling. If the windings are potted in such a manner as to eliminate voids and entrapped air, excellent performance will be achieved: the apparatus will run cooler than a unit insulated with conventional varnish, and the thermal shock properties will be good (8-7).

Encapsulation and the sealing techniques are particularly valuable for field and one-shot applications, where the ease of handling and the speed of cure are virtually indispensable. In production situations, encapsulation techniques generally involve the use of molds to provide esthetic surfaces and highly reproducible thicknesses of insulation.

Table 8-2 presents a comparison of phenolic, polyester, and epoxy-resin potting compounds.

TABLE 8-2. Comparison of Synthetic Potting Compounds*

Property	Class A phenolic	Class A polyesters	Class A epoxy	Class B epoxy	Class H silicone
Specific gravity	1.30–1.32	1.10–1.46	1.11–1.23	1.15	1.70–1.90
Tensile strength, psi	6,000–9,000	6,000–10,000	12,000	12,000–15,000	3,000–7,000
Elongation, %	1.5–2.0	5	5	1.5	
Modulus of elasticity in tension, psi $\times 10^{-5}$	4.5	3.0–6.4	4.5	6	
Compressive strength, psi	12,500–15,000	13,000–27,000	16,000	15,000	9,000–18,000
Flexural strength, psi	11,000–17,000	8,500–17,000	18,800	15,470	9,800
Impact resistance, Izod	0.25–0.40	0.2–0.4	0.5–1.7	0.192	4.20
Hardness, Rockwell M	120	115	100	112	45
Coefficient of thermal expansion $\times 10^6$, °C	60–80	80–100	60	60	308
Resistance to heat, °C, continuous	71	121	149	177	249
Heat-distortion temperature, °C	78–82	60–100	120	300	
Volume resistivity, ohm-cm	10^{12}–10^{13}	10^{14}	10^{16}–10^{17}	10^{17}	10^{11}–10^{13}
Dielectric strength, volts/m	350–400	380–500	400–500	450–500	185
Dielectric constant, 60 cycles	6.5–7.5	3.0–4.36	3.8	3.8	4.0–5.0
Power factor, 60 cycles	0.10–0.15	0.003	0.0013	0.002	0.0055
Arc resistance, sec	100–125	125	50–180	100–140	
Water absorption, 24 hr, %	0.12–0.36	0.15–0.60	0.14	1.10	
Effect of weak acids	Slight	Slight	None	None	Slight
Effect of strong acids	Attacked	Attacked	Attacked	Slight	Attacked
Effect of weak alkalies	Slight	Slight	None	None	Slight
Effect of strong alkalies	Decomposed	Decomposed	Very slight	Very slight	Attacked
Effect of organic solvents	Attacked by some	Attacked by ketones and chlorinated solvents	Resistant	Resistant	Attacked by some
Shrinkage, %	8–10	4–6	1–2	1–2	4–8
Adhesion to metals, glass, plastics, ceramics, etc	Excellent	Fair	Excellent	Excellent	Poor

* From *Modern Plastics* and trade literature.

FORMULATION

Although the epoxy resins are versatile casting materials, their formulation is a somewhat specialized art. The most satisfactory results are achieved only when adequate engineering thought is given to the specific problem. It is the purpose of this section to touch on the more important of the factors involved in the selection of a specific epoxy compound and to present appropriate practical data.

The specific resin–curing agent system will, to a very considerable extent, determine the ultimate properties. Seldom, however, will such an uncomplicated system provide the most satisfactory compound.

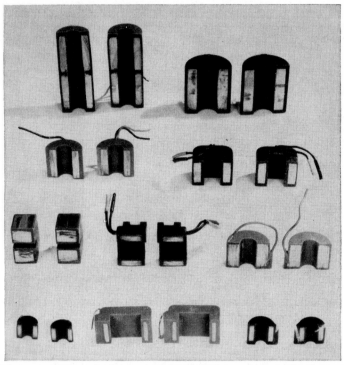

Solenoid, motor contactor, telemetering, starter, and other precision coils are encapsulated in epoxy compounds to protect them against moisture, contamination, and mechanical abuse. (*Deluxe Coils, Inc., and Bakelite Co.*)

Specific properties must be modified while desirable properties are maintained, and where necessary, a number of practical disadvantages must be accommodated.

Resin–Curing Agent Complex

For nearly all casting, potting, encapsulating, and sealing operations, liquid low-molecular-weight epoxy resins are employed. Powders and preformed pellets may be formulated from higher-molecular-weight resins and anhydride curing agents for a limited number of molding

Industrial open-type 10-hp motors are encapsulated in epoxy-resin compound to provide protection against severe caustic and solvent conditions. (*The Epoxylite Corporation.*)

Wound rotor for 25-hp a-c welder is encapsulated in epoxy-resin compound to provide protection against steel machine particles and cutting oils. (*The Epoxylite Corporation.*)

applications, but the solid compounds are of limited utility. Resins having molecular weights from 350 to 450 are the preferred class for most commercial applications.

The maximum operating temperature required for a specific application will determine the class of curing agent to employ. Rigid systems giving

Large 100-hp totally enclosed motor encapsulated in epoxy-resin compound. Windings are protected against moisture and severe acid dust which destroyed phenolic varnish insulation in 3 to 4 months, leading to immediate burnout. One hundred and fifty such motors were encapsulated in epoxy for this manufacturer over a 3-year period. Not a single failure occurred. (*The Epoxylite Corporation.*)

heat-distortion temperatures as high as 300°C may be formulated with anhydrides. Aromatic amines provide heat-distortion temperatures up to about 180°C, and thoroughly postcured aliphatic amines provide heat-distortion temperatures in the neighborhood of 120°C. The room-temperature-cured systems will produce good general-purpose compounds, completely satisfactory where operating temperatures are below 100°C.

The heat-distortion temperature is a somewhat arbitrary value, indicating that loss of load-bearing properties will be rapid at temperatures in excess of it. For some applications, the heat-distortion temperature may be exceeded for limited periods; but if it is exceeded by a considerable value, performance will be unsatisfactory.

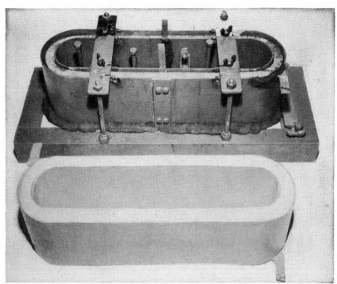

Large 60-lb field coil for 1,800-hp rubber mill motor is encapsulated in epoxy-resin compound (using a five-piece steel mold) to seal out carbon black. (The Epoxylite Corporation.)

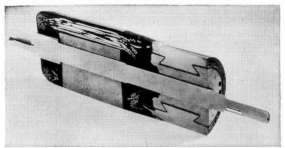

Small d-c motor armature is encapsulated in epoxy-resin compound for service under conditions of severe vibration and rotational loads (8,000 rpm), high temperatures (—65 to 200°C), and severe moisture environment. (Bakelite Co.)

Figure 5-12 reveals the general performance of various resins and curing agents at temperatures above the heat-distortion temperature. Some systems continue to deform rapidly within the ranges tested. Some deform rapidly until they can deform no more—presumably because of maximum stretching of the bonds involved, complete untwisting of the coiled and twisted polymer segments in line with the direction of stress, and completion of any internal slippage and flow possible. When these samples reach this end point, either they hold the load with no further deformation, or they break.

It is difficult to predict the exact performance of a resin–curing agent system under such conditions. The resin, the curing agent, the percentage curing agent, the cure cycle, all are important in determining performance. Resins with higher functionality appear to give higher heat-distortion values and better strength retention above the heat-distortion temperature. The novolac resins are very promising in this regard.

Electrical properties—in so far as they have been correlated with physical properties—are also governed to an extent by heat-distortion temperature. For many compounds, electrical losses increase rapidly above the heat-distortion temperature. (The "unfreezing" of various radicals in the polymer accompanying the general volume expansion which occurs in the region of the heat-distortion temperature permits these radicals to respond to inductive electric vibrations, thereby increasing electrical losses.) A rule of thumb suggested is that compounds which are to be exposed to frequencies above 10^3 cycles/sec at temperatures above the heat-distortion temperature should be checked closely with regard to electrical losses.

Since, in general, the higher-temperature curing agents are less conveniently handled than the lower temperature ones, preference should be given to the class of curing agents providing the minimum acceptable heat-distortion temperatures. Typical data for unfilled casting formulations are presented in Chaps. 3 to 5.

In many cases, the specific curing agent within a given class may be selected on the basis of handling characteristics, chiefly pot life and irritation potential, although the viscosity of the catalyzed system may sometimes be considered.

The selection of a convenient pot-life curing agent should be considered in terms of required cure temperatures and cure cycles. Significantly increased pot life is obtained only through the expenditure of increased cure times or higher-temperature cures.

In production situations, the irritation potential of the curing agent may present somewhat of a problem. Frequently, the most convenient agent from the standpoint of other handling characteristics has a high irritation potential. Most amines, both aliphatic and aromatic, are skin sensitizers; certain of the anhydrides can cause serious systemic injuries (Chap. 12). The least irritating curing agent consistent with other production requirements and ultimate properties should be preferred.

Modification of Properties

If it is necessary to improve selected properties in the epoxy-resin system, the formulator may employ various of the materials described in Chaps. 6 and 7. The number of specific considerations of consequence include, but are not limited to, cost, viscosity, exotherm, shrinkage, pot life, and coefficient of thermal expansion.

Cost can best be reduced by holding the amount of resin employed to a minimum. This can be accomplished, where practical, by the incorporation of large loading volumes of inexpensive fillers or resinous modifiers. Minimum-resin molds should be designed for potting and encapsulation operations.

Viscosity is most critical for potting operations where a high degree of impregnation is required and for casting operations where large loading volumes of fillers are necessary. Assuming that the resin–curing agent system is of the lowest practical viscosity, this can be further reduced by working the catalyzed mix hot or by the addition of diluents, either reactive or nonreactive. High-viscosity systems for encapsulating and sealing operations can easily be achieved by the use of thickening agents or high loading volumes of more conventional materials.

Exotherms are likely to present severe problems in the casting of larger masses. Exotherms may be reduced by the incorporation of fillers and resinous modifiers and selection of curing agent, although the practical minimum value is about 50°C for reasonable cure times. Excessive exotherms can cause volatilization of the curing agent or resinous modifier to produce castings of unsatisfactory quality, may adversely affect the temperature-sensitive components involved, and subject the compound to too great a thermal cycle during cure. Reactive diluents should be avoided in rigid formulations if this parameter is critical.

Shrinkage may be conveniently reduced by the incorporation of fillers and modifiers. The slight shrinkage of even an unfilled epoxy compound usually does not present cause for concern. But when integral molds are employed and larger components are being potted, the excellent adhesion of the epoxy to the mold may cause cracking of the system during cure. For other potting applications, involving delicate components, the shrinkage of an unfilled epoxy may be sufficient to crush the insert.

Pot life dictated by other considerations can be somewhat increased with fillers, diluents, and resinous modifiers, although, again, usually only at the expense of increased cure times or higher cure temperatures. In the case of certain acid anhydrides, where the pot life—in terms of requisite cure cycles—is too long, the pot life can be reduced, and hence cure shortened by the addition of amine accelerators.

Coefficients of thermal expansion of unfilled epoxy resins can be regarded as critically high for a limited number of potting and sealing applications involving rapid temperature cycling. The coefficient of the unmodified resins is higher than that of many materials likely to be involved in the potted system as inserts.   It is often possible to match closely the value of the involved material by the use of suitable filler loading volumes.   The

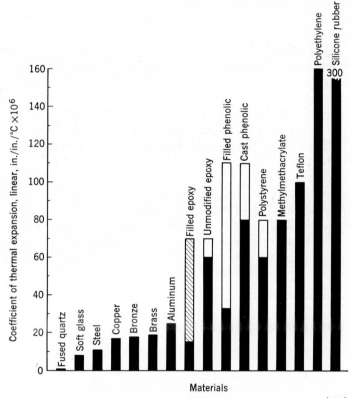

Materials

FIG. 8-6. Effect of filler content on coefficient of thermal expansion (4-5).

effect of a high loading volume on several casting resin systems is indicated in Fig. 8-6.   When such loading volumes cannot be tolerated, it is often possible to formulate a satisfactory ductile compound capable of absorbing resultant strains, and such a system is likewise feasible if several materials are involved and it is necessary for the epoxy resin to absorb differing stress levels within the system.   Ductile systems, however, do not give satisfactory performance at higher temperatures.

The preceding factors, as well as numerous others, may dictate modifications in the epoxy-resin system.   Care should be taken that the requisite modifications do not too greatly degrade the desirable properties.   As indicated in Chap. 6, most modifications designed to accommodate a specific parameter have the effect of reducing the values for the over-all system.

Frequently it is necessary to accommodate a specific parameter by improved production techniques.   For example, if an aluminum case is potted for operations in the 0 to 125°C range and the extreme conditions are encountered, where the aluminum is suddenly raised to the upper

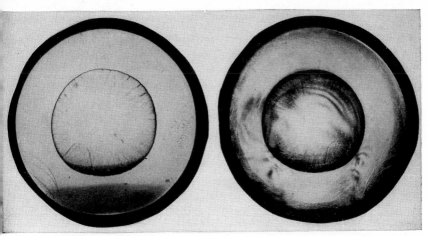

Spherical casting of epoxy resin containing stress cleavage in center, illustrating effect of shrinkage and compressive forces on center as casting is cooled suddenly prior to complete cure and dissipation of exothermic heat.   Polaroid photograph reveals actual stress patterns.   (The Epoxylite Corporation.)

temperature limit (because of the power requirements) and the surface of the potting compound is reduced to the minimum design condition (because of altitude), stresses on the order of 3,000 to 5,000 psi will be established in the plastic.   These stresses, coupled with residual stresses in the potting compound caused by shrinkage and exothermic peaks during cure (8-8), will be sufficient to cause failure.   Since the operating temperatures preclude flexibilized compounds, it will be necessary to design the production techniques in such a fashion so as to minimize residual stresses.

PRODUCTION TECHNIQUES

Although many production difficulties can be eliminated by the proper selection of the resin–curing agent system, frequently an uncompromising decision against optimum handling characteristics must be made.   Production techniques must then accommodate the specific compound.

Installation of continuous mixing equipment may be required. Efficient ovens or cooling devices may be necessary to reduce exothermic peaks. Physical means of eliminating the irritation potential of the curing agent must be devised, etc. Other examples will become apparent from the discussion. In short, consideration must often be given to designing the production process to the compound, rather than the reverse. The factors of general interest in most epoxy formulations are presented in Chap. 12, together with specific handling recommendations. Chapter 10 presents a general discussion of laminates, the use of which should be considered alternatively to casting and encapsulation where extremely high structural strengths are required. Chapter 9 discusses adhesives and surface preparations, factors which may require consideration in some potting, encapsulating, and sealing operations.

The following specific considerations will be discussed in this section: the mold, application techniques, the casting of large or complex shapes, and the use of high filler loading volumes.

The Mold

Where the specific configuration of the molded unit is of secondary importance, the mold should be designed with a slight draft or taper and have a nearly uniform cross section. The taper will facilitate release, and the nearly uniform cross section will minimize stresses during cure. The interior surface of the mold should be smooth and free of rough edges. If the specific cast configuration is complex and contains undercuts, it may be necessary to employ a two-piece mold; but consideration should be given to one-piece molds made from flexible plastisols or, for more or less custom runs, to inexpensive expendable molds.

Encapsulating small transformer in epoxy resin using flexible vinyl plastisol mold. (*Bakelite* Co.)

Molds may be made from any convenient material possessing the required dimensional stability. Teflon or Teflon-coated molds are particularly convenient for longer production runs. However, in some situations, the epoxy may pull the Teflon away. Hence, a release agent is often used on the Teflon to fill the pores of the sintered Teflon coating.

Because of the excellent adhesion of the epoxies to most materials and the low shrinkage during cure, integral molds may be employed when they are conveniently present or sufficiently inexpensive. For certain applications, the integral mold can be formed by the use of a cure-in-place epoxy-based paste.

Exterior molds, if not coated with a permanent releasing film, should be cleaned with a solvent (or, if slightly porous, filled) and then coated with a suitable releasing agent. The mold may be heated to expedite drying of the release agent, to facilitate penetration of the resin, and/or to accelerate cure.

Application Techniques

Excluding the simple application of an epoxy paste by spatula, four distinct application techniques may be employed in forming the systems

Tough epoxy drop-hammer dies withstand repeated impact and shock of forming sheets of aluminum, annealed steel, or stainless steel. (*Bakelite* Co.)

under discussion: bench casting, vacuum impregnation, pressure impregnation, and open-mold or dip casting.

Bench Casting. Bench casting is defined as pouring or casting in the open air under workshop conditions. It is relatively difficult for inexperienced personnel to obtain a bubble-free casting by bench techniques, using even a moderately low-viscosity compound. Bubbles are entrapped in the resin during mixing of the curing agent and the filler; more are incorporated during the pouring operation. The entrapped bubbles can be virtually eliminated by a combination of several techniques. Stirring should be conducted in such a manner as to hold the bubbles to a minimum. The catalyzed system may then be allowed to stand at room temperature, pot life permitting, until the bubbles have escaped. Where practical, warming the catalyzed mixture will expedite bubble release, as will drawing a vacuum on it. Once the bubbles have been allowed to escape to the degree practical, the compound should then be poured slowly and carefully into the mold. The cast system should immediately be exposed to initial cure temperature. If this temperature is higher than ambient, there will be a progressive reduction in viscosity, which will facilitate escape of the bubbles, until crosslinking is initiated and the trend reversed. Care should be taken, however, that the initial cure temperature is not great enough to volatilize any of the components in the resin system.

The bench-casting technique need not be complex. For example, in tooling applications, it is often possible to cast jigs for compound-angle

Epoxy die-face model cast from aluminum master.   Die-face model is used in duplicator machine to reproduce the design in steel.   (*Bakelite* Co.)

tooling by preparing a wooden box mold (with caulked seams), positioning the inserts and guides on a prototype part, then filling the surrounding cavity with coarse gravel. The low-viscosity catalyzed resin mix is then poured over the gravel, which it penetrates readily, and allowed to harden at ambient. Once the mold is stripped, the jig is ready for service.

Vacuum Casting. Vacuum techniques are particularly useful for critical potting applications and may, on occasion, be employed in connection with pressure impregnation.

In determining the degree of vacuum to employ, consideration should be given to the difficulty of the filling operation and to the vapor pressures of the resin-system components. Some reactive diluents, for instance, can be pulled off rather easily, and care must always be taken to avoid volatilizing the curing agent. Moisture traps should be provided in the ines to catch any released material; otherwise, it may polymerize in the pump or vacuum condenser.   When lower vacuums provide satisfactory fill, they should be used.   If high vacuums are necessary, redesign of the resin system may be required to eliminate high-vapor-pressure elements.

It is sometimes also necessary to give consideration to the pretreatment of the foreign components involved.   If considerable moisture is present in the system to be potted, it should be driven off by baking or vacuuming just prior to the potting operation.   If pressure-sensitive devices, such as vacuum tubes, are involved, they may be encapsulated in advance with flexible sheaths to prevent cracking during cure.   If the adhesion to some components is likely to be critical, these should be pretreated.   In some instances, redesign of the foreign system may be necessary to eliminate critical wire coatings, etc., susceptible to the solvent action of the catalyzed resin mix.

Where possible, the resin should be poured under vacuum.   This permits the removal of entrapped air in the resin system and moisture and entrapped air in the component.

If the resin is poured at room pressure and the vacuum pulled subsequently, foaming, bubbling, and frothing will occur at lower pressures, and the volume will expand considerably.   This expanded volume must be accommodated by an ullage reservoir.   For optimum results, all foaming, frothing, and bubbling should cease before the component is returned to ambient pressure.   In actual practice, the vacuum is usually held until all foaming and frothing cease, then slowly increased until bubbling ends, then brought rapidly to ambient pressure.   If foaming and frothing are excessive, too much moisture and entrapped gases are present in the foreign component.   If bubbling is excessive, too much material is being volatilized.

Several vacuum cycles may be employed to enhance the fill.   It is not advisable, however, to permit the resin to cure while vacuum is being applied, since higher exotherms may volatilize the curing agent; and cycling should not be continued after viscosity begins to increase.

Pressure Casting.   Pressure impregnation may be employed in connection with vacuum potting techniques by pressurizing the chamber after the potted system has undergone the high-vacuum cycle.   Pressures of 50 to 100 psi result in extremely dense fill and thorough impregnation.

With electrical coils and similar small components, centrifugal action may be employed to obtain the requisite pressure.   The centrifugal apparatus consists essentially of a motor, vertical shaft, chamber, and spinner assembly.   The spinner assembly is composed of spinner arms radiating from a central core and attached at the opposite ends to pivoted molds.   The molds are filled, and the assembly is spun rapidly.   With such equipment, excellent results can be obtained with room-temperature curing agents. The spinner assembly may be preheated, the resin added, and the assembly spun throughout cure. Spin rates providing pressures on the order of 1,000 psi will form pressure heads that will eliminate foaming and suppress any tendency for the curing agent to volatilize. The resultant castings will be dense, void free, and, in all probability, superior to those obtained by vacuum impregnation (8-9, 8-10).

For some casting, encapsulation, and potting applications, the resin mix may be injected under pressure while the mold remains at ambient pressure.

Powders and preforms may be used with matched mold pressure forming techniques. In this instance, the mold is heated to fluidize the resin until all interstices are filled and the pressure is maintained during the initial stage of cure. Pressure-forming techniques, however, are more common to fabrication with thermoplastic resins.

Open-mold or Dip Casting. This technique consists in dipping the item to be sealed into a catalyzed resin mix and then removing it. The dip compound is formulated for controlled runoff, and the curing agent must, in production situations, provide long pot life.

Casting of Large or Complex Shapes

When casting larger volumes, unless high filler loading volumes are used, there is danger of encountering cracking and runaway exotherms. Temperature variations throughout the mass and localized shrinkage will establish excessive stresses and strains during cure. High exotherms will volatilize the curing agent and/or modifiers to result in entrapped bubbles. Acid anhydride curing agents or epoxy-phenolic blends should be considered for larger castings, because of their lower exotherms. Efficient ovens should be employed during cure. Fillers and flexibilizers should be considered to reduce critical parameters. In many cases, the most satisfactory solution will be stage casting, by which method the larger casting is formed of layers of compound, each cured, or at least gelled, before the next is added.* In encapsulation and sealing work, care should be exercised to maintain a reasonably constant resin build-up throughout the system. Even moderate temperature cycling will impose an excessive stress concentration on thin integral build-ups of resin, and cracking is likely to occur.

The stresses and strains established during the cure of complex castings

* Using sand at a high loading volume, Shell Chemical personnel successfully cast a 1,400-lb batch of catalyzed resin in a bath tub. Ciba personnel in Europe have made 2,000-lb castings in transformers.

will frequently result in cracking.   These can be offset by the incorporation of flexibilizers.

Casting High Loading Volumes of Filler

For some applications, it is possible to employ high loading volumes of filler without increasing the viscosity of the resin compound.   This is very useful when potting configurations that require high internal impregnation but a highly filled surface sheath.   Rather than perform the operation in two steps, it is possible to surround the unit with a coarse dry filler and subsequently vacuum-pressure impregnate the construction with an unfilled resin.

TYPICAL FORMULATIONS

Consideration of the material presented in the preceding chapters will assist in the formulation of compounds for casting, potting, encapsulation, and sealing.   The following formulations are suggested as examples to illustrate the nature of the modifications that may be involved.   The resin, in all cases, is the commercial diglycidyl ether of bisphenol A.

Low-temperature Potting Compound
100 parts 0.005-in. diam glass beads
18 parts epoxy resin
2 parts butyl glycidyl ether
2 parts diethylamino propylamine

Flame-resistant Potting Compound
100 parts epoxy resin
90 parts chlorendic anhydride

Potting Compound for Miniaturized Circuits
100 parts epoxy resin
10 parts allyl glycidyl ether
10 parts polysulfide
10 parts tridimethyl amino methyl phenol

Low-viscosity Potting Compound
100 parts epoxy resin
50 parts calcium carbonate
80 parts hexahydrophthalic anhydride
1 part benzyldimethylamine

Low-exotherm Potting Compound
100 parts epoxy resin
100 parts silica
30 parts phthalic anhydride

Flexible Potting Compound
100 parts epoxy resin
50 parts polysulfide
10 parts triethylene tetramine

Electrical Encapsulating Compound
100 parts epoxy resin
5 parts uncompressed silica
75 parts clay
12 parts diethylene triamine

Machinable Compound
100 parts epoxy resin
10 parts allyl glycidyl ether
200 parts powdered aluminum
11 parts diethylene triamine

High-thermal-conductivity Casting Compound
100 parts epoxy resin
100 parts silica
14 parts metaphenylene diamine

Low-exotherm Casting Compound
100 parts epoxy resin
80 parts powdered aluminum
70 parts pumice
25 parts polysulfide
10 parts dimethylamino methyl phenol

These formulas, of course, represent only a few of the many thousands possible and should not be considered optimum. They are given merely to indicate, in a general way, the type of formulations employed commercially.

LIGHTWEIGHT FOAMS

Various epoxy-resin formulations are suitable for use in foaming applications to provide rigid structures with good insulating properties but with significantly reduced weights. The excellent adhesive properties of the epoxies make them particularly useful for foam-in-place applications, thus obviating the slow and costly operation of machining parts from prefoamed solids or of constructing presized sandwich laminates.

The foams find use as lightweight potting compounds for electrical equipment and as structural potting compounds for reinforcing load-bearing sections of honeycomb members. The foams may be used as structural supports, in which case they frequently see end service in conjunction with a laminate in a sandwich construction. Lightweight foamed castings can be employed in special applications, such as rifle stocks, etc., where the weight saving is particularly advantageous.

The foams may be formed by one of two methods: by chemical action during cure or by the incorporation of prefoamed fillers into the liquid system.

Chemical Foams

Each shape, size, and density of chemical foam poses a different problem of heat dissipation, cure rate, and optimum ratios of the various

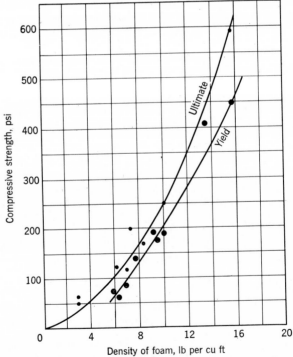

FIG. 8-7. Relation of compressive strength to density of epoxy foam (3-7).

reactants. Sufficient empirical evidence is available, however, to make the application of commercial significance.

Chemical foams are formed during cure by the action of the curing agent involved or of a special material (called blowing agent) incorporated to liberate gases which perform the foaming reaction.

In the first case, aconitic acid, in connection with a second acid, is reported (5-2) to provide rigid foams yielding a density of about 13 lb per

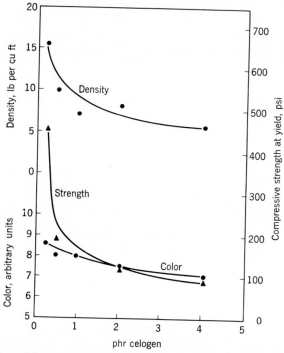

FIG. 8-8. Effect of foaming agent concentration on properties of epoxy foam (3-7).

cubic foot, the exact density being capable of regulation by varying the ratio of the two curing agents employed. Temperatures between 150 and 200°C are required, however, to produce the foaming reaction. At these temperatures, the volume expands rapidly to produce a uniform cellular structure.

More commonly, ammonium carbonate or similar material is employed as a blowing agent. The blowing agent is used in the resin mix in amounts on the order of 2 phr. A typical proprietary commercial materials is Celogen.*

Primary aliphatic amines are employed as curing agents, the less

* Naugatuck Chemical, a Division of U.S. Rubber Co.

reactive amines being preferred for larger volumes of foam.   A wetting agent, such as Tween 20,* is used in low concentration to provide for a fine and uniform dispersion of the gas bubbles.   A solvent is used to dilute the resin and control the foaming process by absorbing excessive heats of reaction.   Either liquid or solid epoxy resins may be employed, since the reaction is conducted at elevated temperature.

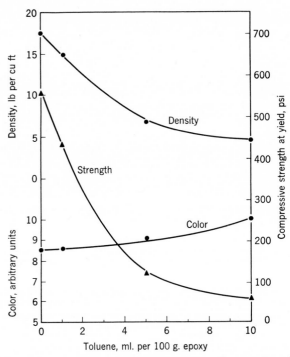

FIG. 8-9. Effect of toluene content on properties of epoxy foam (3-7).

A typical foaming formulation is given in the accompanying table (3-7):

Epoxy resin, 450 molecular weight...........	100 grams
Celogen..................................	2 grams
Tween 20...............................	2 drops
Toluene.................................	5 grams
Diethylene triamine......................	6 grams

The mixing procedure for this formulation requires that the resin be heated to 110°C and added to the mixture of wetting agent, blowing agent, and solvent.   After thorough mixing is achieved, the curing agent is quickly stirred in.   If approximately 100 grams of mixture is involved, the material will initiate foaming in about 30 seconds, and the preceding

* Atlas Powder Co.

formulation will provide a foam having a density of approximately 7 lb per cubic foot. Postcure will improve the properties of the foamed solid, with temperatures on the order of 75 to 100°C being employed for 1 to 2 hours. This postcure should be initiated before the foam has been allowed to cool, since the low thermal conductivity of the solid makes it slow to reheat, especially at the inner portions of thick sections.

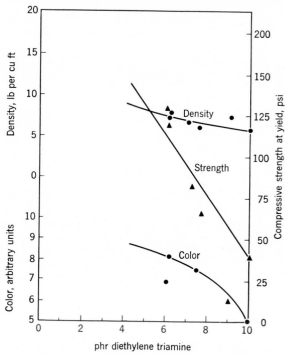

FIG. 8-10. Effect of curing agent percentage on properties of epoxy foam (3-7).

The density of the foam may be determined by regulating the parameters involved, and the specific ultimate properties will be in part a function of the density. Figure 8-7 expresses this relationship in terms of compressive strength.

A study (3-7) of the effect of varying blowing agents, curing agent concentration, solvent content, initial temperature, and type of epoxy resin indicates that all these variables have a strong influence on the density and strength of the foam produced.

The effect of variations in the amount of blowing agent, solvent-diluent content, curing agent, and initial temperature upon the strength and color of the ultimate foam is presented in Figs. 8-8 to 8-11. The effect of various blowing agents on properties is presented in Table

3-3.   The data, however, are of a preliminary nature, and considerably improved epoxy foams may be achieved.

From these illustrations, it is seen that the concentration of curing agent is critical and that less than stoichiometric amounts provide superior products in terms of strength and color.   The minimum amount of diethylene triamine required to achieve a cured system is 6 phr.

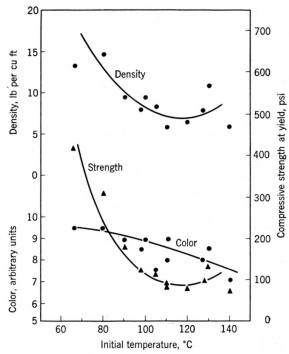

FIG. 8-11. Effect of initial temperature on properties of epoxy foam (3-7).

Increasing this percentage only serves to reduce the properties of the ultimate composition, although it does not affect the density of the product.   Density and strength are inversely proportional to the amount of blowing agent and solvent employed.   The effect of progressively greater initial temperatures justifies the mixing temperature of 110°C for the particular formulation just given.   At higher temperatures, scorching of the foam is more likely to occur.

Syntactic Foams

The second method for producing foamed epoxies involves the utilization of microscopically small hollow spheres made of a phenolic resin and filled with nitrogen gas. Although these spheres might be considered as a filler, they impart to the cured system properties very similar to those obtainable with a chemical foam.

The spheres were originally developed to provide a floating barrier for minimizing oil-evaporation losses from cone-roof storage tanks. The inherent insulating properties of the spheres, coupled with their size (the

TABLE 8-3. Effect of Different Foaming Agents upon Properties of Cured Foam (3-7)

Formulation:
Epoxy resin, molecular weight 450 . . . . 100 grams
Toluene. . . . . 5 grams
Tween 20. . . . . 2 drops
Diethylene triamine. . . . . 6 grams

Foaming agent	Proportion foamant, phr	Final temp., °C	Density, lb/cu ft	Compressive strength, psi	
				Ult	At yield
Ammonium carbonate.	1	185	7.5	187	167
Ammonium carbonate.	2	. . .	7.5	159	110
Celogen.	1	175	8.5	131	118
Di-nitroso pentamethylene tetramine.	1	195	10.7	289	289
Salicylic acid.	1	178	9.0	189	127
Diazo amino benzene.	1	182	9.5	180	148
Water.	10*	110	4.4	23	22
Water.	3	110	14.5	320	252
Phenolic foamant.	1	. . .	NF†		
Dihydrazine oxalate.	2	. . .	NF†		

* 8 phr diethylene triamine.
† No foam produced.

average diameter is 0.0013 in.), have led to their use in controlled foams and sandwich core structures.

The preparation of lightweight syntactic foams can be accomplished without considerable difficulty. Foams in density as low as 8 lb per cubic foot may be produced, depending on the concentration of the phenolic spheres. The upper limit of concentration is about 40 phr or no more than 70 per cent by volume.

In order to obtain sufficiently high loading volumes, automatic agitation is required, and fluidized resins are employed. The spheres are usually mixed into the resin catalyzed by an aliphatic amine, to receive the advantage of the further lowered viscosity. The spheres are added stepwise, and stirring is continued until the components are well dispersed. The resulting mixture is quite thixotropic. Curing temperatures should not exceed 100°C.

The principal advantage of the spheres as lightweight foams is the ease of cure and the simplicity of formulation. Consistent results can be achieved without concern for the more critical parameters of the chemical foaming formulations. Physical properties at lower densities are somewhat less than those of the chemical foams.

Puttylike in consistency, uncured syntactic foam can be molded to shape, troweled onto a suitable surface, and forced into cavities as well as pressed into sandwich cores.

CONCLUSION

A considerable number of factors are involved in the formulation of a specific casting, potting, or encapsulation compound. The ultimate system may be rigid, flexible, or porous and lightweight, to accommodate the specific service environment. The chemical resistance, the structural strength, and the electrical properties of such compounds are outstanding. In many cases, handling ease alone can overcome the somewhat higher cost of the epoxies as compared with more conventional thermosetting materials; in other cases, the superiority of the properties offsets the slightly increased material cost.

The underlying assumption of this chapter has been that the requirements for a specific application can be fulfilled in a straightforward manner. It is only necessary to select the specific curing agent on the basis of the operating temperature limits of the cured system and the handling characteristics convenient to the production situation and to modify the resultant system in easily determined directions to accommodate specific parameters.

It will be recognized that, while such a process may generally be adequate, there are numerous situations where the problem of formulation is vastly more complex, and suitable modifications, both from the chemical and engineering standpoint, will be required to meet critical specifications. The directions these modifications should take are indicated, in a general way, by the text as a unit rather than by any specific chapter.

References

8-1. Epoxy Patterns, *Modern Foundry*, July, 1955
8-2. Epoxy Potting Compounds, *Insulation*, May, 1956.
8-3. Rejda, Epoxy Resins Make Bid for Motor Insulation, *Power*, November, 1954.

8-4. Graves and Pizzino, Effects of High Humidity on Dielectric Properties of Casting Resins, *Electrical Manufacturing*, April, 1956.

8-5. Doctor and Franklin, Corrosion of Copper Wire by Resins, *Electronic Equipment*, July, 1956.

8-6. Manfield, Electrical Applications of Epoxide Resins, Particularly in the Electronics Industry, paper presented at Symposium of British Society of the Chemical Industry, April, 1956.

8-7. Lee, The Use of Epoxy Resins for Protecting Electrical Equipment in Severe Service Environments, paper presented at AIEE Rubber Group Symposium, Akron, Ohio, April, 1956.

8-8. Nichols, The Control of Chemical and Physical Factors in the Application of Casting Resins, Jet Propulsion Laboratory Report, 1955.

8-9. Firth, Centrifugal Method of Impregnating Coils, U.S. 2,695,856 (1954).

8-10. Firth, Electrical Potting and Encapsulation, paper presented at Symposium of Society of Plastics Industry, 1954.

9

ADHESIVES

Epoxy resins possess outstanding adhesive properties. The properties can be improved selectively by the addition of suitable fillers, diluents, and/or resinous modifiers, thus providing a class of adhesives of great versatility. Depending on the formulation, bonds may be either rigid or

Large transformer bushing (insulator) is mended with air-cure epoxy adhesive. High mechanical and adhesive strengths, high arc resistance, and quick-setting characteristics make such on-the-job adhesive applications of significant importance. (*The Epoxylite Corporation.*)

flexible, and for certain applications, short-time temperatures above 300°C may be tolerated.

Investigations of a monomolecular layer of diglycidyl ether of bisphenol A and its homologs at an air-water interface have been conducted (9-1) in an effort to elucidate the nature of the adhesive bond. This work indicated that the adhesion to the aqueous subsurface seemed primarily dependent on the polar hydroxyls, with the unreacted epoxy groups exerting a strongly cohesive effect on the resin chains. It is further suggested (9-2) that the epoxy groups assist in adhesion to solid surfaces.

The better adhesion obtained with higher-weight polymers (containing initial hydroxyl groups) is additionally enhanced by the cohesive forces attributable to the intertwining of the chain molecules. However, in actual practice, optimum adhesion is often obtained with mixed polymers, containing both low- and higher-weight species, perhaps because of the better over-all wetting action achieved with the reduction in viscosity. Thorough chemical cleaning of the bonding surfaces appears to eliminate the need for mechanical roughening (9-12).

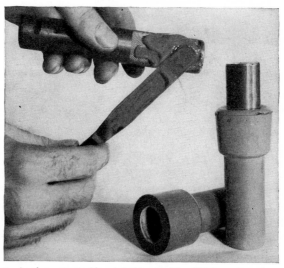

Bonding polyester insulator to steel brush-holder stud for 500-hp railroad motor. Slippage of either piece, prevented by the epoxy, could lead to vibration failure of the insulation or carbon brushes. (*The Epoxylite Corporation.*)

An additional important aspect of the epoxies which makes them excellent in adhesive systems is that curing is accomplished with very slight shrinkage, so that the established bond and the adhesive layer are relatively undisturbed during phase change.

Although the nature of the adhesive bond is little understood, the critical parameters can be established empirically, and within these limits, it is possible to vary formulations quite widely.

ADHESIVE SYSTEMS

The majority of the epoxy-adhesive systems are of the two-container type and may be applied either as liquids or as hot melts. However, other systems may be used, as listed below:

1. The latent curing agents—as discussed in Chap. 4—give bonds of good adhesive strength and permit the formulation of extremely convenient one-container 100 per cent solids systems, where the curing temperatures can be accommodated.

2. One-container adhesive solutions may be formulated with high-weight epoxy resins, as discussed in Chap. 11. The retained solvents in the adhesive layer will, however, blister in the glue line unless handled correctly, and the reduction in bond strengths may be as high as 15 per cent, when compared with the strengths obtained with a similar hot-melt system.

3. Both supported and unsupported tapes may be employed. The tapes virtually eliminate handling difficulties and provide highly reproducible results in production situations. Tape formulations, however, have limited shelf lives at room temperature and may require storage under refrigeration.

4. One-container adhesive powders are available and prove useful for a limited amount of adhesive work, such as bonding larger areas and in special production situations.

5. Solid heat-flowing adhesive solders are useful for a number of structural applications and provide economical bonded joints.

6. Solid two-part adhesive systems may be formulated for special applications. This formulation involves the preparation of a high-weight resin adduct curing agent (see Chap. 3) soluble in acetone. This is applied in solution coating to one bonding surface. A solution coating of a higher-molecular-weight homolog of diglycidyl ether of bisphenol A is applied to the second bonding surface. The prepared system is indefinitely stable at room temperature, but if the two layers are joined under heat and pressure, good bonds may be obtained (9-3).

GENERAL DISCUSSION

The significant variables to be considered in the formulation and application of an epoxy adhesive system are:

Curing Agent. Curing agents should be selected on the basis of over-all requirements; and, as is the case when formulating casting compounds, handling convenience may be a strong factor in the ultimate selection. If two-container systems are employed, the curing agent providing the greatest reduction in viscosity—other things equal—is frequently preferred. Differences that exist between variously cured systems will, however, be reflected to a greater or less extent in the actual performance of the adhesive in a specific application. If bond strengths are critical, an extensive evaluation of curing agents should be considered. Recommended curing agents are given below.

Degree of Cure. Room-temperature curing agents provide satisfactory adhesives for metal-to-metal bonding and related applications, although the adhesion can be increased considerably by postcuring at temperatures not exceeding 120°C. When larger loading volumes of fillers are employed (100 phr and above), a room-temperature cure of about 6 days or more may be required to obtain maximum shear strengths, with heat and chemical resistance increasing even more slowly. When heat cures are used, the initial phase should be at lower temperatures, in order to minimize shrinkage, and the cure should then be continued at high temperatures until crosslinking is virtually complete.

Glue-line Regulation. The epoxy resins appear to be somewhat unique in that the thickness of the glue line can be varied from 1 to 12 mils, although closer regulation may be required for more complex joints. For supported tapes, thicknesses up to 30 mils may be used, depending on the nature of the bond. The production tooling may, to a very considerable degree, dictate the gage for a specific application.

Curing Pressures. Contact pressure is usually adequate for unsupported adhesives. Pressures up to 100 psi may be employed with supported tapes, although the usual range is from less than 5 to about 50 psi. In all cases, pressure should be sufficient to assure complete wetting and even distribution of the adhesive over the bonding surface but not high enough to starve the glue line. The selected pressure should be maintained throughout the initial phase of the cure.

Materials to Be Bonded. Epoxy-based adhesives will give excellent bonds to steel, aluminum, brass, copper, and most other metals; to most thermosetting plastics (phenolics, alkyds, epoxies) and most thermoplastics (vinyl, butyrates, styrenes, etc.), though here formulation may become increasingly critical; and to glass, wood, concrete, paper, cloth, etc. The exact materials will, in many cases, dictate the formulation, as discussed later.

Surface Preparation. For many applications, thorough surface degreasing, with solvents, wire brushing, or sandblasting, will provide satisfactory bonds. However, when higher adhesive strengths are required, attention should be given to chemical means of surface preparation. Careful preparation has resulted in up to a fourfold increase in bond strengths. The following treatments may be recommended. Where appropriate, they are followed by a neutralizing rinse and drying. In some cases, however, it may be necessary to apply a primer coat to the adherends if inservice moisture and vibration are severe.

Steel. Sandblast with clean grease-free sand or wire brush, and degrease with a 10 per cent solution of sodium metasilicate for 10 minutes at 60°C.

Stainless Steel. Dip for 10 minutes at 65°C in the following cleaning solution, parts by weight:

Concentrated hydrochloric acid	50 parts
30% hydrogen peroxide	2 parts
Formalin solution	10 parts
Water	45 parts

Copper Alloys. Etch for 1 to 2 minutes at room temperature in the following solution, parts by volume:

42% ferric chloride	15 parts
Concentrated nitric acid	30 parts
Water	197 parts

Titanium Alloys. Dip for 20 minutes at 50°C in the following solution, parts by volume:

Concentrated nitric acid	9 parts
50% hydrofluoric acid	1 part
Water	30 parts

This treatment will provide increased bond strength, but it does not appear to be optimum.

Glass and Aluminum. Dip for 10 minutes at 70°C in the following solution, parts by weight:

Sodium dichromate	66 parts
96% sulfuric acid	666 parts
Water	1,000 parts

Rubber. Immerse for 10 ($\pm$5) minutes at room temperature in concentrated sulfuric acid, or apply a sulfuric acid paste made by adding barytes. Bonding strengths can frequently be improved by flexing the rubber to produce tiny surface cracks.

Plastics. Sanding, buffing, or flame treatment is recommended in some cases.

Wood. Plane the surface for maximum bond.

Porous Surfaces. Porous surfaces, such as concrete, do not require special treatment, but sufficient adhesive should be used to allow for absorption.

Selection of Resin. Either aromatic- or aliphatic-based epoxy resins may be used for adhesive formulations. In a 100 per cent solids system, a blend of a low-viscosity liquid resin with higher-weight species will frequently improve bond strength.

Selection of Modifiers. Modifications are usually designed to improve selected properties, and no single optimum compound can be given. A detailed discussion and specific formulations are given subsequently.

Application Techniques. Depending on the system and the situation, the adhesive may be applied to the bonding surfaces by tapes or by dipping, brushing, rolling, or spraying. The latter technique appears to provide slightly better bonds, but for practical purposes, the application method can be dictated by convenience. Tapes can be prepared as discussed in Chap. 10. If the tape adhesive is in B stage (i.e., the tape is dry), the initial curing cycle should be sufficiently high to cause flow and ensure wetting. When employing liquid 100 per cent solids systems, each surface to be bonded should be coated with adhesive and the surfaces joined immediately. If the layers are allowed to stand for an appreciable time before joining, some of the curing agent may evaporate to weaken the ultimate strength of the bond. On the other hand, with liquid solvent systems, the optimum results are obtained by allowing time for the solvents to escape prior to joining the surfaces; in all such cases, the solvents must be driven off as thoroughly as possible. Once the bonding surfaces have been joined, they should not be disturbed until cure has progressed well beyond the gel stage. A minimum of handling is recommended, and where possible, clamps should be employed to preserve the bond and alignment.

Test Procedures. The properties of adhesives are reported in terms of shear strength in pounds per square inch and in peel strength in pounds per linear inch. Actual test procedures are performed on small-area standard samples and may vary in detail from laboratory to laboratory, but the results are comparable. A lap-shear test procedure is discussed in Specification MIL-A-8331, and a description of peel-test procedure can be found in ASTM Method D-90-49. A stripping-test procedure involving curing the adhesive in contact with metal foil and subsequently stripping the foil from the resin is discussed in Ref. 9-9. Reference 9-10 outlines a technique for correlating sonic energy absorption to bond quality to permit nondestructive testing. Other tests are conducted in accordance with the procedures outlined in Chap. 2.

SELECTIVE IMPROVEMENT OF CHARACTERISTICS

The commercial epoxy resins, used with an appropriate curing agent, may provide a satisfactory rigid adhesive without modification. However, the handling of such a compound is complicated by the tendency of the resin to flow, particularly during cure, with resultant irregularities in the glue line and starved areas on the bonding surface. The temperature range is limited; the coefficient of thermal expansion is high; the viscosity (depending on the resin and/or the curing agent) may not be sufficiently low to provide complete wetting action; shrinkage rates, while quite low, may be too high for many applications; and peel strengths are poor. These characteristics can be improved selectively.

Controlling Flow. Flow characteristics may be regulated by the incorporation of fillers, by the use of tapes, or by the careful regulation of the curing cycle. If required, thixotropic pastes may be formulated that will not flow during cure and that are useful for bonding non-close-fitting joints.

Extending Temperature Ranges. Flexibilizers improve low-temperature bond strengths to $-50°C$ and for some applications provide satisfactory performance at considerably lower temperatures. They appear to offer no immediate promise for improving performance at temperatures much above 100°C because of the loss of strength of such modified resins at these temperatures.

Phenolic resins, in higher loading volumes, have been used with limited success in epoxy adhesives for operations in the 250°C range. Considerable effort is being directed toward extending the upper operating temperature limits to even higher values. Three approaches are being followed to achieve adhesives for higher-temperature operations: development of more satisfactory resinous modifiers, development of better curing agents, and synthesis of epoxy resins with improved temperature resistance. For intermediate-range work, "bodying" resins with phenolics and anhydrides has been suggested, but little work has been accomplished.

Even below 250°C, the upper temperature limit is critical for many compounds. With systems suitable for operation in the 150 to 200°C range, there is usually a moderate increase in bond strength as temperature rises; but thereafter, the bond strength decreases with further temperature increase to a drop-off point beyond which loss of properties is rapid. Since a single batch of adhesive for a single application will give drop-off strengths that vary over a 5 to 10°C range, the formulator should allow a safety margin in design work.

Because the high (compared to metals) coefficient of thermal expansion of the unmodified epoxy resins does much to disrupt the adhesive bond with changes in temperature, reductions in this value have the effect of extending the upper operating temperature limit.

Lowering the Coefficient of Thermal Expansion. Thorough cure will result in some decrease in the coefficient of thermal expansion, but since higher temperatures are required to achieve it, the method is somewhat self-defeating.   Fillers, as discussed in Chap. 6, are most effective in reducing the value.   Ideally, the coefficient of thermal expansion should be lowered to match that of the material being bonded (or, in the case of like-on-unlike bonds, to a value between the two materials).   In practice, however, it is often not possible to employ a sufficiently large loading volume.   High loading volumes increase viscosity to the point where thin, regular glue lines cannot easily be obtained and in other ways tend to degrade, rather than improve, the bond.   For some applications and some fillers, loading volumes up to 200 phr may be employed, but optimum shear-strength values are usually obtained with lesser amounts. Suggested loading volumes for some good adhesive fillers are mica, 14 phr; short-fiber asbestos, 25 phr; aluminum oxide, 50 phr; talc, 80 phr; and zinc dust, 100 phr.   Some fillers promote oxidative degradation at elevated temperatures (9-13), and these, of course, should be avoided.

When temperature limits permit, it is useful to compensate for differentials in the coefficient of thermal expansion by the use of flexibilizers to absorb the internal stresses during thermal cycling.   For short periods at higher temperatures, supported tapes will somewhat improve performance by more uniform distribution of stresses.

Improving Wetting Action.   Wetting action can be improved by warming the adhesive and/or by the incorporation of reactive or nonreactive diluents into the system.   However, when a low coefficient of thermal expansion is critical, diluents should be avoided.   In production situations with two-component systems, there will be a progressive increase in viscosity, which may alter reproducibility of the optimum bond; this can be avoided by mixing small quantities at a time or using automatic blending equipment.

Reducing Shrinkage.   Not only are fillers useful for controlling flow and for reducing the coefficient of thermal expansion to permit substantial retention of the bond up to the temperature limit of the particular compound, but also, by bulk displacement, they serve to reduce the rate of shrinkage.   Their total effect is impressive.   Field and laboratory data indicate that fillers will improve operational bond strengths by 50 to 100 per cent.   Figures 9-1 and 9-2 indicate the effect of fillers on an adhesive system cured with DMP-30.

Modifying Other Properties.   The mechanical and electrical properties and the chemical resistance of the adhesive systems are not specifically cited in this chapter.   Such data for a variety of similar compounds are provided elsewhere in the text.   One point, however, deserves general comment.   The excellent chemical resistance of the epoxies is reflected in the performance of most adhesive systems.   For example, with a typical formulation for bonding 24 ST aluminum, a shear strength of optimum cure at room temperature will be approximately 2,300 psi.   This value may even increase somewhat after 30-day immersion in tap water, salt water, alcohol, hydraulic oil, etc.   Stronger solvents will bring about some decrease in performance, with, for example, shear strengths dropping to 1,400 psi after 30 days immersion in methyl ethyl ketone.

Some fillers and modifiers will affect chemical resistance and electrical properties adversely.   Where a particular nonadhesive property is impor-

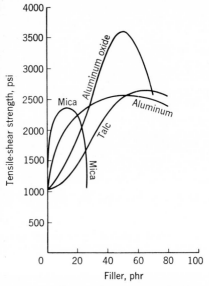

FIG. 9-1. Effect of fillers on tensile shear strength of epoxy adhesive formulation at room temperature (9-8).

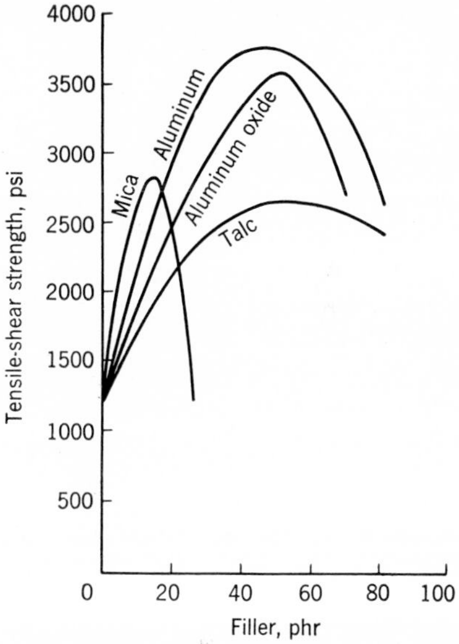

FIG. 9-2. Effect of fillers on tensile-shear strength of epoxy adhesive formulation at 57°C (9-8).

tant, a compound designed also to accommodate it may provide less than the optimum in shear strength but be best suited for the application.

APPLICATIONS

Since it is possible to obtain shear strengths of over 12,000 psi on steel-to-steel bonds, the epoxy adhesives are excellent for structural work.   In many cases, they are superior, in terms of over-all strength, fatigue resistance, and handling characteristics, to established metal-joining methods such as bolts and welds.

In the aircraft industry, where weight saving is at a premium and where lightweight hard-to-bond materials are used extensively, the epoxy adhesives are extremely popular.   Providing bond strengths above

8,000 psi on aluminum-to-aluminum bonds, an epoxy system offers increased strength and reliability over that obtained with conventional solders. Not only is the adhesion excellent for aircraft "sandwich" constructions (9-11), but the flow characteristics enable the formation of the necessary fillets at the juncture of the core-cell edges and the facing material. One aircraft company, for instance, produced over 40,000 epoxy-bonded sandwich parts in 4 years.

With the epoxy adhesives, such multiple advantages are not uncommon. For instance, one adhesive formulation is used in a playback cartridge to bond polyester film, aluminum, mu-metal, sintered iron, alloyed magnets, plastic insulated copper wire, rubber, and silver-plated brass. By the time the assembly of these components is completed, the applied adhesive has thickened sufficiently to permit the anchoring of a diamond stylus arm for the final operation. Or again, an epoxy adhesive system can be used to bond centrifugal brake linings with greater convenience than can rivets, and since the rivets (which protrude halfway down toward the brake drum) are eliminated, the lining can be worn down 100 per cent and still will not score the drum on failure.

FORMULATION

There are hundreds of adhesive formulations in use by industry. For many general-purpose applications—metal-to-metal, wood-to-glass, phenolic-to-acrylic—where service environments are not unusual and temperatures do not vary markedly from normal ambient, the selection of the adhesive formulation can be based on cost and convenience.

For many jobs, special compounds, which use commercial recommendations merely as starting points, are necessary; in some cases, their design may require considerable developmental effort.

For convenience, the epoxy adhesives may be considered to fall into either the flexible or rigid category. Both flexible and rigid materials are suitable for the various adhesive systems discussed previously, although, to some extent, the particular system selected will dictate the range of possible properties, with, in general, the two-container systems being more versatile.

Flexible Systems

Although severely limited by higher temperatures, the flexible systems (as discussed in Chap. 7) considerably extend the versatility of the epoxies as adhesives and permit bonding to a number of hard-to-bond materials, such as rubber and flexibilized plastics. For rigid surfaces, the increased flexibility permits stable phase changes during cure, with the consequent improvement of the ultimate bond, and by absorbing a considerable amount of strain and stresses improves the impact resistance and moderates the effects of varying rates of thermal expansion in the adhesive joint. Peel strengths and low-temperature performance will be improved.

The flexible systems are normally two container. With certain polymeric flexibilizers, solvent systems can be employed, particularly to lay down high-peel-strength primer coats, and flexible tapes can be made which are convenient in some production situations.

Monomeric plasticizers and flexibilizers are sometimes used, and proprietary grades are present in a number of commercial adhesives. These materials will produce some reduction in viscosity and a moderate improvement in bend strength, impact strength, and shear strength after thermal cycling. For instance, with rigid systems, there is a tendency for local ruptures in the adhesive bond to propagate, particularly under severe vibration. Where there is danger of such ruptures occurring, plasticizers such as polyvinyl formal, even in small percentages, will reduce the tendency to peel, probably by effecting a reduction in the secondary valence forces in the film.

But if major improvement is required, it will be necessary to consider the use of the larger percentages of polymeric flexibilizers. The polyamides will be treated as typical of the class, although other polyfunctional flexibilizers can be employed with excellent results.

Polyamides. The polyamides are excellent thermoplastic adhesives, since they contain polar amine, carboxyl, and amide groups, as discussed in Chap. 7. Some higher-weight species have even been suggested for bonding polyethylene. As flexibilizers which react directly with the epoxies, the polyamides become an integral part of the cured epoxy-resin system, thus distributing the stresses and impact loads throughout the adhesive bond.

The commercial polyamides all have relatively high viscosities. Even with the most fluid compound, the viscosity of the epoxy-polyamide blend will be somewhat high and the handling difficulties increased over those to be expected with less viscous polymers.

Viscosity can be lowered by preheating the two components but with a consequent reduction in pot life. Where highly fluid systems are required, it may be necessary to accommodate pot lives on the order of 20 minutes. When longer pot lives are necessary, some reduction of viscosity can be accomplished by the use of reactive diluents.

The polyamides will bring about improvements in adhesive strength and versatility. For instance, a typical polyamide with a fluidized epoxy resin and a filler loaded at 40 phr will give 200-lb bend strengths and 16-lb peel strengths on metal. The shear strength to aluminum after an impact of 80/in.-lb will be about four times that of a rigid system and only slightly below that of the pre-impact strength. The increased surface tack of the more viscous blends will assist in holding together the faying surfaces prior to cure. Shear strengths and other physical properties, however, will decline rapidly with increase in temperature. For instance, shear strengths on aluminum-to-aluminum surfaces will drop from 3,200 psi at 25°C to 1,500 psi at 82°C to 600 psi at 120°C.

The optimum ratio of polyamide to epoxy will depend on the specific application and the commercial resin employed. Higher percentages of polyamide will improve peel strengths; lower percentages will permit retention of bond at somewhat higher temperatures. The more flexible bond required, of course, the higher the amount of polyamide. An optimum formula might contain as much as 250 phr polyamide. For bonding rigid materials, as little as 40 phr may be used with good effect.

Cure cycles, likewise, will depend on application. Thorough cure can be obtained by baking 4 hours at 66°C, followed by $\frac{1}{2}$ hour at 120°C, although for many applications, long room-temperature cures will prove adequate. If production situations permit, cure temperatures of 150°C for 20 minutes may be used to give extremely fast cures without significantly reducing the adhesive properties.

Two typical epoxy-polyamide formulations are listed below.

Metal bonding formulation:

Polyamide (amine value 210–230) . . . . 50 parts
Epoxy resin (fluidized) . . . . 50 parts
Tabular alumina . . . . 20 parts

This formulation will give such typical shear-strength values at room temperature as:

3,200 psi on aluminum
2,800 psi on cold-roll steel
2,100 psi on Naval brass
1,400 psi on hard copper

Rubber bonding formulation:

Polyamide (amine value 210–230) . . . . 50 parts
Epoxy resin . . . . 50 parts

This formulation, cured for 48 hours at room temperature, will give shear strengths of 1,000 psi on aluminum-rubber bonds, with failures mostly in the rubber.

A careful determination of the various properties required of the particular flexible bond should be undertaken prior to initiating formulation work.

Rigid Systems

Rigid adhesive systems may, arbitrarily, be divided into room-temperature curing type and heat-curing type. The room-temperature curing type, while always a two-container system, is extremely useful for field and one-shot miscellaneous uses and frequently is very satisfactory for production situations, particularly when heat-sensitive materials are involved. In nearly all cases, however, ultimate properties will be improved by a postcure, and often postcure is recommended. The heat-curing type adhesive systems are used to a limited extent to provide higher bond strengths at elevated temperatures and for the formulation of more convenient adhesive systems.

Rigid systems will give excellent bonds to steel, rigid plastics, Fiberglas, aluminum, glass, bronze, copper, nickel, iron, wood, concrete, tin, etc., the exact shear strengths depending on the formulation and the surface preparation.

Room-temperature Curing Adhesives. Typical of the room-temperature curing agents useful in adhesive formulations are such cross-linking aliphatic amines as diethylene triamine, triethylamine, and diethylamino propylamine and catalytic amines such as tridimethyl amino methyl phenol. Strong organic acids, such as oxalic, are also reported to give good room-temperature shear strengths.

With room-temperature curing agents, the adhesive drop-off point will be between 100 to 120°C, the exact point depending considerably on the filler, the specific resin, and the length of cure. For instance diethylene triamine in a typical adhesive formulation will give a room-temperature shear strength on aluminum-to-aluminum bonds of over 2,000 psi after an 8-hour cure at 25°C. If, however, the temperature is rapidly increased to 85°C, the shear strength will be reduced to about 10 per cent of the room-temperature value. On the other hand, using triethylamine, about 8-days room-temperature cure will be required to establish comparable room-temperature shear strengths, but at 85°C the value will be somewhat increased over that at room temperature. Pot life for diethylene triamine will be in the neighborhood of 30 minutes; for triethylamine, 7 hours.

Table 9-1 presents a comparison of the effects of selected fillers on shear strengths when used with a typical room-temperature curing agent in the following formulation:

Mixed polymer/epoxy resin......... 100 parts
Allyl glycidyl ether............... 10 parts
Filler............................ 100 parts
Triethylamine.................... 12.5 parts
(The mixed-polymer epoxy resin contains 25 parts of a glycerol-based epoxy)

From an examination of this table, some idea can be gained of the importance of the use of fillers in adhesive formulations. It will be seen that the surfaces to be bonded as well as the operating temperatures will influence the selection of the optimum filler. The excellent performance of zinc dust appears to be caused by a degree of catalytic action. Table 9-2 and Figs. 9-1 and 9-2 present data indicating the importance of loading

TABLE 9-1. Effect of Fillers on Shear Strength of Adhesive Formulation (3-7)

Fillers, at 100 phr	Shear strength, psi					
	Phenolic linen laminates tested at				Aluminum blocks tested at	
	23°C	75°C	90°C	105°C	23°C	105°C
Aluminum powder............	2,790	.....	1,470	1,390		
Ignited Al₂O₃...............	4,600	1,360	1,195	530	1,650	1,150
Short-fiber asbestos*...........	1,740	1,270	580	510	2,180	3,910
Carbon black...............	2,000	555	980	910	2,000	1,170
Silica......................	2,840	1,600	1,250	830	1,530	600
Zinc dust..................	2,510	600	300	225	4,080	3,865

* 24 phr.

volumes with a specific filler. The formulation employed for this test series was

Mixed polymer/epoxy resin................ 100 parts
Tridimethyl amino methyl phenol............ 10 parts

It should be noted however, that the specific loading volume is somewhat dependent on the viscosity of the resin used and also will be a function of cure time, since higher loading volumes will appreciably lengthen cure time required for optimum adhesive values.

A good general-purpose room-temperature curing adhesive may be formulated with 100 parts of an epoxy resin having a molecular weight in the neighborhood of 400 with a talc filler loaded at 80 phr and with diethylene triamine as the curing agent. This material can be handled easily and will prove adequate for many industrial applications, where optimum shear strengths are not required.

Consideration of the curing agents listed earlier in the text will indicate the viscosities and pot lives to be expected from particular formulations, and the discussion of fillers in Chap. 6 will aid in the development of specific compounds.

Heat-curing Adhesive Formulations. With heat-curing adhesive formulations employing such curing agents as 4,4′ methylene dianiline and metaphenylene diamine, some increase in the upper operating temperatures will be realized, as indicated by the increased heat-distortion temperatures. For instance, metaphenylene diamine will give shear strengths over four times as great as diethylene triamine at temperatures

TABLE 9-2. Effect of Filler Loading Volumes on Shear Strength of Adhesive Formulation (9-8)

Filler	Amount, phr	Tensile shear strength, psi Aluminum blocks	
		23°C	60°C
None...................	...	1,030	1,205
Aluminum................	40	2,525	3,725
	60	2,525	3,580
	80	2,390	2,620
Aluminum oxide............	30	2,505	2,805
	50	3,615	3,600
	70	2,555	2,665
Mica.....................	6	2,210	1,810
	14	2,360	2,815
	26	1,055	1,210
Silica....................	40	600	610
	90	1,460	1,225
Talc.....................	30	1,870	2,360
	60	2,650	2,655
	80	2,520	2,400

of 105°C, with correspondingly better performance at somewhat higher ranges. However, aromatic diamines possess several disadvantages:

1. They provide increased shear strengths over an intermediate range, from 120 to 175°C. For the lower end of this range, room-temperature curing agents are, with the proper selection of fillers, satisfactory; and for the upper part of the range, there appears to be a limited number of industrial applications where such constant temperatures are encountered.

2. The curing agents as cited above provide poorer bond strength at room temperature and are sensitive to temperature cycling. The shrinkage rate is fairly high and cannot as easily be offset by the addition of fillers.

3. The increased brittleness, impact sensitivity, and low peel strengths cannot be offset by the use of flexibilizers for higher-temperature operations.

Acid anhydrides, in general, possess, for adhesive applications, the disadvantage of requiring a long cure cycle.

The largest potential commercial application of heat-curing adhesives appears to be in the formulation of one-container systems.

One-container systems dispersed in a solvent vehicle may employ curing agents of the normal room-temperature type, but for the purpose of this discussion, they are considered to be heat curing, since the adhesive system requires heat.   The ketones and esters, which are excellent solvents for the epoxies, are not, however, to be preferred in adhesive formulations, since they tend to remain in the glue lines during cure.   More highly volatile solvents are more satisfactory.   A solvent adhesive system,

TABLE 9-3. Properties of One-container Adhesive System (3-7)

Shear strength, psi:

At 25°C	3,000
At 82°C	3,600
At 120°C	2,200
At 150°C	1,100
At −58°C	3,100
At 25°C, after 200 hr, 25°C	3,000
At 82°C, after 200 hr, 82°C	2,700
Impact strength, ft-lb, at 25°C	21
Bend strength, lb, at 25°C	175

formulated as discussed in Chap. 11, will offer excellent bond strengths on most materials and will lend itself readily to convenient application techniques, such as spraying.   Such systems are useful for laminates, sandwich constructions, honeycombs, foams, etc., where surface areas are not too large or where the bond may be reasonably exposed to the atmosphere.

Typical of the curing agents employed in one-container hot melts and fluid systems is dicyandiamide.   This curing agent may be ground, along with the filler, into low-melting-point epoxy resins to provide a powdered adhesive that will cure readily at temperatures in the neighborhood of 175°C.   Likewise it may be milled into a fluid epoxy containing a filler to provide a long-shelf-life one-container fluid.   Dimethyl cyanamide, a toxic liquid, may be used at about 5 phr to provide stable one-container adhesive systems.

A typical proprietary one-container adhesive system, formulated from a liquid epoxy resin, a latent curing agent, and employing an asbestos filler, requires a cure schedule of 175°C for 90 minutes and provides a shelf life at room temperature in excess of 2 years.   The cured adhesive will provide bond strengths on 24 ST aluminum as indicated in Table 9-3.

High-temperature Adhesives. The military services are vitally interested in the development of high-temperature adhesive compounds and have undertaken a continuing development program for their realization. Much of the work has been accomplished with epoxy-phenolic resin blends. A typical formulation (Epon 422J) is as follows:

Epoxy resin (molecular weight 1,000)	100 parts
Phenolic resin	49 parts
Aluminum dust	149 parts
Dicyandiamide	9 parts
Copper 8-quinolinolate	1.5 parts

This compound can be employed as a hot melt or as supported or unsupported tapes. Unlike more conventional epoxy-based adhesives, it

TABLE 9-4. Shear Strengths of Phenolic-Epoxy Adhesive Using Aluminum Powder and Dicyandiamide (3-7)

Test temperature, $C°$	Shear strength, psi
−58	2,300
21	2,300
159	1,900
204	1,900
260	1,600
100 cycles, 25–250	1,000
200 hr, 250	700

does not demonstrate the characteristic rise and fall and drop-off with temperature increase. The decline is gradual and regular throughout the temperature range from 60 to 260°C. Table 9-4 presents the range in terms of shear strength to 24-ST-3 aluminum.

A discussion of this formulation is presented in Ref. 9-5. Of particular interest is the use of 8-quinolinol and its derivatives as a stabilizer to improve long-time aging characteristics. While still not providing completely satisfactory values after long-time aging, the reagent increased the shear strengths from the 0- to 350-psi range to the 700- to 800-psi range after 200 hours at 260°C. A number of standard antioxidants were investigated in Ref. 9-5. No satisfactory antioxidant was, however, discovered, although carbon black appeared the most promising.

A second high-temperature adhesive formulation (9-6) consists of the following:

Phenolic resin	500 parts
Epoxy resin (molecular weight 2,000)	100 parts
Methyl ethyl ketone	100 parts
Hexamethylene tetramine	20 parts

This material gives somewhat better high-temperature bond strengths on aluminum surfaces than the previous formulation but lower bond strengths throughout the temperature range, as indicated in Table 9-5.

An interesting high-temperature adhesive formulation based on a liquid epoxy resin and employing pentamethyl diethylene triamine at 4 phr is discussed in Ref. 9-7. Shear strengths for this compound on aluminum are presented in Table 9-6.

TABLE 9-5. Shear Strengths of Phenolic-Epoxy Adhesive Using Hexamethylene Tetramine (9-6)

Test temperature, °C	Shear strength, psi
−58	1,366
26	1,497
232	1,328
316	1,074

TABLE 9-6. Shear Strengths of Epoxy–Pentamethyl Diethylene Triamine Adhesive Formulation (9-7)

Test temperature, °C	Shear strength, psi
−58	3,240
26	3,110
121	2,950
149	1,040
204	570
260	380

Solders

Epoxy-resin solders have proved more economical than metallic solders. The initial costs are comparable, but the low specific gravity of the epoxy solders provides greater coverage per pound. No primer coat is required. Additionally, the thixotropic nature of the epoxy formulation practically eliminates runoff.

The epoxy solders may be worked easily with standard power tools. Despite the rigidity of the cured system, it may be ground, sanded, buffed, or machined.

The epoxy solders may be employed in stick or paste form. Because the formulations can readily be modified, end properties can be tailored to the specific application.

A typical stick solder formulation can be given as:

Epoxy resin (molecular weight 400)	100 parts
4,4′ methylene dianiline	28.5 parts
Powdered aluminum	60 parts
Uncompressed silica	10 parts

The ingredients are prepared as a hot melt and cast into small-diameter tubes. The resin mix will harden slowly at room temperature and give a usable life without refrigeration in excess of one month. To apply, the area to be filled is warmed with a torch until it is sufficiently hot to cause the resin to flow when drawn across the surface. Excessive heat should be avoided, however, if bubbling is to be prevented. Postcure will be required for small masses of solder. After cure, the solder may be finished by conventional techniques as required.

A typical paste-solder formulation can be given as:

> Epoxy resin (molecular weight 400).......... 100 parts
> Diethylene triamine..................... 11 parts
> Aluminum powder....................... 30 parts
> Uncompressed silica.................... as required

The stiffness of the mix is governed by the amount of thixotropic agent employed. To apply, troweling techniques prove satisfactory.

CONCLUSION

It can be concluded that the epoxy resins provide versatile adhesives for a wide range of commercial applications. They can be formulated as both one- and two-container systems, and their handling characteristics can be varied to accommodate specific production situations. A number of variables are involved in the formulation of a specific compound, and ultimate adhesive strengths will be influenced by cure cycles, application techniques, and surface preparation. Through the use of fillers, diluents, and resinous modifiers, systems can be formulated that have superior shear strengths at temperatures as low as $-50°C$ and good shear strengths as high as $300°C$.

The direction of development appears to be toward extending the upper operating temperature performance to the theoretical limits for organic compounds and to improving the long-time-aging characteristics of such high-temperature formulations. In the temperature range of $150°C$ and below, the development effort is directed toward improving the adhesive performance, extending the versatility, and further improving the excellent handling characteristics of the adhesive systems.

References

9-1. Glazer, Monolayer Studies of Some Ethoxyline Resin Adhesives and Related Compounds, *Journal of Polymer Science*, April, 1954.

9-2. Bruyne, The Adhesive Properties of Epoxy Resin, paper presented at Symposium of British Society of the Chemical Industry, April, 1956.

9-3. Shokol, Newey, and Bradley, Process for Forming Cured Glycidyl Ether Resinous Bonds between Two Solid Surfaces, U.S. 2,651,589 (1953).

9-4. Elam and Morrill, Structural Adhesives for Use at Elevated Temperatures, *Western Plastics*, March, 1956.

9-5. Naps, Elevated Temperature-resistant Modified Epoxide Resin Adhesives for Metals, WADC Technical Report 53-126, parts I, II, and III, 1953–1956.

9-6. Black and Bloomquist, Metal-bonding Adhesive with Improved Heat Resistance, *Modern Plastics*, December, 1954.

9-7. Black and Bloomquist, Metal-bonding Adhesives for High Temperature Service, *Modern Plastics*, June, 1956.

9-8. Epstein, Epoxy-based Adhesives, Theoretical Calculations, paper presented at Division of Paint, Plastics, and Printing Ink Chemistry, ACS, Atlantic City, September, 1956.

9-9. Snoddon, Metal-to-resin Adhesion as Determined by a Stripping Test, paper presented at the meeting of the American Society for Testing Materials, Los Angeles, Calif., September, 1956.

9-10. Arnold, An Ultrasonic Technique for Non-destructive Evaluation of Metal-to-metal Adhesive Bonds, paper presented at the meeting of the American Society for Testing Materials, Los Angeles, Calif., September, 1956.

9-11. Steele and Marshall, Recent Developments in Sandwich Constructions, Including Heat-resistant Materials, paper presented at the meeting of the American Society for Testing Materials, Los Angeles, Calif., September, 1956.

9-12. Alter and Soller, Molecular Structure of Epoxy Polymers as a Basis for Adhesion, paper presented at Division of Paint, Plastics, and Printing Ink Chemistry, ACS, New York City, September, 1957.

9-13. Black and Bloomquist, Metal Surface Effects on Heat Resistance of Adhesive Bonds, paper presented at Division of Paint, Plastics, and Printing Ink Chemistry, ACS, New York City, September, 1957.

10
LAMINATES

Epoxy resins may be used as binders in the preparation of laminates of paper, polyester cloth, fiber-glass cloth, wood sheets, mica, etc. The epoxy resin–fiber glass laminate is the most important commercially, and such laminates are discussed in detail as representative. The formulations and techniques useful in the preparation of glass-cloth laminates are also generally applicable to laminates of most other materials.

THEORY OF GLASS-FIBER LAMINATES

Although glass has extremely high tensile and compressive strengths, these properties are not readily apparent in a cylindrical specimen. Surface flaws, occurring randomly, cause cracking and failure of the specimen at values far below theoretical. However, if glass is reduced to fiber form, the same number of random flaws will occur in only a few particular fibers, the balance of the material being of theoretical strength, and the over-all strength of the fiber bundle will reflect more nearly the theoretical value.

To make practical use of the high strength of these fibers, it is necessary to isolate them one from another in order to prevent abrasion and the formation of new surface flaws. Such constructions result in fiber-glass cloth. By using synthetic resins, it is possible to bond fiber-glass cloth into a solid laminate having very high strength-to-weight ratios (i.e., tensile strength divided by specific gravity) as shown in the accompanying table.

Comparison of Strengths and Strength-to-Weight Ratios

	Tensile strength, psi	Specific gravity	Tensile strength/ specific gravity
Steel, structural.................	60,000	7.80	7,700
Steel, piano wire................	300,000	7.80	38,500
Aluminum......................	15,000*	2.88	5,200
Epoxy–glass cloth laminate........	46,000–66,000	2.20	20,700–30,000

* Up to 70,000 for high-strength aluminum alloys.

233

A study of the nature of the bonding forces in laminates by Outwater (10-1) indicates that upon initial loading there is a tendency for the adhesive bond between the glass and resin to be broken, with the subsequent high-strength properties attributable to the friction of the resin against the fiber.   Figure 10-1 indicates this effect on two laminate specimens.   However, that there is some retention of the adhesive bond is

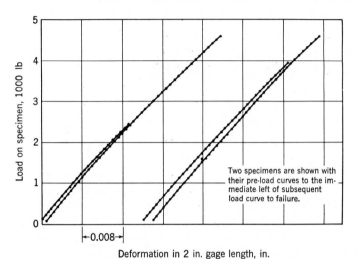

Deformation in 2 in. gage length, in.

FIG. 10-1. Breaking of resin-glass bond by initial tensile loading (10-1).

indicated by the improved strengths obtainable with specially treated cloth, as discussed subsequently.   Test data on properly prepared cylindrical glass specimens, likewise, indicate that retention of the bond will be achieved until failure of the glass.   It is probable, therefore, that the wetting action of the epoxy-resin binder, together with its adhesive strength, conjoin, to a yet undetermined degree, to provide the ultimate strength properties of the laminate.

COMMERCIAL APPLICATIONS OF EPOXY–GLASS CLOTH LAMINATES

The use of the better known and less expensive phenolic and polyester resins as binders for glass-cloth laminates is more common than the use of epoxies.   However, the epoxy laminates offer higher compression strengths, higher resistance to delamination, and higher moisture resistance than do the more conventional thermosetting resins.   For example, the flexural strengths at room temperature for typical compounds are as follows (3-7):

	Flexural strength, psi
Polyester A	51,300
Polyester B	46,400
Epoxy	79,000

The time to failure for these compounds immersed at 66°C in water under a constant flexural load is shown in the accompanying table.

Compound	Initial flexural stress, psi	Time to failure, hr
Polyester A	25,700	1.9
Polyester B	23,200	0.2
Epoxy	39,500	54.0
Epoxy	25,000	685.0

Epoxy laminates are becoming increasingly important in the aircraft industry, where they are employed as structural sheeting in ducts, tail sections, and elevators and as materials for lightweight honeycomb sections, etc. The laminates find use in electrical switch gear, instrumentation panels, high-performance moisture-resistant printed circuit bases, electric-coil insulation, etc. The laminates are used in low-pressure bearing surfaces and similar specialized applications throughout industry. In tool and die work, the epoxy laminates are used for many punching, stamping, forming, and hobbing operations. Providing increased structural strengths and dimensional stability over castings, they are frequently used in their stead (Chap. 8) to provide extremely tough, durable components capable of long service lives. In the chemical engineering industry and petroleum fields, epoxy laminates are used for the fabrication of lightweight corrosion-resistant pipes. In the automobile industry, epoxy–glass cloth laminates are useful in repairing damaged bodies and fenders. Epoxy laminates can be used as reinforcements for pressure vessels, providing a unit much lighter in weight than one composed exclusively of metal. Convenient wet lay-up techniques, combined with room-temperature cures, permit the application of laminates for emergency patching of pipes and other pressure-bearing equipment. The high resistance of the epoxy laminates to water makes them preferable to polyester resins for boat fabrication. The list could be extended, but in summary, the laminates may be used in any conventional application where the superior properties justify the slightly higher cost. References 10-2 to 10-6 discuss specific applications.

TECHNIQUES OF MANUFACTURE

Essentially two techniques are used to prepare laminates: (1) wet lay-ups and (2) dry lay-ups.

Wet lay-ups involve the impregnation of the cloth with a 100 per cent solids nonsolvent-containing resin and the immediate (or essentially immediate) application of the cloth to the laminating operation. The lower-viscosity resins, such as the commercial-grade diglycidyl ether of bisphenol A, are most commonly used, since the higher-molecular-weight resins are too viscous to provide satisfactory wetting action unless worked hot.

Dry lay-ups involve the impregnation of the cloth with either a 100 per cent solids or a solvent-containing resin system in advance of the production operation. If a 100 per cent solids system is employed, the resin is then applied to the glass fiber and gelled or B-staged to produce a dry tack-free cloth capable of flow on the application of heat. If a solvent system is employed, the cloth is coated and the solvent driven out as best possible to provide a tack-free surface capable of cure by the subsequent application of heat.

Terminal boards from epoxy laminates have high dimensional stability and low moisture absorption. *(Taylor Fibre Company.)*

In order to obtain the requisite flow characteristics, the liquid low-viscosity resins are employed with the dry lay-up 100 per cent solids systems, and the curing agent is selected on the basis of the ease with which B-stage can be achieved. Curing agents such as 4,4′ methylene dianiline, for example, can be B-staged in laminating work. The B-staged cloths are effective in that they contain no solvents, but their shelf life is short, and it is frequently necessary to store them under refrigeration.

The higher-molecular-weight resins are customarily employed in solvent formulations for dry lay-ups; here, they possess the advantage of

Wet lay-up technique is demonstrated in manufacture of automatic lathe housing with complex curved shape. Concave mold is coated with repeated layers of glass mat and epoxy resin. Finished product, removed from mold, needs only touch up and painting. (*Bakelite* Co.)

Low cost highly stable fender welding fixture built up from epoxy resins and glass-cloth demonstrates wide usefulness of epoxy tooling. (*Bakelite* Co.)

Lightweight epoxy laminates and reinforced epoxy tubing form a huge airplane inspection fixture at about a fourth the weight and half the cost of equivalent steel tooling. (*Bakelite* Co.)

Wet lay-up technique is demonstrated in insulation of 400-kva transformer primary coil. Glass tape and brushable epoxy compound form tough moisture-resistant laminate. (*Shell Chemical Co. and Larsen-Hogue Electric Co.*)

lower cost. Suitable solvents are acetone, methyl ethyl ketone, and Cellosolve. The resin is dissolved, together with the curing agent, into the solvent vehicle. In some instances, however, complicated procedures may be required. For example, when using phthalic anhydride—only slightly soluble in acetone—as a curing agent for the higher-weight resins, it is necessary to fuse the resin and curing agent at about 150°C prior to dissolving the mix into the solvent. In some cases, refluxing may be required.

Sufficient solvent is used to achieve a viscosity low enough to provide for thorough wetting action. The mixture is applied to the cloth by squeeze rolls or coating bars in such a manner as to control the resin build-up, and the solvents are driven off to leave a dry, but unpolymerized, coating. If the higher-weight species are employed, the resultant laminates will be stiff and possess poor drape characteristics; such cloths are most advantageously used in the preparation of flat-press laminates. To improve drape characteristics, mixtures of high- and low-molecular-weight resins may be employed in connection with solvent system dry lay-ups. The specific drying cycle may be adjusted to suit production equipment but must not be sufficiently high to polymerize the resin mix.

Cross section of Epoxylite molded motor coil reveals dense air-free insulation achieved by use of epoxy resin—glass cloth laminate molded directly to copper conductors under heat and pressure. (*The Epoxylite Corporation.*)

Formation of the Laminate

The laminate may be formed under contact (or so-called zero) pressure, in which only the weight of the plies is applied to the binder; under low pressure; and under high pressure.

Contact laminates usually possess high resin contents and are chiefly useful where the expense of equipment and considerations of production do not justify the increased performance obtained with pressure laminations.

Low-pressure laminates may be formed by a variety of methods, the most common of them being the "vacuum bag impregnation" technique. In this process, the laminate is placed over the contoured mold and a thin sheet of plastic draped over the unit and anchored airtight along its edges, or alternatively, the mold and laminate can be placed into a plastic bag. The vacuum is then pulled on the laminate, whereupon the plastic sheet is drawn in to force the laminate to assume the contour of the mold. If the vacuum is low, it may be helpful to assist formation of the laminate by

A 600-hp rubber mill motor is rewound with Epoxylite molded coil. Coil resists carbon black, plasticizer vapors, and vibration. Absence of air pockets in insulation provides better cooling of the copper, longer thermal life. (*Larsen-Hogue Electric* **Co.**)

exerting pressure on the collapsed sheet by means of a spatula or other convenient device. Customary procedure is to cure the laminate under vacuum.

High-pressure laminates are formed by the use of matched molds or platens pressed together mechanically and heated, with the pressure being retained until the laminate has hardened into the desired shape.

FORMULATION

The major factors involved in the formulation of the laminates are:
1 Type of glass cloth and its surface treatment.
2. Resin, modifier, and curing-agent system.
3. Laminating pressure, resin content, and curing cycle.

Type of Glass Cloth and Its Surface Treatment

The basic components of glass cloth are called filaments and are slender fibers of glass ranging from 0.00018 to 0.00075 in. in diameter. These are grouped into strands, each strand usually containing either 102 or 204 filaments (10-7).

The strands may then be twisted into yarns (discussed in detail below) or collected into untwisted rovings.

The *rovings* are used in less expensive "mat" cloths. The strands of the roving are cemented together with a binder, which, in large measure, determines the ultimate properties of the laminate. The mat may consist of continuous rovings or of chopped ($\frac{1}{4}$- to 2-in.) rovings. Epoxy resins can be used as a mat binder to impart highly desirable properties (10-9).

The *yarns* are woven into a variety of fabrics, with the strands which run parallel to the length of the fabric designated "warp" and the cross threads designated "filling." The specific type of weave dictates, to some degree, the properties of the fabric, and the specific laminating application will, in many cases, determine the best suitable weave.

Some of the most common weaves are as follows (10-8):

Plain Weave. In this type, the warp and filling threads cross alternately. Fabrics with this weave are the least pliable, but they are also the most stable.

Basket Weave. This weave is similar to the plain woven fabrics except that two or more warp threads cross alternately with two or more filling threads. Basket-woven material is flatter, stronger, and more pliable than the plain woven type but less stable.

Crowfoot Weave. In this type of weave a filling thread crosses over three warp threads and then under one. Fabrics of this type are more pliable than either of the aforementioned. Consequently, they are easy to form around curved surfaces.

Long Shaft or Satin Weave. A fabric with this type of weave has a filling thread passing over seven warp threads and then under one, thus causing the material to be the most pliable yet mentioned. It is also flatter and stronger. Its pliability allows excellent draping around compound curves but restricts porosity because of the high thread count.

Leno Weave. Two or more warp threads crossing over each other and interlacing with one or more filling threads constitute a leno weave. This produces a very open fabric.

Unidirectional Weave. These fabrics are made with strong warp threads and weaker filling threads. This gives maximum strength in one direction without additional weight.

It is necessary to consider certain inherent properties of the cloth selected for use. Should the warp and filling have unequal breaking strengths, for instance, the flexural and tensile strengths of the laminate will depend on how the fabric is cut. Additionally, in building plies, consideration should be given to the proper positioning of each layer. It is generally recommended that the warps be parallel and side by side rather than stacked.

In addition to the various weaves, a variety of finishes are available for the glass cloth. The specific finish will, to some degree, determine the ultimate properties of the laminate.

During manufacture of the glass cloth, the filaments are coated with a starchlike material called sizing, which serves to prevent flaws as the strands are being twisted and woven into the fabric. The sizing is not compatible with most of the laminating resins, and consequently, it should be removed. Removal may be accomplished by heat or by a combination of chemical treatment and heat. For best strengths, the chemical treatment should be used. It consists of applying a primer coating (or keying agent) to the heat-cleaned fabric. The keying agent bonds to the adsorbed moisture layer of the glass, and the epoxy bonds to the keying agent through available unsaturated groups. The application of this material is called finishing, and the material is called a finish. With the development of effective finishes, room-temperature flexural strengths for epoxy laminates have been increased by 20,000 to 30,000 psi. Most finishes, however, have been designed for the polyesters, and such finishes are not necessarily optimum for epoxy resins.

Several types of finish are available (10-7). These fall into three general classifications:

Heat Cleaned. Heat-cleaned glass fabrics may be employed with epoxy laminates because of the highly adhesive nature of the resins, but properties will be less satisfactory than with a finished cloth. An epoxy system cured with a tertiary amine will give flexural strengths up to 80,000 psi in a heat-cleaned glass-cloth laminate.

Chrome Finished. Chrome finishes such as methacrylato chromic chloride (Volan A) will give flexural strengths of about 90,000 psi in an epoxy system cured with a tertiary amine.

Silane Finished. Silane finishes such as the reaction product of resorcinol and allyltrichloro silane will give flexural strengths of about 105,000 psi in an epoxy system cured with a tertiary amine (10-7).

Resin, Modifier, and Curing-agent System

The resin-modifier-curing-agent system provides a major variable in laminating formulations. Both low- and higher-molecular-weight resins may be employed in laminating formulations, with the lower-weight resins being preferred for wet lay-ups, the higher-weight species for dry lay-ups. The solid resins having a molecular weight in the 1,000 range appear to be the preferred class of higher-weight species.

Most of the curing agents discussed in Chaps. 4 to 7 have been employed in laminates with varying degrees of success. Specific formulations will be discussed in connection with properties.

In general, the aliphatic amines are useful in wet lay-ups because of the speed with which they cure at room temperature. They cannot, however, be B-staged, although they do find application in solution coatings. The aromatic diamines, the amides, and selected anhydrides are successful in both wet and dry lay-ups and provide systems having higher heat-distortion temperatures. Postcuring, in these instances, is necessary, either in an oven or in service. Some of the materials can be B-staged, but they are most commonly used in dry lay-ups as solution coatings. Phenolic resins (Chap. 6) are employed as resinous modifiers in dry lay-ups to increase the heat-distortion temperatures over those of the aromatic diamine and amide cured systems. Flexibilizers (Chap. 7) are employed in both wet and dry lay-ups to provide laminates of high impact resistance and good low-temperature performance.

Fillers may be used with epoxy laminates, as they are with polyester laminates, to reduce cost and shrinkage, but they have the effect of decreasing the room-temperature flexural strengths on the order of 20 per cent. Certain fillers, such as zinc tetraoxychromate, will improve corrosion resistance; and some may be employed to modify other selected properties. Diluents, used in smaller percentages, do not affect room-temperature structural strengths adversely but will, of course, somewhat reduce higher-temperature performance.

Laminating Pressure, Resin Content, and Curing Cycle

Laminating pressure, resin content, and curing cycle are treated under one heading because they are mutually interdependent with regard to their effect on properties. They are likewise dependent, to some extent, on the application technique.

Laminating Pressure. One of the advantages of the epoxy resins is that they can be laminated with only contact pressure. Flexural strengths of a system thus obtained will be adequate for many production situations, where ease of manufacture is of considerable economic importance. Seldom, however, is a dense void-free fill achieved, and the laminate will possess resin-rich areas. Because of the low pressure, the resin content will be in the neighborhood of 50 to 60 per cent. This results in flexural strengths of 30,000 to 45,000 psi.

Low-pressure laminates, in contrast with contact-pressure laminates, will have correspondingly better strength properties. Here, the higher glass content of the laminates accounts for much of the improvement. The following room-temperature strengths may be considered typical of the relationship between laminating pressure and flexural strengths:

Pressure, psi	Flexural strength, psi
3	38,000
25	63,000
200	78,000

However, when the resin content is held constant, the effect of laminating pressure will be slight:

Pressure, psi	Flexural strength, psi	Flexural modulus, psi $\times 10^{-6}$
30	67,000	2.8
100	67,000	2.8
300	70,000	3.0

Resin Content. The resin content may be determined by the application technique, but is quite dependent on the laminating pressure. As an interrelated parameter, it determines the strength of the ultimate laminate.

The effect of resin content can be approximated by the equation (10-1)

$$E_c = \frac{E_g}{2.26/R} - 1.26$$

where E_c = modulus of elasticity of laminate, psi

E_g = modulus of elasticity of glass, psi

R = weight percentage of glass present

Increasing the percentage of glass decreases the denominator on the right-hand side of the equation and thereby increases the modulus of the laminate.

The variations that can be expected with resin content within the working range of 25 to 35 per cent are not overly significant:

Resin content	Flexural strength, psi	Compressive strength, psi
18	49,000	31,000
26	78,000	56,000
30	76,000	. . . . . .
33	. . . . . .	54,000
37	67,000	57,000

The effect of resin content on flexural strengths for various temperatures is indicated in Fig. 10-2.

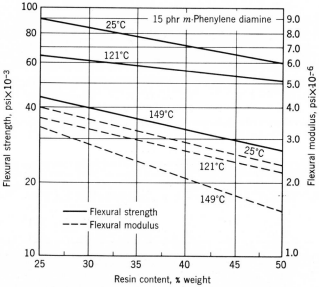

FIG. 10-2. Effect of resin content on glass laminate (3-7).

Cure Cycle. The cure cycle for laminates may be considered to be somewhat more complex than for castings, coatings, and adhesives. It may be accomplished in one or more of three stages: (1) precure, (2) cure during pressure, and (3) postcure.

Precure is of considerable consequence when using wet lay-up techniques in conjunction with high pressure for forming the laminate or with an initial high-temperature curing cycle. Precure serves to body the resin and prevent excessive flow upon application of heat and/or pressure.

It will be realized that the presence or absence of a precure may influence the resin content to a considerable degree.

For instance, if a hot press is employed to form the laminate, and if the full laminating pressure is applied as soon as the wet lay-up is inserted in the heated press, the resin usually flows so rapidly that the laminate is starved and contains porous nonsaturated areas. This can be corrected by holding the laminate in the hot press for a period of reduced pressure and is sometimes followed by a complete release of pressure, known as breathing, to allow the entrapped fumes to escape. A normal hot-press cycle may, for example, utilize a 3-minute precure at 150°C and a 30-second breathing period.

If the precure period is extended beyond the optimum time for the particular resin system involved, the resin will not flow sufficiently under

TABLE 10-1. Effect of Postcure on Properties of Contact-pressure Laminate (10-10)

(Epoxy resin: fluidized)

Mechanical properties	Cured at room temperature	Postcured 8 hr at 160°C
Tensile strength, psi	36,100	40,700
Tensile modulus, psi	2.03×10^6	2.35×10^6
Compressive strength edgewise, psi	38,100	43,000
Compressive modulus edgewise, psi	2.94×10^6	2.83×10^6
Flexural strength, psi	52,500	61,800
Flexural modulus, psi	2.51×10^6	3.25×10^6
Flexural strength at 70°C, psi	7,600	46,600
Flexural modulus at 70°C, psi	0.38×10^6	2.37×10^6
Flexural strength after 2 hr in 100°C water, psi	46,200	57,400
Flexural modulus after 2 hr in 100°C water, psi	2.29×10^6	2.79×10^6
Impact strength, Izod	12.4	10.4

pressure to provide a sufficiently dense, void-free laminate, and as in the case of too early application of pressure, a porous laminate will result. And, again, if the breathing cycle is too extended, too much volatile curing agent may escape.

Optimum precure and precure cycle must be determined for each resin system and is dependent not only on the system but on the cure temperature, the precure pressure (if any), and the size of the laminate. It is best determined empirically.

A second form of precure, having the reverse effect, may be employed with dry lay-ups in order to improve their drape. In this instance, the laminate is subjected to a high initial temperature to cause resin flow and permit the convenient forming of the laminate to the surface contour.

Rather than apply a precure temperature, as such, it is sometimes advantageous to allow the wet lay-up laminate to proceed to the B-stage at room temperature before heating is initiated, particularly in the case of exceptionally thick plies. This procedure not only minimizes the resin flow but allows dissipation of much of the exothermic heat at low tem-

TABLE 10-2. Typical Cure Cycles and Properties for Metaphenylene Diamine Laminate (3-7)

(Epoxy resin: molecular weight 350 to 400)

Cure cycles	Cure temperature, °C	Cure time, min	Cure pressure, psi
A	107	30	200
B	143	15	200
C	224	15	200

(Test conditions: room temperature)

Properties	Initial value	After 3 hr in boiling acetone	After 3 hr in boiling water
Flexural strength, psi × 10⁻³:			
Cure A	79.5	59.4	69.1
Cure B	86.5	82.1	72.1
Cure C	80.5	78.7	76.3
Flexural modulus, psi × 10⁻⁶:			
Cure A	3.4	1.8	3.8
Cure B	4.0	4.0	3.4
Cure C	3.5	3.1	3.3
Hardness, Barcol:			
Cure A	70	40	70
Cure B	70	70	70
Cure C	70	68	68
Weight increase, %:			
Cure A	....	2.8	0.25
Cure B	....	0.12	0.17
Cure C	....	0.09	0.18

perature, thus providing minimum distortion from thermal stresses in the laminate.

Cure during pressure is usually determined by the temperature required for the laminate to achieve a progressed cure in a reasonable time. The exact time will be dependent on the temperature and the curing agent. At 150°C, 15 minutes will often prove adequate.

Postcure will determine, to an extent, the properties of the ultimate laminate, and its length and the requisite temperatures will generally be determined on the basis of parameters discussed in the previous chapters. Likewise, of course, it will depend on the previous precure and pressure-cure cycles.

Two specific examples will serve to illustrate typical cure cycles. In the case of a wet lay-up laminate, not involving pressure and employing a

TABLE 10-3. Effect of Cure Pressure and Postcure on Elevated Temperature Performance of Metaphenylene Diamine Laminate (3-7)
(Epoxy resin: molecular weight 350 to 400)

Cure cycle	Cure temperature, °C	Cure time, min	Cure pressure, psi	Postcure at 240°C, hr
A	150	15	200	
B	150	15	200	1
C	150	15	25	
D	150	15	25	1

Properties	Tested at		
	25°C	150°C	260°C
Flexural strength, psi $\times 10^{-3}$:			
Cure A....................	75.3	18.5	8.8
Cure B....................	72.3	56.9	11.1
Cure C....................	74.2	18.1	6.2
Cure D....................	68.7	26.3	7.0
Flexural modulus, psi $\times 10^{-6}$:			
Cure A....................	3.2	1.4	1.3
Cure B....................	3.0	3.2	1.6
Cure C....................	3.2	1.5	1.3
Cure D....................	2.8	1.8	1.2

polyfunctional primary amine as curing agent, cure can be accomplished in an oven or under infrared lights at 90 to 120°C in 30 minutes to 1 hour. The infrared lights rather than ovens have been found to be particularly effective with plaster molds, since it is then unnecessary to heat the entire mass to obtain cures. The effect of postcure is indicated in Table 10-1.

A dry lay-up, employing metaphenylene diamine in a solvent-impregnated system, cured in matched molds, and employing pressure to provide adequate flow, will have physical properties dependent on both cure temperature and cure pressure. Selected data are presented in Table 10-2. The effect of postcure on the same system is presented in Table 10-3.

PROPERTIES OF THE CURED LAMINATE

The properties of the cured laminate can be indicated only in a general way, in view of the number of factors involved in the formulation and processing of each system.   Data for a number of specific formulations prepared as ⅛-in. thick 12-ply laminates of Volan A 181 cloth will be given.   For convenience, the discussion will consider, in order, mechanical properties, electrical properties, and chemical resistance.   It will be realized that data furnished in prior chapters will have utility in the formulation of laminates for a specific application.

Mechanical Properties

As indicated previously, the mechanical properties of epoxy–glass cloth laminates are excellent.   Although the specific values will be determined

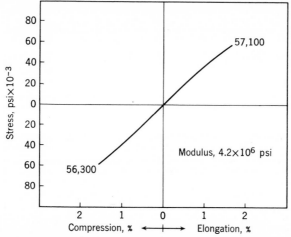

FIG. 10-3. Stress-strain curve in tension and compression for a glass-fiber laminate, cured with diethylamino propylamine (10-11).

by a number of variables, data for representative systems will indicate ranges to be expected.

Flexural strengths are most frequently recorded in the literature, because they are determined with relative ease.   Tensile and compressive strengths, however, are high, as indicated in Figs. 10-3 to 10-5.

Typical rigid systems, employing wet lay-ups at contact pressure and cured with various aliphatic amines, give flexural strengths as indicated in Table 10-4.   The effects of moisture conditioning and thickness of laminate on one particular system are presented in Fig. 10-6.

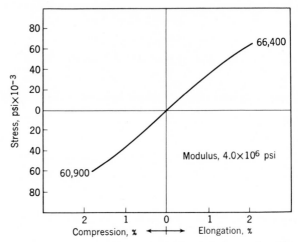

FIG. 10-4. Stress-strain curve in tension and compression for a glass-fiber laminate of 1,000 mol. wt epoxy resin cured with dicyandiamide (10-11).

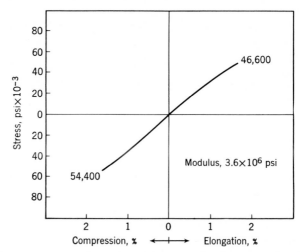

FIG. 10-5. Stress-strain curve in tension and compression for epoxyphenolic glass-fiber laminates (10-11).

A typical rigid system employing a dry lay-up in conjunction with a pressure cycle and postcure, with 4,4′ methylene dianiline as curing agent, will provide mechanical properties as indicated in Table 10-5. The same curing agent, used in dry lay-ups at similar pressures and postcure cycles with higher-weight species, provides properties as indicated in Table 10-6. The effect of temperature on an aromatic-diamine cured system is compared with an aliphatic-amine cured system in Fig. 10-7.

TABLE 10-4. Typical Properties for Laminates Cured by Various Aliphatic Amines (3-7)

(Epoxy resin: molecular weight 450)

Curing agent	Phr	Resin, %	Cure		Flexural strength, psi $\times 10^{-3}$	Flexural modulus, psi $\times 10^{-6}$	Flexural yield, psi $\times 10^{-3}$	Water absorption, 30 days immersion at 25°C, %
			Time, min	Temp, °C				
Tridimethyl amino methyl phenol......	6	31	60	80	63.4	3.2	63.4	0.9
Diethylene triamine...	8	29	30	115	69.0	2.8	69.0	0.6
Dimethylamino propylamine........	6	31	60	80	63.9	3.0	63.9	0.8
Dimethylamino methyl phenol......	16	32	60	80	67.1	3.4	62.5	1.5
Diethylamino propylamine............	6	29	60	115	64.0	3.1	63.8	0.8
Benzyldimethylamine.	6	29	60	80	66.7	3.3	66.7	0.9
Piperidine...........	6	33	180	80	68.3	3.2	64.3	0.2
Diethylamine........	12	29	150	115	64.0	3.2	62.0	1.0
Pyridine.............	15	32	120	80	71.0	3.2	63.3	0.7

TABLE 10-5. Typical Mechanical Properties of Laminate Cured with 4,4' Methylene Dianiline (10-10)

Epoxy resin: molecular weight 350 to 400
Cure cycle:
  Pressed 1 hour at 160°C
  Postcured 2 hours at 150°C
    plus 6 hours at 200°C

Properties

Tensile strength, psi...	50,000–58,000
Tensile modulus, psi $\times 10^{-6}$.....................................	3.3–3.6
Compressive strength, edgewise, psi.............................	49,000–51,000
Compressive modulus, edgewise, psi $\times 10^{-6}$......................	3.5–3.6
Flexural strength, psi:	
At 25°C...	79,000–89,000
At 127°C...	52,000–60,000
After 2 hr in 100°C water.................................	77,000–82,000
Flexural modulus, psi $\times 10^{-6}$:	
At 25°C..	3.6–3.9
At 127°C..	3.0–3.5
After 2 hr in 100°C water.................................	3.2–3.6
Impact strength, Izod....................................	12–15
Hardness, Rockwell M....................................	115–117
Water absorption, 24 hr at 25°C, weight gain, %................	0.05–0.07

Rigid systems for higher-temperature operations may be formulated from epoxy-phenolic blends and from anhydrides. A typical phenolic blend will provide excellent flexural strengths at higher temperatures. Flexural strength vs. temperature for one such system is presented in

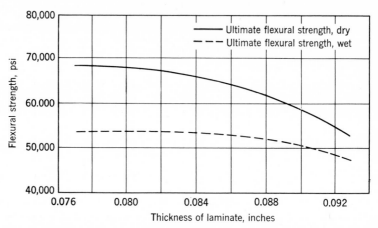

FIG. 10-6. Flexural strength of a glass-fiber laminate, cured with diethylene triamine at 10 phr, as a function of laminate thickness (3-9).

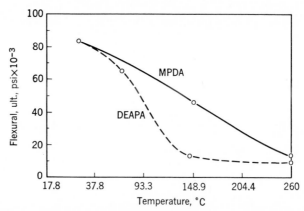

FIG. 10-7. Effect of temperature on the flexural strength of glass-fiber laminates cured with metaphenylene diamine and diethylamino propylamine (10-11).

Fig. 10-8. For comparison, a system cured with dicyandiamide is also shown. In both cases, an epoxy resin having a molecular weight of 1,000 was employed. The high-temperature flexural strength of a 400-molecular weight resin cured with chlorendic anhydride is presented in Table 10-7. Table 10-8 presents the high-temperature properties of a liquid

TABLE 10-6. Typical Mechanical Properties vs. Molecular Weight of Resin for Laminate Cured with 4,4′ Methylene Dianiline (10-10)

Cure cycle:
Pressed at 400 psi for 1 hour at 160°C
Postcured 8 hours at 160°C

Properties	Epoxy resin, molecular weight 1,000	Epoxy resin, molecular weight 1,500
Tensile strength, psi...................	52,000–59,000	61,000–66,000
Tensile modulus, psi × 10^{-6}...............	2.9–3.4	3.5–4.0
Compressive strength, edgewise, psi.........	45,000–50,000	48,000–52,000
Compressive modulus, edgewise, psi × 10^{-6}...	3.5–3.7	3.9–4.5
Flexural strength, psi:		
At 25°C...........................	80,000–85,000	95,000–100,000
At 127°C..........................	69,000–74,000	70,000–75,000
After 2 hr in 100°C water...............	77,000–79,000	85,000–90,000
Flexural modulus, psi × 10^{-6}:		
At 25°C...........................	3.6–3.9	4.4–4.6
At 127°C..........................	3.5–3.7	4.0–4.2
After 2 hr in 100°C water...............	3.4–3.7	3.8–4.0
Impact strength, Izod....................	12–15	16–18
Hardness, Rockwell M....................	110–112	102–107
Water absorption, 24 hr at 25°C, weight gain, %	0.04–0.06	0.04–0.08

TABLE 10-7. Typical Strength Properties vs. Temperature for Laminates Cured with 120 Phr Chlorendic Anhydride (5-8)

Epoxy resin: molecular weight 350 to 400
Cure cycle:
Cure A—pressed at 100 psi for 2 hours at 180°C
Cure B—pressed at 100 psi for 24 hours at 180°C

Properties	Temperature, °C				
	23	138	177	204	260
Cure A:					
Flexural strength, psi............	87,900	75,500	73,500	29,800	9,700
Flexural modulus, psi × 10^{-6}.....	4.17	3.28	3.33	2.22	1.20
Cure B:					
Flexural strength, psi............	86,700	76,600	74,000	39,300	9,800
Flexural modulus, psi × 10^{-6}.....	4.01	3.36	3.35	2.71	1.20

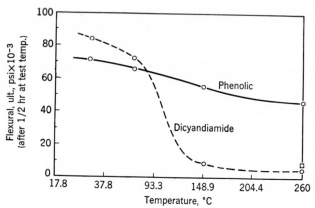

FIG. 10-8. Effect of temperature on flexural strength of glass-fiber laminates of 1,000 mol. wt epoxy resin in phenolic blend and cured by dicyandiamide (10-11).

TABLE 10-8. Typical Strength Properties vs. Temperature for Laminate Cured with Pyromellitic Dianhydride and Maleic Anhydride Mixtures (5-7)

Epoxy resin: molecular weight 350 to 400
Cure cycle:
    Pressed at 100 psi for 15 min at 150°C (with 2 min zero pressure precure)
    Postcured 16 hours at 160°C

Properties	PMDA	PMDA/MA
Flexural strength, psi:		
23°C.............................	73,000	74,000
150°C............................	45,000	46,000
260°C............................	15,000	16,000
260°C (after aging at 200°C)..........	23,000 (500 hr)	24,000 (500 hr)
260°C (after aging at 260°C)..........	17,000 (192 hr)	26,000 (500 hr)
Flexural modulus, psi $\times$ 10^{-6}:		
23°C.............................	3.4	3.5
150°C............................	2.6	2.9
260°C............................	2.2	2.3
260°C (after aging at 200°C)..........	2.4 (500 hr)	2.7 (500 hr)
260°C (after aging at 260°C)..........	2.4 (192 hr)	2.9 (500 hr)
Weight loss, %:		
500 hr at 200°C.....................	1.2	1.2
192 hr at 260°C.....................	6.0	
500 hr at 260°C.....................	....	7.5

TABLE 10-9. Typical Mechanical Properties of Laminates Flexibilized with Polyamide Resin (7-2)

(Test conditions: room temperature except as noted)

Resins: Epoxy, molecular weight 350 to 400
 Polyamide, amine number 210 to 230
Cure cycle:
 Pressed 10 to 20 minutes at 150°C

Properties	Polyamide, phr			
	Unfluidized resin		Fluidized resin	
	43	75	66	100
Tensile strength, psi..............	37,000	39,000	34,000	50,000
Tensile strength at 121°C, psi.......	17,000	19,000	14,000	20,000
Flexural strength, psi.............	50,000	60,000	55,000	60,000
Flexural modulus, psi × 10⁻⁶.......	2.5	2.5	2.5	2.5

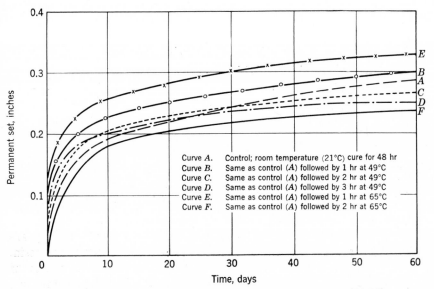

Curve A. Control; room temperature (21°C) cure for 48 hr
Curve B. Same as control (A) followed by 1 hr at 49°C
Curve C. Same as control (A) followed by 2 hr at 49°C
Curve D. Same as control (A) followed by 3 hr at 49°C
Curve E. Same as control (A) followed by 1 hr at 65°C
Curve F. Same as control (A) followed by 2 hr at 65°C

FIG. 10-9. Creep vs. time for filled epoxy–glass cloth laminates (10-12).

resin cured with pyromellitic dianhydride and PMDA/MA mixtures. In all three cases, solvent systems were employed in formulation of the resin system. Although the flexural strengths of the epoxy–glass cloth laminates are not so high at elevated temperatures as those provided by some epoxy-phenolic blends, the higher-temperature phenolic blends are quite brittle and possess somewhat less satisfactory room-temperature properties.

Where very high impact resistance is required, as in tooling applications, flexibilizers such as the polyamides and polysulfides may be employed. The increased impact resistance will be achieved at the

TABLE 10-10. Typical Mechanical Properties of Laminates Flexibilized with a Polysulfide Resin (7-6)
(Test conditions: room temperature)

Resins: Epoxy, molecular weight 350 to 400
      Polysulfide, molecular weight 1,000
Curing agent: Tridimethyl amino methyl phenol at 10 phr
Cure cycle:
    Pressed 30 to 60 minutes at 120°C

Properties	Polysulfide, phr						
	0	16.7	20	25	33.3	50	100
Compressive strength, edgewise, psi × 10^{-3}	35	35	33	31	30	27	17
Flexural strength, psi × 10^{-3}	65	63	61	60	59	35	10
Flexural strength, after 2 hr in 100°C water, psi × 10^{-3}	38	37	32	31	30	20	15
Flexural modulus, psi × 10^{-6}	3.1	3.0	2.9	2.8	2.6	2.1	1.3
Flexural modulus after 2 hr in 100°C water, psi × 10^{-6}	2.6	2.5	2.5	2.4	2.4	1.7	0.6
Impact strength, Izod	11	11	12	12	14	15	>16

expense of higher-temperature performance, as expected from the discussion in Chap. 7. The more elastic nature of the laminates is, likewise, reflected in the lower strength and moduli at room temperature. Tables 10-9 and 10-10 provide typical data for flexibilized systems.

Creep properties of epoxy laminates under sustained loading are good, as might be expected from the dimensional stability of the resin. Attempts are being made, however, to improve this parameter in view of its importance in high-pressure environments. Thorough cure will improve performance to a degree. Typical data, based on a filled laminate, are presented in Fig. 10-9.

Electrical Properties

The electrical properties of epoxy glass laminates are equal to the electrical properties of casting compounds, except that the presence of glass increases dielectric constant. Table 10-11 presents the electrical properties of dry lay-up laminates of three resin systems cured with 4,4′ methylene dianiline. Table 10-12 presents similar properties for resin systems

TABLE 10-11. Typical Electrical Properties of Laminates Cured with 4,4′ Methylene Dianiline (10-10)

(Test conditions: room temperature, except as noted)

Cure cycle:
Pressed 1 hour at 160°C
Postcured 2 hours at 150°C
plus 6 hours at 200°C

Electrical properties	Molecular weight of resin		
	350–400	1,000	1,500
Power factor, 10° cycles/sec:			
Dry	0.017–0.019	0.015–0.018	0.010–0.014
After 2 days in water	0.010–0.025	0.019–0.021	0.015–0.018
After 2 days in water at 50°C	0.010–0.035	0.020–0.025	0.015–0.020
Dielectric constant, 10^6 cycles/sec:			
Dry	4.2–4.6	4.5–4.7	4.7–4.9
After 2 days in water	4.4–4.8	4.5–4.9	4.8–5.1
After 2 days in water at 50°C	4.6–5.3	4.6–5.2	4.9–5.2
Loss factor 10^6 cycles/sec:			
Dry	0.07–0.09	0.07–0.09	0.05–0.07
After 2 days in water	0.08–0.12	0.09–0.10	0.08–0.09
After 2 days in water at 50°C	0.10–0.20	0.11–0.12	0.08–0.10
Dielectric strength:			
Perpendicular to laminations, volts/mil	500–550	450–480	450–500
After 2 days in water at 50°C	400–500	300–350	350–450
Arc resistance, sec	130–180	140–180	155–185
Insulation resistance, megohms	5–10 × 10^5	1 × 10^6	1–3 × 10^6

cured by diethylamino propylamine and metaphenylene diamine as well as dicyandiamide and an epoxy phenolic blend catalyzed by dicyandiamide. Table 10-13 presents electrical properties of a second phenolic-epoxy blend, catalyzed with alpha-methylbenzyl dimethylamine. Laminates cured with PMDA are not greatly affected by temperature (Table 10-14). Table 10-15 presents electrical properties for a laminate flexibilized by a polysulfide.

TABLE 10-12. Comparison of Typical Electrical Properties of Four
Laminates (10-11)
(Test conditions: room temperature)

Epoxy resins: molecular weight 350 to 400 with DEAPA and MPDA, molecular
weight 1,000 with other compounds

Curing agent	Frequency, cycles/sec			
	10^2	10^3	10^4	10^6
Diethylamino propylamine:				
Power factor.................	0.0192	0.0167	0.0131	0.0222
After 24 hr in water..........	0.0292	0.0195	0.0141	0.0226
Dielectric constant.............	5.16	5.01	4.91	4.77
After 24 hr in water..........	5.26	5.08	4.96	4.82
Metaphenylene diamine:				
Power factor.................	0.0231	0.0180	0.0163	0.0202
After 24 hr in water..........	0.526	0.0347	0.0213	0.0211
Dielectric constant.............	5.68	5.25	5.38	5.22
After 24 hr in water..........	6.03	5.66	5.44	5.23
Dicyandiamide:				
Power factor.................	0.0093	0.0080	0.0102	0.0219
After 24 hr in water..........	0.0213	0.0106	0.0108	0.0226
Dielectric constant.............	5.35	5.27	5.22	5.05
After 24 hr in water..........	5.44	5.35	5.27	5.12
Phenolic resin:				
Power factor.................	0.0218	0.0197	0.0127	0.0157
After 24 hr in water..........	0.0866	0.0784	0.0331	0.0213
Dielectric constant.............	4.65	4.49	4.38	4.33
After 24 hr in water..........	5.69	5.10	4.76	4.51

TABLE 10-13. Typical Electrical Properties of Epoxy-phenolic Blend Laminate Catalyzed by 0.5 Per Cent Alpha-Methylbenzyl Dimethylamine (10-10)

(Test conditions: room temperature, except as noted)

Cure cycle:
Pressed at 400 psi for 1 hour at 160°C
Postcured 8 hours at 160°C

Electrical Properties

Power factor, 10^6 cycles/sec:	
Dry...	0.010–0.018
After 2 days in water........................	0.010–0.020
After 2 days in water at 50°C................	0.014–0.021
Dielectric constant, 10^6 cycles/sec:	
Dry...	4.2–4.9
After 2 days in water........................	4.6–5.1
After 2 days in water at 50°C................	5.0–5.2
Loss factor, 10^6 cycles/sec:	
Dry...	0.04–0.09
After 2 days in water........................	0.05–0.10
After 2 days in water at 50°C................	0.06–0.11
Dielectric strength:	
Perpendicular to laminations, volts/mil..........	450–500
After 2 days in water at 50°C................	350–450
Arc resistance, sec.............................	150–180
Insulation resistance, megohms..................	$1–3 \times 10^5$

TABLE 10-14. Effect of Temperature on Electrical Properties of Typical
PMDA and PMDA/MA Cured Laminates (5-7)

(Test conditions: 10^3 cycles/sec)

Electrical properties	PMDA		PMDA/MA	
	Cured 24 hr at 180°C	Aged 200 hr at 200°C	Cured 24 hr at 180°C	Aged 200 hr at 260°C
Dielectric constant:				
At 23°C	4.06	4.67	4.11	4.20
At 100°C	4.94	4.72	4.43	5.21
At 150°C	4.96	4.69	4.51	5.21
At 200°C	4.97	4.77	5.38	5.21
Power factor:				
At 23°C	0.0031	0.0052	0.0041	0.0044
At 100°C	0.0053	0.0031	0.0034	0.0036
At 150°C	0.0071	0.0035	0.0047	0.0038
At 200°C	0.0650	0.0052	0.0136	0.0042

TABLE 10-15. Typical Electrical Properties for Laminates Flexibilized with
Polysulfide (7-6)

(Test conditions: room temperature)

Resins: Epoxy, molecular weight 350 to 400
       Polysulfide, molecular weight 1,000
Curing agent: Tridimethyl amino methyl phenol
Cure cycle:
    Pressed 30 minutes at 120°C

Electrical properties	Polysulfide, phr						
	0	16.7	20	25	33.3	50	100
Dielectric constant:							
At 10^3 cycles/sec	4.4	4.6	4.6	4.7	4.9	5.0	5.2
At 10^9 cycles/sec	3.6	3.6	3.8	3.8	4.0	4.1	4.2
Loss factor:							
At 10^3 cycles/sec	0.0020	0.0026	0.0028	0.0030	0.0033	0.0035	0.0040
At 10^9 cycles/sec	0.021	0.011	0.013	0.014	0.016	0.019	0.023

Chemical Resistance

Chemically resistant rust-free pipes represent one of the largest potential markets for epoxy laminates.   Because of this, increasing attention is being given to studies intended to show loss of strength or other changes in properties caused by exposures to chemical environments.

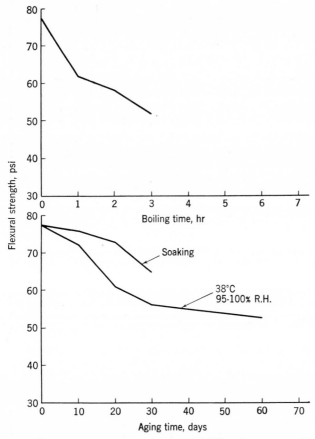

FIG. 10-10. Effect of water on glass-fiber laminate of 1,000 mol. wt epoxy resin cured with 4 phr dicyandiamide (10-13).

Water is the most common fluid which must be resisted, and in this connection, epoxy laminates are superior to both phenolics and polyesters (10-10).

The general effect of water on resin strength and glass strength is augmented by the lubricating effect of water on the coefficient of friction between the resin and glass fiber.   Thus, as outlined earlier, once the

TABLE 10-16. Chemical Resistance of Metaphenylene Diamine Laminate (3-7)
(Test conditions: room temperature)

Epoxy resin, molecular weight 350 to 400
Cure cycle:
  Pressed at 150°C at 200 psi for 15 minutes
  Postcured 1 hour at 204°C

System tested in	Per cent weight gain, immersion period, days			Flexural strength after 1 year immersion, psi	Flexural modulus after 1 year immersion, psi $\times 10^{-6}$
	30	180	365		
Sulfuric acid 95%	Delaminated after 7 days				
Sulfuric acid 70%	0.20	0.34	0.42	72,000	3.4
Sulfuric acid 3%	−0.09	−0.45*	0.09	48,000	2.2
Hydrochloric acid 37%	−0.21	−5.7	......	40,200†	2.6†
Hydrochloric acid 10%	0.00	−0.09	−0.32	49,900	2.6
Nitric acid 50%	Top layer delaminated				
Nitric acid 30%	−0.21	−4.8	......	13,700†	1.9†
Phosphoric acid 98%	0.10	0.74	0.90	67,300	2.9
Phosphoric acid 10%	0.27	0.54	0.65	66,600	2.9
Acetic acid, glacial	0.34	0.42	0.25	65,200	3.0
Acetic acid 10%	0.29	0.62	0.73	61,300	3.3
Oxalic acid, saturated	0.24	2.5	......	43,000†	2.4†
Sodium hydroxide 50%	−0.23	−1.3	......	66,900†	2.3†
Sodium hydroxide 1%	0.17	0.36	0.50	64,500	3.0
Ammonium hydroxide 28%	0.70	2.3	2.4	24,400	2.8
Sodium chloride 20%	0.24	0.40	0.67	69,300	3.4
Sodium sulfate 30%	0.24	0.64	0.74	67,200	3.5
Ammonium nitrate 50%	0.21	0.60	0.73	56,200	2.7
Acetone	0.33	1.0	......	53,000†	2.8†
Ethyl acetate	0.45	0.45	0.72	65,500	2.9
Ethylene dichloride	0.35	0.59	0.55	66,000	2.7
Ethylene glycol	−0.03	−0.23	0.09	70,300	3.1
Hydraulic brake fluid	0.18	0.40	0.54	64,800	3.5
Jet fuel	0.08	0.14	0.32	71,800	3.2
108 octane gasoline	0.07	0.13	0.31	66,400	3.1
Methyl ethyl ketone	0.24	0.34	0.35	72,700	2.9
Isopropyl alcohol	−0.02	−0.05	0.01	65,700	3.5
Allyl chloride	0.08	0.72	1.1	69,400	2.9
Hydrogen peroxide	Delaminated				
Water, distilled	0.21	0.67	0.63	70,900	3.7

* 90-day data.
† 180-day data.

adhesive bond between the glass fiber and resin has been broken by stressing, then only the resin shrinkage pressure against the glass fiber holds the laminate in place. Because this is a friction mechanism, and water is a lubricant, the strength of the laminate is appreciably reduced (Fig. 10-10). Studies are in progress designed to improve this parameter. Other chemicals than water also result in significant reduction in properties. The action of some of these is emphasized by any tendency of the

TABLE 10-17. Chemical Resistance of Chlorendic Anhydride Laminate (3-9)
(Test conditions: room temperature, 30 days immersion)

Epoxy resin: molecular weight 400 to 450
Cure cycle:
  Pressed 90 minutes at 150°C

System tested in	Weight gain, %	Dimensional change, %	Flexural strength retained, %	Flexural modulus retained, %
Distilled water...................	0.272	0.000	91	100
Hydrogen peroxide 3%...........	0.188	0.000	32	61
Sulfuric acid 3%.................	−0.266	0.000	86	100
Hydrochloric acid 10%..........	−3.61	0.000	49	70
Nitric acid 10%.................	−0.119	0.000	41	82
Acetic acid 5%.................	0.173	0.000	100	100
Ammonium hydroxide 10%.......	0.236	0.000	91	100
Sodium chloride 10%............	0.015	0.000	100	100
Isopropyl alcohol 98%...........	0.017	0.000	100	100
Hydrocarbon fluid 100%.........	0.089	.....	98	100
Boiling water, 3 hr..............	....	.....	83.4	100
Refluxing acetone, 3 hr..........	....	.....	78.8	70

reagent to swell or dissolve the cured resin. Chemical resistance of a particular system can be estimated from data provided for unfilled castings. Specific data for a laminate cured by an aromatic amine are presented in Table 10-16 and for an anhydride cured system in Table 10-17.

The effect of oxidizing environments, particularly long exposure at elevated temperatures, is of interest in many applications. Typical weight-loss data for systems cured with pyromellitic dianhydride are given in Table 10-8.

CONCLUSION

Epoxy–glass cloth laminates are extremely versatile and may be used for a variety of industrial applications, from lightweight printed circuit bases to large chemically resistant piping.

The laminates depend, for their ultimate properties, on the particular glass cloth or mat selected, together with the resin system, the exact cure cycle, and the cure pressure employed.

Wet lay-ups employing liquid resins together with amine, amide, or anhydride curing agents may be formulated.   Dry lay-ups may be used, formulated from B-staged 100 per cent solids or solvent systems, and may use either liquid or solid epoxy resins, the latter being more common.   In general, the B-staged systems give short storage lives; the solvent systems, extended storage lives.

Production techniques may involve contact-pressure laminating, low-pressure laminating, or high-pressure laminating, with the particular system being based, to an extent, on the ultimate properties, but strongly considering the exact production situation.

The epoxy–glass cloth laminates provide mechanical properties superior to the polyesters, electrical properties superior to the phenolics, and moisture resistance superior to both.   The properties of the laminate can be varied rather widely, as is the case with other epoxy systems, by the selection of modifying agents, and because of this versatility, the epoxy–glass cloth laminates are finding increasing use in industry.

References

10-1. Outwater, The Mechanics of Plastics Reinforcement in Tension, *Modern Plastics*, March, 1956.
10-2. Charity, New Honeycomb Processing Method, *Machine and Tool Blue Book*, February, 1954.
10-3. Rejda and Moreland, Epoxies Get Tough Guard Duty, *Plant Engineering*, May, 1956.
10-4. Plastic Tooling, *Industrial Design*, October, 1954.
10-5. Epoxy Low-pressure Laminates, *Machine Design*, July, 1954.
10-6. Swackhammer, Reinforced Plastic Replaces Aluminum, *Aero Digest*, January, 1955.
10-7. Brookfield, Some Aspects of the Use of Glass Fibres for the Reinforcement of Epoxy Resins, paper presented at Symposium of British Society of the Chemical Industry, April, 1956.
10-8. Marblette Corporation, sales literature.
10-9. Parallel Glass Fibre Reinforcement for Plastic Laminates, U.S. Department of Commerce, OTS PB 111719, 1954.
10-10. Godard, Thomas, and Welch, Epoxy Resins in Reinforced Plastics, paper presented at Eleventh Conference, Reinforced Plastics Division of the Society of Plastics Industry, 1956.
10-11. Elam and Hopper, Structural Laminates from Epoxy Resin Adhesives, *Modern Plastics*, October, 1954.
10-12. Sokol, Epoxies for Tools and Dies, *Tooling and Production*, August, 1955.
10-13. Elam, private communication, Shell Development Corp.

11

COATINGS

Coating formulations absorb the majority of epoxy-resin production. In coating formulations, the epoxies provide chemical resistance superior to the alkyds, and it was, in fact, the search for a chemically resistant thermosetting coating containing no vulnerable ester linkages that helped lead to their discovery and synthesis.

In addition to chemical resistance, epoxy resins possess tenacious adhesion and extreme toughness (for a rigid coating), and their exploitation awaited only the end of World War II, when epichlorohydrin became commercially available to make large-scale production of the resins feasible.

Since that time, the use of epoxy resins in coatings has grown rapidly, with the expectation that they will outstrip practically all other types of coating resins, despite their somewhat higher cost.

Coating formulations may be of three types: (1) 100 per cent solids coatings, (2) nonesterified solution coatings, and (3) esterified solution coatings.

100 PER CENT SOLIDS COATINGS

Coatings designated as 100 per cent solids coatings contain no volatiles which must be driven off during cure. Such coatings are based on the low-viscosity liquid epoxy resins, and the resin itself thus serves as a vehicle and wetting agent for the pigmenting and opacifying fillers and flow-control agents which may be required.

The 100 per cent solids coatings are formulated in much the same fashion as are the compounds employed for encapsulating operations (Chap. 8) and can be designed to provide build-ups of a few mils to $\frac{1}{16}$ in. or more in a single pass. Such compounds possess inherent advantages and disadvantages which combine to make them of significance only in specialized applications.

The 100 per cent solids coatings provide for thick build-ups in a single application, and since cure is accomplished without the release of solvents, there are no minute pinholes and passageways present in the film to admit contaminants to the protected components.   This ultimate protection, together with the maximum electrical properties and chemical resistance of the liquid epoxy resins, may be achieved without baking cycles and within a very few hours at ambient temperature.   The coatings can be applied to heat- or solvent-sensitive surfaces, and they are

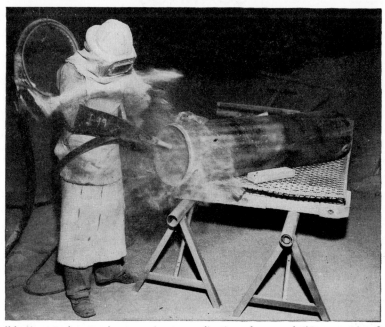

Sandblasting steel water heater prior to application of epoxy baking varnish. Sandblasting assures grease-free bonding surface as well as surface roughening desired to provide mechanical as well as chemical bonding of coating.   (*Shell Chemical Co.*)

particularly convenient for coating small areas exposed to extremes of environment and for protection of in-place structural members.

The disadvantages of the 100 per cent solids coatings have militated against their widespread use.   These can be summarized as (1) brittleness, (2) poor resistance to higher temperatures and thermal cycling, (3) comparatively high cost, and (4) short pot life.

The brittleness is inherent in the thickness of the coating.   It may be greatly reduced by flexibilizers, although at the expense of chemical resistance.   The poor performance during thermal cycling is attributable to the build-ups and the high coefficients of thermal expansion of the only slightly filled resins.   The high cost is a direct reflection of the high resin content.   The short pot life is a function of the curing agent.   Since

100 per cent solids coatings are not conveniently amenable to baking cycles, room-temperature curing agents must be employed. If baking-type curing agents are used, the coated component must be allowed to stand at room temperature until the coating has progressed well into B-stage; otherwise, upon application of heat, runoff will be uncontrollable. The high viscosities have militated against spray equipment, but progress at developing guns capable of handling the systems is being made.

Epoxy-resin varnish on steel panel at left, held at 88°C for 2 years, blistered slightly but did not rupture. Porcelain-coated panel at right, after same exposure, shows rust spots in center. (*Shell Chemical* Co.)

As is expected, a variety of 100 per cent solids coatings may be formulated, depending on the end use. A typical formulation can be given as:

Epoxy resin (molecular weight 350–400)	100 parts
Chemically treated Bentonite	15 parts
Black oxide	5 parts
Diethylene triamine	10 parts

NON-ESTER CONTAINING SOLUTION COATINGS

Non-ester containing epoxy-resin films are extremely tough, hard, and chemically resistant. Electrical properties and moisture resistance are outstanding. In spite of the toughness of the cured film, it can be flexed or bent as much as 180 degrees without cracking. This flexibility has been attributed to the long chains and well-spaced hydroxyl groups of the epoxy resins. Unlike most film-forming resins, no flexibilizers need be introduced into the formulation to degrade the excellent properties.

The color properties of the films are good, and in most cases, white and pastel shades may be achieved easily. This parameter will depend to some extent on the curing agent employed and whether or not phenolic hydroxyls are present in the cured film. It may likewise be a function of

Four solvent tanks with a top coat of white amine-catalyzed air-cure epoxy paint. Solvents attacked previous coatings. (*Shell Chemical* Co.)

baking schedules. In all cases, darker colors with good stability are realizable. Resistance to weathering is generally good. The adhesion, like the chemical resistance, is extremely high, and the coatings can, therefore, be applied without the use of time-consuming primers—or, in fact, can be used as highly resistant primer coatings.

For general-purpose coating work, the relatively high cost of non-ester epoxy formulations is not always justified. Wear and abrasion resistance makes them suitable for durable industrial floor coatings. Resistance to staining and acid and caustic attack makes them valuable as enamels for some items of household equipment. Excellent electrical insulating varnishes may be formulated; and the coatings can be used as can linings where flexibility and chemical resistance are mandatory. Because of their highly adhesive nature, epoxy varnishes can, in a limited number of instances, be employed as extremely convenient and inexpensive structural adhesives.

Epoxy coatings may be formulated either as air-dry or baking-type films, depending on the selection of curing agent. They may be applied by all conventional techniques, but the faster air-drying enamels require the use of spray equipment containing dual-metered nozzles in order to prevent polymerization in the spray gun.

Tanks containing hydrochloric acid, sulfuric acid, and solvents, as well as plant structure in background, are protected by air-cure epoxy paint. (*Shell Chemical* Co.)

Although emulsions are theoretically possible and some data are available on their properties, the coating formulations are based primarily, and almost exclusively, on solvent systems.

The principal considerations for these reduced-solids coatings are (1) resin, (2) solvent vehicle, (3) curing agents and modifiers, and (4) pigments.

These factors will be considered in sequence, and typical formulations will be given in conclusion.

Resin

The higher-molecular-weight resins are preferred to the liquids in solution coatings from the standpoint of both cost and cured properties. These molecules have a degree of polymerization between $n = 3$ and $n = 12$. Although some overlapping of applications occurs, the resins

TABLE 11-1. Compatibility of Solid Epoxy Resins with Various Coating Materials (11-12)

(Test specimen: 1½ mil dry film—force dried 1 hour at 100°C)

	Molecular weight of resin and per cent present											
	1,000			1,500			3,000			4,000		
	90 %	50 %	10 %	90 %	50 %	10 %	90 %	50 %	10 %	90 %	50 %	10 %
Typical commercial alkyd resins:												
Alkyd, short, soy	I	I	I	I	I	I	I	I	I	I	I	I
Alkyd, medium, soy	SI	I	I	I	I	I	I	I	I	I	I	I
Alkyd, long, soy	C	I	I	I	I	I	I	I	I	I	I	I
Alkyd, styrenated	C	I	I	I	I	I	I	I	I	I	I	I
Alkyd, nondrying	C	C	C	C	C	C	C	C	C	C	C	C
Alkyd, nondrying	C	I	C	I	I	I	I	I	I	I	I	I
Typical commercial phenolic resins pure and modified:												
Phenolic	C	C	C	C	C	C	C	C	C	C	C	C
Phenolic, rosin mod	I	I	I	I	I	I	I	I	I	SI	I	I
Typical commercial cellulose derivatives:												
Cellulose acetate	I	I	I	I	I	I	I	I	I	I	I	I
Cellulose nitrate, RS	I	I	I	I	I	I	I	I	I	I	I	I
Ethyl cellulose	SI	I	I	I	I	I	I	I	I	I	I	I
Typical commercial amino resins:												
Melamine formaldehyde	SI	I	I	I	I	I	I	I	I	I	I	I
Sulfonamide	C	C	C	C	C	C	C	C	C	C	C	C
Urea formaldehyde	C	C	C	C	C	C	C	C	C	C	C	C
Typical commercial chlorinated derivatives:												
Chlorinated biphenyl	C	C	I	C	C	I	C	C	I	C	I	I
Chlorinated rubber	SI	SI	SI	I	I	I	I	I	I	I	I	I
Typical commercial vinyl derivatives:												
Polyvinyl acetate	C	C	C	C	C	C	C	I	I	I	I	I
Polyvinyl chloride acetate	I	I	I	I	I	I	I	I	I	I	I	I
Polyvinyl formal	C	C	C	C	C	C	C	C	C	C	C	C
Typical miscellaneous commercial compounds:												
Blown linseed oil	C	I	I	I	I	I	I	I	I	I	I	I
Butyl acetyl ricinoleate	C	I	C	C	I	I	I	I	I	I	I	I
Dammar	C	SI	C	SI	I	C	SI	I	SI	SI	I	SI
Ester gum	I	I	SI	I	I	I	I	I	I	I	I	I
Ester gum, maleic	I	C	C	I	I	C	I	I	I	I	I	I
Terpene resin	I	I	I	I	I	I	I	I	I	I	I	I
Cumarone resin	I	I	C	I	I	C	I	I	I	I	I	I
Styrenated polyester	SI	I	I	I	I	I	I	I	I	I	I	I

C—Compatible, bright clear film.
SI—Slightly incompatible, slight haze or smoke appearance.
I—Incompatible, cloudy films.

having molecular weights in the 1,000 range (and consequently containing a greater number of epoxy groups) are most suitable for use with amine curing agents. The resins having molecular weights from 3,000 to 4,000 are preferred for use with urea and phenolic resinous curing agents. The resins of an intermediate degree of polymerization (i.e., with molecular weights from 1,500 to 2,000) are best suited for ester formation, as discussed subsequently. Liquid resins may be employed alone or with the higher-weight species when necessary to achieve solution coatings of high solids content (11-11).

The epoxy resins are compatible with a number of other coating materials, for which they may be used as up-grading agents. They may be used with vinyls, for instance, to improve performance at higher temperatures (Chap. 6) and even in amounts on the order of 1 per cent are effective antichalking agents, although straight epoxy coatings themselves have poor chalk resistance. Table 11-1 indicates the compatibility characteristics.

It is necessary, of course, not only to select the proper resin for the given application, but to determine, as well, the solids content most suitable for the job. The solids contents of commercial formulations will vary from about 20 to 70 per cent for most applications. The concentration will determine the thickness of a single build-up, but should not be considered as a qualitative guide to performance. Several coats of a low-solids system will provide increased resistance over single coats of high-solids systems, primarily because the multiple coats reduce the possibility of continuous passageways (formed during the evaporation of the solvent) from the surface of the coating to the surface of the component being protected.

Solvents

The solvent system is employed to provide a fluid carrier for the solid resin, enabling convenient deposition of a smooth, continuous film on the surface to be coated; the solvent is thereafter evaporated.

The uncured epoxy resins are soluble in oxygenated solvents, such as ketones, esters, and ethers, and in highly halogenated hydrocarbons, although the efficiency of the solvents declines with increasing polymerization. Aromatic solvents, such as toluene and xylene, as well as simple alcohols, such as isopropyl and n-butyl alcohol, are not active solvents for the epoxies; however, in combination, they develop latent solvency for the resins. Table 11-2 presents data on various solvents vs. viscosity for epoxy resins in the 1,000 to 4,000 molecular-weight range.

Coating formulations inevitably involve a combination of true solvents

TABLE 11-2. Solubility Characteristics of Solid Epoxy Resin (11-12)

Solvent	Viscosity of 50% w resin solution (Gardner-Holdt, 25°C) Molecular weight of resin			
	1,000	1,500	3,000	4,000
Ketones:				
Acetone			$G-H$	
Methyl ethyl ketone	A_3	A	$I-J$	$U-V$
Methyl i-butyl ketone	A	F	W	Z_{1-3}
Diacetone alcohol			Z_{5-6}	
Isophorone			Z_6	
Esters:				
Ethyl acetate			Y	
n-Butyl acetate			X	
Cellosolve* acetate	F	Q	Y	Z_5
Ether alcohols:				
Methyl Cellosolve			Y	
Ethyl Cellosolve	F	Q	$Y-Z$	Z_{4-5}
Butyl Cellosolve			Z_3	
Ethyl Carbitol*			Z	
Butyl Carbitol			Z_5	
Chlorinated solvents:				
Trichloropropane			Z_6	
Chloroform	$H-I$	W	Z_{5-6}	Z_6
Mixed solvents:				
Toluene-acetone, 1-1			K	
Toluene-methyl ethyl ketone, 1-1			N	
Toluene-methyl i-butyl ketone, 1-1	A_1	$G-H$	$U-V$	Z_{1-2}
Toluene-diacetone alcohol, 1-1			Y	
Toluene-isoporone, 1-1			Z_{1-2}	
Toluene-i-propyl alcohol, 1-1			X	
Toluene-s-butyl alcohol, 1-1			$Z-Z_1$	
Toluene-methyl i-butyl carbinol, 1-1			Z_1	
Toluene-Cellosolve acetate, 1-1	A	K	Z	Z_2

* Union Carbide Chemicals Company.

and thinners. The thinners are employed to reduce cost and regulate the viscosity. Fast evaporating solutions are based on low-boiling ketones, such as acetone or methyl ethyl ketone; slow evaporating solutions are based on the higher-boiling materials and, when used to improve leveling properties, may contain up to 25 per cent cyclohexanol added to the thinner. Typical solvent systems might consist of methyl isobutyl ketone, Cellosolve acetate, and xylene at a 1:1:1 ratio. Figure 11-1 pre-ents viscosity vs. solids content for two typical solvent solutions and various molecular weight epoxy resins.

By proper combination of solvents and thinners, it is possible to reduce viscosity of a given resin system while preserving the solids content at a given per cent. For instance, in a typical formulation (11-12) involving

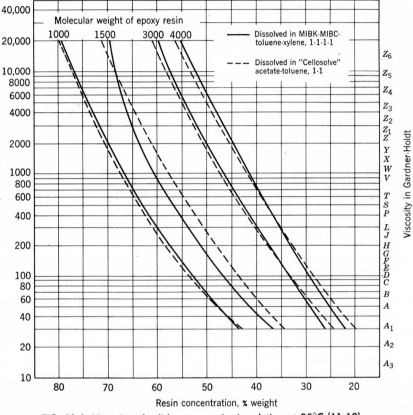

FIG. 11-1. Viscosity of solid epoxy resins in solution at 25°C (11-12).

70 per cent solids the resin may be combined with

Methyl isobutyl ketone........... 33
Cellosolve...................... 33
Xylene......................... 34

at a 70:30 ratio to give a brushing viscosity of 5,000 centipoises at room temperature. At the same ratio, combined with

Methyl isobutyl ketone........... 45
Butyl Cellosolve................ 5
Toluene........................ 50

a varnish having a spraying consistency of 2,400 centipoises at room temperature will be achieved.

If reduced solids content is permissible, the solution may be cut until the desired consistency is reached.   A thinner for the above spraying composition would consist of n-butanol and toluene at $1:1$.   A solvent for the above spraying composition might consist of methyl isobutyl ketone, cyclohexanol, and toluene at $1:1:2$.   If the solids content is reduced to 40 per cent with such thinners, or solvents, the room-temperature viscosity of the coating will be reduced to about 30 centipoises.

Ester-type solvents, such as Cellosolve acetate, should be avoided in formulations employing amine curing agents, since the esters react with the caustic amines and inhibit proper cure.   And, for some applications where sensitive surfaces are involved, the solvent system will be selected with that parameter in mind; likewise, the method of pigmentation employed may dictate the less volatile systems.

Curing Agents and Modifiers

Ureas, phenolics, melamines, polyamides, polysulfides, polyamines, and acids may be employed as curing agents for solution-coating epoxy resins. They may be considered to fall into two classes: the air-dry and the baking type.   The air drys consist of the polyamines, the polyamides, the polysulfides, and certain acids; the baking type are predominantly the ureas and phenolic resins.   With phenolic resins, catalytic amounts of an acid or of dicyandiamide are required to achieve convenient cures; accelerators, likewise, may be used with the ureas, but here stability poses a problem.   The primary use of urea resin modifiers is for controlling flow.

Air-dry Coatings.   *The primary aliphatic amines* are the most widely used curing agents for air-dry solution coatings.   In most respects, they can be considered to provide air-drying films that exceed, in performance, the best that can be offered by baking-type coatings based on other thermosetting resins.

Typical amines employed in solution coatings are ethylene diamine, diethylene triamine, diethylamino propylamine, etc.   Films formed by these agents may readily be hardened at room temperatures or may be forced dried or baked.   "Dry-to-handle" time will depend on the curing agent and on the amount of solvent present.   The range for most will fall between 4 and 6 hours, although ultimate properties may not be realized until up to one week at room temperature.   For this reason, even though the films are air-drying, bakes are often employed.   Baking temperatures are quite low, however, and baking cycles are conveniently short.   The following may be considered typical:

120 minutes at	38°C
90 minutes at	45°C
20 minutes at	93°C
10 minutes at	120°C
4 minutes at	177°C
2 minutes at	204°C
1 minute at	232°C

If multiple coats are employed to reduce pinhole failures in the film, baking schedules should provide for escape of solvents between coatings, with the final cure being the extended value. If higher-temperature bakes are used, ethylene diamine in particular should be avoided, since its low boiling point will permit it to volatilize and escape the film.

The amines, when used with the 1,000 molecular-weight epoxy resins, are employed at about 6 phr. Since they are reactive at room temperature, there will be a progressive increase in the viscosity. The amines are, therefore, packaged separately, usually, for convenience, in a solvent system. For diethylene triamine, for example, the solvent might be n-butanol and toluene at 1:1 employed on a 50 per cent weight basis.

Pot life of the amine-resin blend will depend on the solvent concentration and will range from 8 hours to several days at room temperature. However, the progressive increase in viscosity may require periodic thinning, with the consequent reduction in solids content. Viscosity data for paints containing two typical amines are presented in Fig. 11-2.

If humid conditions prevail, or if the amine-catalyzed system is applied too quickly after mixing (it normally should be allowed to stand an hour or so), blushing is likely to occur. In pigmented coatings, gloss will not be too satisfactory, and the amines in general tend to provide relatively poor color characteristics in clear films if the bakes are on the order of 100 to 120°C or higher. Diethylamino propylamine and benzyldimethyl-amine are reportedly superior in this property.

Polyamine-cured epoxy-resin coatings modified with coal-tar products have also been introduced and offer good over-all properties (11-9).

The polyamides may be employed in solution coatings where high orders of adhesion and flexibility are required, such as for paper coating. Additionally, the surface-active nature of the polyamide resins makes it possible to deposit firmly adhering films even on wet and rusty surfaces. Loose, flaky rust, of course, must be removed. Rusty panels which have been coated in this manner with a 1.5-mil protective layer show no further signs of corrosion after 336 hours in salt spray. Cold pipes or machinery can thus be painted while in a humid atmosphere.

As presented in Chap. 7, the low-melting-point solid resins and the high-viscosity liquid polyamides are the preferred class. They provide for somewhat extended pot lives, but in respect to most other handling characteristics, they are similar to the primary amines, and, as is the case with primary amines, cure can be accelerated by bakes, if required, the curing schedules cited previously being considered typical.

The polyamides are employed with the 400 and 1,000 molecular-weight resins.   In the case of low-melting-point solid polyamides, a ratio of about 100 phr is employed; in the case of the fluid polyamides, about 54 phr.

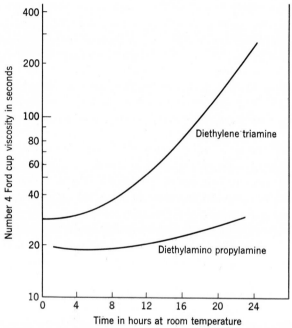

FIG. 11-2. Effect of amine curing agents on room-temperature viscosities (11-10).

The amount will be critical in terms of cured properties, and the manufacturer's recommendations should be adhered to.

Like the polyamines, the polyamides must be packaged separately. The solid materials may be dissolved in isopropyl alcohol and toluene at 1:1, or the solvent system used for the resin may be employed.   The liquid polyamides may be packaged with the solvent-containing flow-control agent (when used) or may be cut with a thinner such as xylene and butanol at 9:1.

In addition to greater flexibility and impact strength, the polyamides, compared to the more widely used polyamines, provide superior gloss retention and somewhat better blush resistance, although initial color is inferior (11-1). Some loss of chemical and solvent resistance will be experienced.

Water-based polyamide-epoxy emulsion paints can be prepared without special equipment from a commercially available polyamide-emulsion base. Films from emulsion mixtures offer nearly the same protection as solvent coatings, but have less gloss and clarity. Because the polyamide is a corrosion inhibitor, these emulsion paints can be used even on steel surfaces and are also suitable for masonry surfaces.

Organic acids may be used in catalytic amounts to provide extremely fast-drying surface coatings, but the cure is too fast for most applications. Sulfonic acids are reported to be extremely efficient in this regard (11-2). Using, for example, 1 phr of *m*-benzene disulfonic acid, a gel time of 4½ minutes will be realized. Where such drying speeds are essential, the solution coating can be applied with a dual-nozzle spray gun which provides proper metering of the ingredients. With *p*-toluene sulfonic acid, a suitable solvent is *n*-butyl acetate at 9 parts solvent to 1 part acid. If this system is used to cure a urea formaldehyde-epoxy resin film, sprayed coatings will be dry to touch in 10 minutes and hard enough for sanding at the end of 1 hour. Full cure is apparently realized thereafter by room-temperature aging.

Polysulfides may be employed, as the polyamides are, to produce extremely flexible and impact-resistant coatings. As would be expected from the discussion in Chap. 7, although a second curing agent is employed, the polysulfide and resin are packaged separately. If tri-dimethyl amino methyl phenol is used, the following cure schedules are adequate:

30 minutes at	66°C
15 minutes at	93°C
5 minutes at	120°C
4 minutes at	150°C
3 minutes at	177°C

Room-temperature cures will be realized in about 3 days.

The amount of polysulfide may conveniently be regulated to provide the desired properties, with a 50 phr ratio being satisfactory for high flexibility. The polysulfide and curing agent, when compatible, are packaged in one container, the resin in the other. The polysulfide may be thinned with a suitable material, such as methyl ethyl ketone.

Heat-convertible Curing Agents. Although less oxidation resistant than the vinyls, the baking-type coatings are highly flexible, tough, and heat resistant and provide better all-around properties than do the air-dry types. A quantitative study of the oxidation tendencies of epoxy films (11-13) indicated that the time and temperature of the final bake influenced the subsequent oxidation rate of the film (and hence, higher temperature performance)—lower baking temperatures yielding better stability. The more complete the cure, however, in terms of epoxy conversion, the greater the resistance to oxidation. The nature of the solvents, solvent concentration, air-dry time prior to bake, and film thickness appear to have little effect on oxidation rates.

Baking-type coatings, unlike the air dries, may be formulated as indefinitely stable one-container systems. The improvement in properties must be weighed against the high baking temperatures required to achieve cured films.

The urea formaldehyde and phenol formaldehyde resins are the most widely used curing agents for the heat-convertible systems. Although they provide comparable properties, each possesses points of superiority. The ureas provide for lower temperature cures and yield films of superior color; the phenolics provide optimum chemical and solvent resistance and yield films of superior heat stability. As indicated previously, they are used with epoxy resins having molecular weights in the 3,000 to 4,000 range.

Urea formaldehyde resins are used at about 33 phr and may be of varying degrees of reactivity. They are available commercially in solutions at solid contents in the neighborhood of 60 per cent. Common solvents are xylene and butanol at 4:6. A typical commercial product of higher reactivity is Beckamine P-196 (Reichold Chemicals, Inc.). It gives pot lives in the resin mix on the order of 1 to 2 months. A commercial product of lower reactivity is Beetle 227-8 (American Cyanamid Co.), which provides a system stable at room temperature for over 2 years.

A typical formulation using the more reactive curing agent will achieve satisfactory cures at the following schedules:

60 minutes at.......... 120°C
20 minutes at.......... 150°C
6 minutes at.......... 177°C
3 minutes at.......... 204°C

For the less reactive urea formaldehydes, cure temperatures will be somewhat higher for a given time period.

Phenol formaldehyde resins are used at about 43 phr and provide systems indefinitely stable at room temperatures; in fact, an acid catalyst used at 1 to 2 per cent is usually employed to accelerate cure. The preferred class of phenolic resins is apparently the resol type, i.e., containing etherified or unetherified methylol groups (11-3). Typical commercial materials are Durez 15956 (Durez Plastics and Chemical Company, Inc.) and Methylon 75108 (General Electric Company). The phenol formaldehyde system, employing 1.5 per cent phosphoric acid, cures as follows:

60 minutes at..........	150°C
30 minutes at..........	177°C
20 minutes at..........	190°C
10 minutes at..........	204°C

Because of the presence of phenolic hydroxyls in the cured system, the color characteristics will be somewhat less satisfactory than for other curing agents.

Flow-control Agents. Flow-control agents may be required with some formulations to reduce surface tension and improve leveling. Of the various materials evaluated in the literature, three seem extremely good: polyvinyl butyral, certain silicones, and certain ureas. Typical commercial compounds are, in order, Butvar B-76 (Monsanto Chemical Company), SR-82 (General Electric Company), and Beetle 216-8 (American Cyanamid Company).

The flow-control agents are used in small amounts, on the order of 1 to 3 per cent, and their application is indicated subsequently with regard to specific formulations.

Pigments

Most conventional paint pigments can be used with epoxy coating formulations, although a few should be avoided. Zinc fillers tend, in most cases, to affect the curing mechanisms, and alkaline and metallic pigments should be avoided if acidic curing agents are employed. Typical suitable materials are cadmium sulfide, phthlocyanine blue and green, titanium dioxide, lamp black, carbon black, chromic oxide, calcium carbonate, toluidine red, etc. Metal primers based on red lead, red iron oxide, etc., likewise may be used with success.

The resin may be pigmented in the normal manner by the use of ball or roll mills.

As in the case of other coating formulations, gloss may be adjusted by varying the binder/pigment ratio as well as by the selection of curing agents.

Although the specific filler will dictate the effect, the general effect of chemically inert pigments is, as might be expected, to increase the cure time. With room-temperature curing agents, for instance, cure times are about doubled.

Formulation

The typical method for preparing a solution coating is to crush the solid resin and add to it the solvent system. Continuous agitation is maintained, employing a stirrer driven by an explosion-proof motor. At selected intervals, the other system components are added, either in solvent solution or as solids or liquids. The manufacturing procedure generally requires a period of several hours.

The following formulations have been given in the literature and are cited as typical.

Amine Coating (Bakelite VF-1974)

	Per cent by weight
Vehicle nonvolatiles—55%:	
Resin (mol. wt 1000)	97
Flow-control agent	3
Vehicle volatiles—45%:	
Toluene	50 (approx.)
Methyl isobutyl ketone	24 (approx.)
n-Butanol	23 (approx.)
Butyl Cellosolve	3 (approx.)
Amine volatiles:	
n-Butanol	34
Toluene	34
Water (from commercial-grade amine)	32

Curing agent: Diethylene triamine at 6 phr

Polyamide Coating (Bakelite VF-1973)

	Per cent by weight
Vehicle nonvolatiles—38.1%:	
Resin (mol. wt 1,000)	50
Polyamide (amine value 83–93)	50
Vehicle volatiles—61.9%:	
For resin:	
Xylene	50
Methyl isobutyl ketone	50
For polyamide:	
Xylene	90
Cellosolve	10

Polysulfide Coating (Thiokol T140-3)

	Per cent by weight
Vehicle nonvolatiles—80%:	
Resin (solid and liquid epoxy resin at 60/40 blend)	63⅓
Polysulfide (mol. wt 1,000)	31⅔
Flow-control agent	5
Vehicle volatiles—20%:	
For resin, 58%	
Methyl ethyl ketone	100
For polysulfide, 42%	
Methyl ethyl ketone	100

Curing agent: Tridimethyl amino methyl phenol at 10 phr, packaged with polysulfide

Urea Formaldehyde Coating (Shell YU-180)

Per cent by weight

Vehicle nonvolatile—30%:
Epoxy resin (mol. wt 3,000) 70
Urea formaldehyde resin....... 30
Vehicle volatiles—70%:
Methyl isobutyl carbinol... 25
Methyl isobutyl ketone.. 25
Toluene... 25
Xylene.. 25

Phenol Formaldehyde Coating (Shell YP-100)

Per cent by weight

Vehicle nonvolatiles—35%:
Epoxy resin (mol. wt 3,000) 73.1
Phenol formaldehyde resin....................................... 24.4
Flow-control agent... 1
Phosphoric acid.. 1.5
Vehicle volatiles—65%:
Methyl isobutyl carbinol... 25
Methyl isobutyl ketone.. 25
Toluene... 25
Xylene.. 25

Red Lead Primer Dispersion

Per cent by weight

Red lead.. 69
Diatomaceous silica... 6.5
Magnesium silicate.. 5.4
Aluminum stearate.. 0.3
Resin vehicle.. 18.8
Resin, 55%
Toluene, 22.5%
Methyl isobutyl ketone, 20.3%
Butyl Cellosolve, 2.2%
used at 79.5% in let down

Dark Green Enamel Dispersion

Per cent by weight

Phthalocyanine green... 25
Resin vehicle.. 75
Resin, 33⅓%
Butanol, 33⅓%
Toluene, 33⅓%
used at 44% in let down

Tables 11-3 to 11-5 present data for typical coating formulations.

TABLE 11-3. Properties of Typical Amine-cured Coating Formulation (3-7)

Chemical Resistance
(Test specimen: multicoat clear coatings on rounded end probes, average film
thickness 6 to 8 mils)

Solvent or reagent	Exposure time			
	1 week	2 weeks	1 month	2 months
Organic				
Acetone.	ss	ss	ss	
Methyl ethyl ketone.	ss	ss	ss	
Methyl isobutyl ketone.	ss	ss	ss	
Ethyl alcohol.	u	u	u	
Secondary butyl alcohol.	u	u	u	
Methyl isobutyl carbinol.	u	u	u	
Toluene.	u	u	u	
Xylene.	u	u	u	
Mineral spirits.	u	u	u	
Carbon tetrachloride.	u	u	u	
Allyl chloride.	u	s	s	
Formaldehyde 37% w.	Failed in 1 week			
Ethylene diamine.	Failed in 1 week			
Diethylene triamine.	Failed in 1 week			
Linseed fatty acid.	u	u	u	
Acetic acid 5% w.	u	u	u	
Acetic acid 50% w.	u	u	u	
Acetic acid, glacial.	Failed in 1 day			
Sodium methoxide 40% w.	u	u	u	
Detergent solution.	u	u	u	
Citric acid 10%.	u	u	u	
Inorganic				
Sodium hydroxide 20% w.	u	u	u	u
Ammonium hydroxide 27% w.	Failed in 1 week			
Ammonia vapor.	u	u	u	u
Phosphoric acid 85% w.	Failed in 1 day			
Hydrochloric acid 10% w.	u	u	u	u
Hydrochloric acid 20% w.	u	u	u	u
Hydrochloric acid 36% w.	u	u	u	u
Hydrochloric acid vapor.	u	u	u	u
Sulfuric acid 25% w.	u	u	u	Failed
Sulfuric acid 50% w.	u	u	u	Failed
Sulfuric acid 70% w.	u	Discolored	Discolored	Discolored

TABLE 11-3. Properties of Typical Amine-cured Coating Formulation (3-7) (Continued)

Chemical Resistance (Continued)

Solvent or reagent	Exposure time			
	1 week	2 weeks	1 month	2 months
Inorganic				
Sulfuric acid 80% w.............	Failed in 1 week			
Sulfuric acid 90% w.............	Failed in 1 day			
Nitric acid 10% w.............	u	u	u	Failed
Nitric acid 20% w.............	u	u	Failed	
Nitric acid 30% w.............	u	Failed		
Sodium chlorite 25% w...........	u	u	u	Failed
Sodium hypochlorite 5% w........	u	u	u	Failed
Calcium hypochlorite 5% w........	u	u	u	u
Water........................	u	u	u	u

u—Unaffected.
ss—Slightly softened.
s—Softened.

Physical Properties

Flexibility.................	Good
Impact resistance...........	Good
Hardness.................	Excellent
Outdoor durability.........	Excellent
Color....................	Very good
Abrasion resistance.........	Good

TABLE 11-4. Typical Properties of Polysulfide Epoxy-resin Coating (7-6)

Set time, min............................	95–110
Tack-free time, hr.......................	3
Cure time:	
To handle, hr...........................	5
Optimum cure, 5 mil thick, days...........	3
Adhesion to steel.........................	Good
Flexibility:	
0.125-in. rod...........................	Good
Conical mandrel, % elongation............	38
Impact resistance, in.-lb*..................	48
Scratch resistance........................	Good
Clarity..................................	Good
Chemical resistance at 54°C:	
Tap water.............................	Good
Synthetic sea water.....................	Good
Jet fuel, JP-4..........................	Good
Aromatic fuel, SR-6.....................	Good

* Gardner variable test.

TABLE 11-5. Resistance to Chemicals and Solvents of Epoxy Solution Coating Heat Converted by Phenol Formaldehyde Resin (3-7)

Film unaffected by a 3 months immersion in the following reagents at room temperature (all solutions are in water):

Alcohol:
Ethyl
Isopropyl
Secondary butyl
n-Butyl
Methyl isobutyl
Neosol
Neosol A
Diacetone
Hexylene glycol
Glycerine
Organic chlorides:
Carbon tetrachloride
Allyl chloride
Ketones and aldehydes:
Methyl isobutyl ketone
Formaldehyde (30%)
Cyclic hydrocarbons:
Toluene
Xylene
Ethers:
Diethyl ether
Bis (β-chloroethyl) ether

Bases:
Sodium hydroxide
   (all conc.)
Ammonium hydroxide (10%)
Acids:
Acetic: (1%)
Linseed fatty
Sulfuric (up to 75%)
Hydrochloric (up to 20%)
Nitric (up to 10%)
Phosphoric (up to 85%)
Miscellaneous reagents:
Liquid detergent (100%)
Liquid detergent (50%)
Solid detergent (1%)
Resitoxaphene
Sodium methoxide (40% in methanol)
Sodium chlorite (25%)
Sodium hypochlorite (5%)
Calcium hypochlorite (5%)
Ferric chloride (5%)
Water
Salt spray at 38°C for 500 hr

Film unaffected by the following materials, all exposed for 3 weeks at 66°C, except as noted:

Isopropyl alcohol
Secondary butyl alcohol
Methyl isobutyl carbinol
Neosol
Neosol A
Diacetone alcohol
Hexylene glycol

Methyl isobutyl ketone
Allyl chloride
20% sodium hydroxide (boiling, 24 hr)
73% sodium hydroxide (138°C, 2 weeks)
Glycerine
Glycerine (77°C, 6 weeks)
Water

Films slightly soften in 1 month exposure at room temperature to acetone, methyl ethyl ketone, ethylene dichloride, hydrochloric acid (36%), sulfuric acid (78%), and hydrogen peroxide (15%). The coating has limited resistance to sulfuric acid (at concentrations greater than 85%) and hydrogen peroxide (at concentrations greater than 15%).

EPOXY-RESIN ESTERS

It has been estimated that 50 per cent of all solid epoxy resins go into the production of epoxy esters for coating formulations. When used in this connection, the epoxy resins can be considered polymeric, polyhydric alcohols.

The esterification process consists of reacting the hydroxyl-bearing resins with acids:

$$R-\overset{\overset{\displaystyle O}{\|}}{C}-OH + HO-\overset{|}{\underset{|}{C}}- \rightarrow R-\overset{\overset{\displaystyle O}{\|}}{C}-O-\overset{|}{\underset{|}{C}}- + H_2O$$

to produce the ester linked system, with water being given off as a by-product.

The reaction is accomplished by cooking the two intermediates at 200 to 300°C until the reaction has progressed to the desired stage. A description from the literature (11-4) illustrates the process:

To 1 equivalent of a polymeric polyhydric alcohol (e.g., that prepared from bisphenol, epichlorohydrin, and phenol) in an apparatus equipped with a mechanical stirrer is added 0.9 to 0.95 mol of an unsaturated acid mixture, composed of the chain acids derived from drying oils, from semidrying oils, or from nondrying oils, of the glyceride type, or mixtures of such acids. The apparatus is equipped with a condenser attached thereto through a water trap, with a thermometer and with means for bubbling inert gas such as CO_2 through the reaction mixture during esterification Heat is applied, and after the polymeric polyhydric alcohol has melted, stirring is started and continued during esterification. A slow stream of an inert gas such as CO_2 is bubbled through the reaction mixture to aid in removing water formed during esterification. The reaction mixture is heated for, e.g., 4 to 5 hours at, e.g., 250 to 260°C, water of esterification being removed through the water trap. The resulting product is cut to the desired solid content by adding hydrocarbon solvents, and the resulting solutions form excellent compositions for making protective films adapted to harden on air oxidation or heat polymerization or both.

Preferred epoxy resins for esterification are those in the 1,500 to 2,000 molecular-weight range. Higher-weight resins, containing more numerous hydroxyls, will body during cook to yield high-viscosity products. They may however, be used with nonbodying acids.

Epoxy-resin esters may be dissolved in hydrocarbon solvents if sufficient fatty acid modification is present. For short esters, having less than half of the available hydroxyls esterified, an aromatic hydrocarbon is required. However, for long esters, for example, an ester having 0.8 of the available hydroxyls esterified with linseed fatty acid, a completely aliphatic hydrocarbon such as mineral spirits can be used as a solvent.

Epoxy esters may be used in air-dry formulations (for which a small amount of conventional metallic catalyst, called drier, is added), or they may be used with ureas and melamines to provide heat-convertible films (11-5).

The properties of the specific epoxy-ester film will be determined by a variety of factors, among them being the acid and/or oil acid selected, the ratio of reactants, the cooking cycle, the type of equipment used (i.e., open or closed kettle), the type of cook (i.e., azeotropic* or fusion), the molecular weight of the resin, etc.

The variety of films obtainable is considerably extended by the number of feasible esterifying agents. Epoxy esters can be formed from unsaturated oil acids, such as fatty acids (11-6), and from oil acids low in unsaturation, such as tall oils (11-7). These may be employed in connection with selected amounts of saturated oil acids and/or with polybasic acids and anhydrides and high-molecular-weight monobasic acids (11-8). Additionally, modified condensates of phenols and fatty acids may be employed as may rosins.

Generally, the effects of oil length and acid selection on the film properties are similar to the effects experienced with alkyd esters. The production techniques are, likewise, similar. Two formulations from the literature may be given as typical:

Air-dry Enamel Vehicle (Epon Ester LR-8)

Formulation:

Epoxy resin (molecular weight 1,000).................... 43% by wt
Linseed fatty acid..................................... 47% by wt
W. G. gum rosin....................................... 10% by wt

Typical data:

Acid number.. 7.0
Viscosity... Y-Z (Gardner-Holdt)
Color.. 8-9 (Gardner)
Weight per gallon..................................... 7.9 lb
Solvent.. Mineral spirits
Nonvolatile.. 60%

Nondrying Baking Vehicle (Epon Ester YC-3)

Formulation:

Epoxy resin (molecular weight 3,000).................... 75% by wt
Cocoanut fatty acid................................... 25% by wt

Typical data:

Cooking temperature.................................. 232°C
Acid number.. 1
Viscosity... W-Y (Gardner-Holdt)
Color.. 7-9 (Gardner)
Weight per gallon..................................... 9.0-8.1 lb
Solvent.. Xylene
Nonvolatile.. 50%

Although the epoxy esters are similar to more conventional alkyd esters, they offer three advantages: high adhesion, excellent flexibility, and superior chemical resistance. Since the ester linkages are vulnerable

---

* Involving the introduction of a small amount of solvent to assist in removal of water of reaction.

to caustic attack, alkali-resistance tests are a fair measure of chemical resistance. Table 11-6 presents alkali resistance for several cured films. The films were immersed at 70°C in a 2 per cent soap solution.

The over-all properties of the epoxy-ester films are, however, inferior to the properties of the nonesterified films. They possess the overriding advantage of lower cost, arising from the reduced epoxy content and the feasible use of inexpensive solvent vehicles. The ester coatings provide indefinite shelf life without requiring two-container systems. The heat-convertible coatings require only short moderately high bakes. For a melamine-converted film, for example, 30 minutes at 150°C is adequate.

Table 11-6. Comparison of Alkali Resistance of Finishes Based on Epoxy Esters and Finishes Based on Alkyd Resins (11-12)

Vehicle	Age of film, days	Condition of film after immersion for period noted		
		48 hr	186 hr	336 hr
85% epoxy ester 15% melamine	1	O.K.	Small blisters	Some loss of adhesion
85% alkyd 15% melamine	1	Some loss of adhesion	Off panel	
85% epoxy ester 15% melamine	30	Slight blistering	Off panel	
85% alkyd 15% melamine	30	. . . .	Completely off panel	
60% epoxy ester 40% melamine	1	O.K.	Slight blistering	Slight blistering
60% alkyd 40% melamine	1	Some loss of adhesion	Off panel	
60% epoxy ester 40% melamine	30	Slight blistering	Off panel	
60% alkyd 40% melamine	30	. . . .	Completely off panel	

Epoxy esters may be applied by all techniques employed with coatings based on more conventional resins and may be handled as conveniently.

CONCLUSION

By far the largest volume of epoxy-resin production is assigned to the coating industry for use in tough, flexible, chemically resistant films.

Although it is possible to formulate 100 per cent solids coatings based on the liquid epoxy resins, solution coatings are used almost exclusively for coating work.

The solution coatings may be considered to be of two types: those containing no ester linkages and those which do contain them. In the former case, the coatings are cured by amines, acids, and amides to provide fast room-temperature cures and by ureas and phenolic resins to provide the ultimate in resistant baking formulations. In the latter case, the air-dry coatings are formulated conventionally from oil acids; the baking coatings are formulated to contain the ureas or melamines as converting agents.

Both the ester and non-ester containing epoxy coatings exhibit characteristics superior to most conventional coating materials.

References

11-1. Rouse, Curing Agents for Epoxy Resins, *Official Digest Paint and Varnish Production Clubs*, November, 1953.
11-2. Scheibli and Dannenberg, Room Temperature Curing "Epon" Resin Coatings, paper presented at Paint and Varnish Production Club Symposium, Los Angeles, Calif., April, 1952.
11-3. Bruin, Some Aspects of the Chemistry of Epoxide Resins in Relation to Their Application, paper presented at Symposium of the British Society of Chemical Industries, April, 1956.
11-4. Greenlee, Synthetic Drying Compositions, U.S. 2,456,408 (1948).
11-5. Greenlee, Polyepoxide-containing Compositions and Reaction Products, U.S. 2,528,359 (1950).
11-6. Greenlee and Zech, Synthetic Drying Compositions, U.S. 2,502,518 (1950).
11-7. Greenlee, Tall Oil Esters, U.S. 2,493,486 (1950).
11-8. Greenlee, Synthetic Drying Compositions, U.S. 2,504,518 (1950)
11-9. Whittier and Lawn, Coating Compositions Containing Coal Tar Pitch and an Epoxy Ether Resin, U.S. 2,765,288 (1956).
11-10. Union Carbide Chemicals Company, sales literature.
11-11. Hensen, Helmreich, Applegath, and Vranish, Liquid Epoxy Resins in Coatings, Paper presented at Division of Paint, Plastics, and Printing Ink Chemistry, ACS Symposium, Atlantic City, September, 1956.
11-12. Technical Booklets SC:52-3 and SC:54-46, Shell Chemical Co.
11-13. Park and Blount, Oxidative Degradation of Epoxy Resin Coatings, paper presented at Division of Paint, Plastics, and Printing Ink Chemistry, ACS Symposium, Atlantic City, September, 1956.

12

HANDLING METHODS AND SAFETY PRECAUTIONS

The solid epoxy resins are almost exclusively the concern of paint and varnish formulators familiar with synthetic resins generally. The handling characteristics of the solid epoxy resins are very similar to those of the other solid coating materials, and their application in production poses no unusual problems.

The liquid resins, on the other hand, are extremely versatile materials and have invaded a number of industries previously unfamiliar with plastics in general; and because many of the users are unfamiliar with epoxies in particular, their use in production situations may involve a number of initial inconveniences. Most of these can be overcome with foresight.

It is generally advisable for the user and production employees to work with a limited number of laboratory samples in order to become familiar with the general handling properties of the resin system: to experience the exotherm phenomena, the pot-life characteristics, the effect of temperature on viscosities and to assess the other variables influencing the handling characteristics of the system. Such laboratory samples can conveniently be employed in the anticipated service environment or evaluated by suitable test procedures, to establish the suitability of the particular formulation and the specific effect of handling variables on ultimate properties. The total of this activity will indicate the handling characteristics that must be accommodated in subsequent production.

USE OF EPOXY RESINS IN PRODUCTION

The more important factors to be considered in the commercial use of epoxy resins can be listed as:
1. Incorporation of fillers.
2. Proper metering of ingredients.

3. Determination of optimum batch size.
4. Selection of mixing equipment.
5. Use of especially designed application apparatus.
6. Elimination of the dermatitis* potential.
7. Selection of proper curing equipment.
8. Selection of necessary releasing agents.

These will be considered in sequence.

Incorporation of Fillers

It is normally inconvenient to incorporate the fillers during the initial stages of the production process. Optimum results require heating the fillers to drive off any water present and, following their incorporation by thorough mixing, allowing the resin to stand for a suitable period until the bubbles have escaped. In practice, it is most convenient to work the resin warm during the mixing operation, and if the production situation requires room-temperature pot lives, the filled system must be allowed to return to ambient prior to addition of the curing agent. For these reasons, the fillers are usually added well in advance of the production situation by a separate compounding operation, or filled resin formulations are purchased initially.

Metering Curing Agents

Since optimum and reproducible results do not permit wide variations in the amount of the curing agents employed in the system, some weighing or metering device must be used to ensure quality control. Continuous metering equipment is available commercially. This equipment can be preset to the specific formulation and will deliver a considerable volume of material in controlled flow, the value for one commercial metering device being 3,785 cu cm per minute. Mixing is accomplished automatically, at the required temperature, without the introduction of air during the process.

In the absence of automatic equipment, measurements by weight are most convenient, except when the curing agent is a liquid used at 10 to 20 phr, in which case the curing agent may be measured volumetrically in a glass graduate. Often the best solution is to employ two-container systems that have been preweighed in advance, necessitating only that the employee combine the materials as furnished.

---

* Medically speaking, the less commonly used word dermatoses more accurately describes the skin condition.

Optimum Batch Size

The optimum batch size will be dependent on the curing agent employed in the system and the temperatures at which the system is worked.   Generally, the epoxy resins maintain a workable viscosity for the majority of their pot life; once appreciable exotherm is generated,

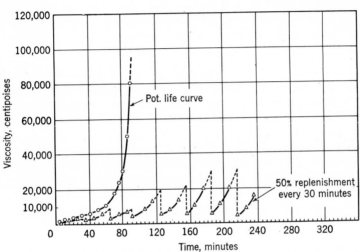

FIG. 12-1. Effect of batch replenishment on viscosity of ethylenediamine catalyzed system (12-1). (*Applied Engineering Associates, Brooklyn, N.Y.*)

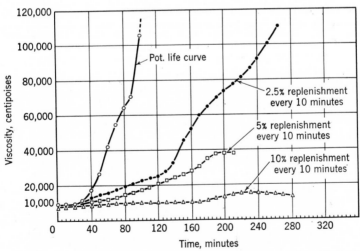

FIG. 12-2. Effect of batch replenishment on viscosity of an amine-resin adduct catalyzed system (12-1).   (*Applied Engineering Associates, Brooklyn, N.Y.*)

however, gelation occurs rapidly thereafter. The size of the batch will establish the pot life, particularly with the more highly exothermic compounds. For given stirring equipment, the larger the mass, the longer the stirring time, thus further reducing the available time for the application operations. With the more reactive amines, batches are usually 1 to 2 lb, with larger amounts (up to 5 lb) sometimes being used. The batch size selected should be such that permits the convenient use of all the material prior to the time of the transition period. Alternatively, a system of batch replenishment may be employed, involving the periodic addition of freshly catalyzed mix to the material being worked. Figures 12-1 and 12-2 indicate the effect of various amounts of batch replenishment on two typical aliphatic-amine catalyzed systems. These figures, likewise, illustrate the nature of the transition period, as reflected in a more or less steep and sudden increase in viscosity.

Selection of Stirring Equipment

Thorough mixing of resin and curing agent is requisite to the attainment of ultimate properties in the cured system. This can be obtained by hand mixing with some systems, although automatic agitation is preferred. In larger batches, and when employing certain of the anhydrides that must be worked hot, the automatic stirrers are virtually indispensable. The mixers normally employed are the propeller type, and typical kitchen mixers are quite satisfactory for smaller batches.

Sealant gun, containing polyethylene liner and operating by compressed air, is used to pot electrical connectors with epoxy compounds. (*The Epoxylite Corporation.*)

Pot life permitting, stirring time can be reduced and better mixing achieved by warming the resin prior to the addition of the curing agent. For mixtures that must be worked hot, water baths may be used to control temperature during stirring.

Use of Application Equipment

The epoxy resins are usually applied by pouring, brushing, or troweling. However, hand guns and spray equipment may be used in their application. The hand guns are convenient for potting connectors, coating strain gages, etc. These generally employ expendable cartridges (made of polyethylene or similar material) preloaded with the catalyzed resin mix. The cartridges may be kept under refrigeration to improve pot life. Conventional spray equipment may be used with solution-type coatings, but to avoid clogging, frequent cleaning may be required. For faster reacting systems, dual-nozzle spray equipment is available. Use of special equipment offers, in addition to handling convenience, the advantage of placing the production employee once removed from contact with the resin mixture.

Elimination of Adverse Physiological Reactions

Many of the liquid epoxy resins and, more particularly, the curing agents used in industrial formulations are primary skin irritants. For this reason, direct contact with the skin must be avoided. The solid epoxy resins, on the other hand, have not been shown to have an irritation potential.

Some materials involved in the epoxy-resin formulations are more irritating than others. Amine curing agents, for instance, are generally the most irritating. They may be considered as strong caustics, and they will produce serious local injury on short exposure. In some cases, systemic injury may result from chronic exposure, and in other cases, the effect has not yet been determined. For these reasons, the amines must be handled with respect. If worked hot, their fumes pose additional hazards. There appears, however, to be no apparent relationship between the basicity or volatility of the amine and its irritation potential, so that some strong organic bases, such as the polyamides and some hydroxyalkylated derivatives of the amines, can be considered to have minimum irritation potential (12-2). The acid anhydrides, like organic acids generally, will cause burns if allowed to remain in prolonged contact with the skin; and if ingested, some, such as pyromellitic dianhydride and phthalic anhydride, may produce serious injury to the liver or gastrointestinal disturbances—although they are less toxic than their corresponding acids.   With a few exceptions, however, the anhydrides are less irritating than the amines; in particular, they do not appear to be skin-sensitizing agents.   Some reactive diluents are particularly irritating, and others (e.g., epichlorohydrin) are highly toxic.   The irritation potential of the liquid epoxies, while present, is of considerably less consequence.   From the literature, it can be concluded that the possibility of serious injury resulting to a worker from handling the materials is almost nonexistent.

Aside from being primary irritants, however, the materials employed in conventional epoxy-resin formulations are sensitizing agents.   Some individuals do not appear particularly vulnerable to this effect and may work with epoxies for extended periods without inconvenience.   The majority will, however, be susceptible unless suitable precautions are exercised. The effect may be considered a form of hypersensitivity and will be reflected as dermatitis or an asthma-like condition.   The dermatitis will appear in the form of a rash resembling poison ivy and will be characterized by mild itching.   It will usually be confined to the hands and forearms, but if steps are not taken to remove the individual involved from contact with the resin system, medical attention may eventually be required.   If contact is not repeated, the rash will disappear without medication within a few days.

It is most important to avoid the development of this hypersensitivity; for once contracted, subsequent resistance will be lowered, and in some cases, the individuals will not be able to continue handling the materials without its reoccurrence.   The majority of individuals appear to have satisfactory initial resistance, which diminishes with continued contact. Hence, the full irritation potential will not immediately appear in a production situation.   This, of course, encourages careless handling.   Proper precautions must be exercised from the beginning of use rather than after the problem appears.   If there is no skin contact, there will be no dermatitis (12-3).   The following conditions, if observed, will prevent the development of hypersensitivity.

Avoid Skin Contact.   The epoxy resins and resin formulations should not be allowed to come in contact with the skin.   This can be accomplished by the use of vinyl plastic gloves and/or suitable barrier creams. Should contact occur, the contaminated area should be washed immediately and thoroughly with soap and water or alcohol—never with a solvent!

Paper towels should be readily available and should be used for wiping up spilled resin and cleaning equipment.   These should not be reused. Care should be taken to avoid spreading the resin throughout the working area. This will occur if employees handle foreign items (e.g., doorknobs, desk drawers, spatulas, light fixtures, scales, etc.) while wearing contaminated gloves.

Practice Personal Hygiene. Work clothes should be changed and laundered every few days. Resin that contaminates the clothes will almost inevitably contact the skin. The underside of shirt cuffs accumulates resin easily, and particularly the fumes from the curing agents. The cuff abrades the wrist to assist the sensitizing process. Long-sleeved shirts should be changed daily. Frequent washing, uncontaminated clothing, and workman-like habits will control inadvertent contact with the resin and eliminate its effect.

During warmer weather, even increased attention should be given to the practice of personal hygiene.

Provide Adequate Ventilation. Displaced-air ventilation should be provided, and when resin mixes are worked hot it should be considered indispensable. Hoods should be used to cover the working benches and the fumes exhausted to the atmosphere through connecting air ducts.

Of course, it may be expected that even if the foregoing procedures are scrupulously adhered to, a fraction of a per cent of individuals will still develop an allergy to the materials. These must be transferred from further contact with it. If the foregoing three conditions are observed, no problems will be encountered with hypersensitivity. If they are not observed, a high incidence of dermatitis will inevitably occur.

The cured system is not a skin irritant.

Selection of Curing Equipment

If temperatures higher than ambient are employed to cure the resin system, three devices are feasible: ovens, infrared heat lamps, and high-frequency heaters. From the standpoint of ultimate properties, forced-air recirculating ovens provide most satisfactory control of exothermic heat and result in castings relatively free of residual stresses. Infrared lamps are convenient cure accelerators for room-temperature-type curing agents and provide a degree of cure adequate for most industrial applications. High-frequency heaters are in limited use.

Production-line tunnel ovens of various constructions may be used in connection with conveyor equipment to provide rapid and continuous processing of smaller potted, sealed, and encapsulated components.

In any event, the curing equipment should be adequate to accommodate the cure cycle best suited to the material being worked. In some cases, temperature variations from batch to batch may be reflected in critical parameters of the cured system.

Selection of Releasing Agents

Since the epoxy resins are extremely adhesive materials, releasing agents should be used to protect molds and other nonintegral components which contact the resin during cure. Releasing agents based on silicone resins are very effective and are available as either greases or liquids. Two typical commercial compounds are Dow Corning DC-20 (liquid) and Epoxylite MG-1 (grease). In general, the releasing agent should be insoluble in the resin mixture, should not melt at the curing temperature employed, and should be applied in a very thin continuous film.

Permanent parting agents can be made from polyethylene and Teflon. Cellophane or similar films can be used conveniently to separate layers of catalyzed resin or to protect surfaces during production. Used on components, it is easily washed off after cure.

STRIPPERS FOR EPOXY RESINS

The epoxy resins, because of their extreme resistance to solvents, are very difficult to remove from surfaces, once cured. Thoroughly cured and filled systems must be soaked for relatively long periods (i.e., from several days to a week) in special solvents before they can be removed, and even then, removal may be a time-consuming job. A typical proprietary solvent that works well with aliphatic-amine cured systems is DeSolv 292 (Ram Chemical). From a practical standpoint, it is often less expensive to scrap small components than to remove the plastic, particularly on aromatic-diamine cured systems. On larger components, the epoxy resins can be sandblasted off about as easily as aluminum. Most efficiently, it is burned off, using temperatures in excess of 400°C. Adequate ventilation should be provided, since, in burning, the resin produces a black, acrid smoke.

When the cured material has contaminated a surface, such as a spatula blade, it may be ground off without difficulty. The uncured resin may be removed with a convenient solvent, such as xylene, or, if polymerization has not progressed too far, with an active solvent, such as methyl ethyl ketone.

Film strippers for solution coatings are available in proprietary grades, and these are more effective. A typical compound will soften or lift films within an hour to the degree that the coating can then be removed by slight scraping. A typical commercial stripper is Sprazee (Wyandotte Chemical Co.).

CONCLUSION

The excellent properties and the extremely versatile nature of epoxy resins in casting, potting, sealing, adhesive, laminating, and coating formulations have resulted in their widespread use in industries hitherto unfamiliar with thermosetting plastics.

It has, therefore, been necessary for these industries to reorient their materials-handling processes to accommodate unfamiliar materials. This is accomplished by an experimental period, followed by the determination of the important variables in the system and the integration of the system into a feasible production process employing specific equipment. Special consideration is given to eliminating the possibility of dermatitis by enforcing proper hygiene and installing adequate ventilation.

When such a sound and well-thought-out approach is employed, the epoxy resins can be used with complete satisfaction and without difficulty to produce all varieties of products wherein their superior properties are utilized to the maximum extent.

References

12-1. Sussman, Processing of Epoxy Resins, *Modern Plastics*, April, 1955.
12-2. Ingberman and Walton, Low Toxicity Aliphatic Amines as Crosslinking Agents for Polyepoxide Resins, paper presented at Division of Paint, Plastics, and Printing Ink Chemistry Division, ACS Symposium, Atlantic City, September, 1956.
12-3. Dorman, Dermatoses and Epoxy Resins, paper presented at Society of Plastic Engineers (Southern California Section) Symposium, Los Angeles, Calif., November, 1956.

CHEMICAL INDEX